Dementia Reconsidered, Rev
the person still comes first

Dementia Reconsidered; the person comes first

Original text by Tom Kitwood

Dementia Reconsidered, Revisited; the person still comes first

Edited by Dawn Brooker

Open University Press

Open University Press
McGraw-Hill Education
8th Floor, 338 Euston Road
London
England
NW1 3BH

email: enquiries@openup.co.uk
world wide web: www.openup.co.uk

and Two Penn Plaza, New York, NY 10121-2289, USA

First published 2019

Commissioning Editor: Vivien Antwi
Editorial Assistant: Karen Harris
Content Product Manager: Ali Davis

A catalogue record of this book is available from the British Library

ISBN-13: 9780335248025
ISBN-10: 0335248020
eISBN: 9780335248032

Library of Congress Cataloging-in-Publication Data
CIP data applied for

Typeset by Transforma Pvt. Ltd., Chennai, India

Praise for this book

"This important book does three things. It brings to a new generation the insight and vision of Tom Kitwood. It highlights the remarkable progress we have made in recent years. But most important of all it reminds us what still needs to be done if we are to fully respect the rights of people with dementia and their family care-givers. Kitwood inspired Alzheimer's Society to knit together research, care, and societal change. We are now re-inspired to make sure all progress is evidenced and evaluated for its impact. We must realise the enormous opportunities the digital age offers people affected by dementia but in doing so constantly listen to and learn from their many and varied voices across nations and cultures."

Jeremy Hughes CBE, Chief Executive, Alzheimer's Society, UK

"This book is a must read for anyone engaged in the field of dementia. Kitwood's contribution is unquestionable and 'Dementia Reconsidered' played a significant part in developing what we now know as contemporary person-centred dementia care. Like many others, his work influenced my thinking greatly and his untimely death was a huge loss. So Dementia Reconsidered Revisited is a welcome publication and reading Kitwood's writing again alongside detailed and critical commentaries by leading scholars in the field is a sheer joy".

Professor Brendan McCormack, Queen Margaret University, Edinburgh, UK

"It doesn't matter if you have read and absorbed the original Tom Kitwood textbook as this version offers so much more. The original theory developed by Tom Kitwood will assist clinicians, researchers and families understanding of dementia and personhood. Importantly, the textbook offers a contemporary understanding of the key concepts outlined in each chapter as written by world leaders in dementia research. This essential, must have and must-read textbook will be a favourite on my book shelf and that of my students."

Professor Wendy Moyle, Program Director, Healthcare Practice and Survivorship; Griffith University, Australia

"Dementia Reconsidered, Revisited; the person still comes first is a remarkable contribution to the literature, bridging time and underscoring the importance of Kitwood's work for today and tomorrow. Cover to cover, it is essential, illuminating reading for all who wish to fully live and work productively in service of all people our ageing world."

Sarah H. Kagan PhD, RN, Lucy Walker Honorary Term Professor of Gerontological Nursing, University of Pennsylvania, USA

"This timely book demonstrates the significant contribution Kitwood has made to ensuring people live well with dementia. Brooker's edited volume will be a lasting legacy to our field."

Murna Downs, Professor of Dementia Studies, Centre for Applied Dementia Studies, University of Bradford, UK

Contents

Contributors

Tom Kitwood (1937–1998) was the Alois Alzheimer Professor of Psycho-gerontology at the University of Bradford in the UK, where he founded the Bradford Dementia Group in 1992. He published *Dementia Reconsidered* in 1997.

Dawn Brooker is Professor of Dementia Studies and Director of the Association for Dementia Studies at the University of Worcester in the UK.

Christine Bryden is a Dementia advocate, Adjunct Research Fellow, Public and Contextual Theology Centre, Charles Sturt University, Australia.

Richard Cheston is Professor of Mental Health Research (dementia) at the University of the West of England and Honorary Senior Research Fellow and Clinical Psychologist, the Research Institute for the Care of Older People (the RICE Centre) in Bath in the UK.

Jan Dewing is Sue Pembrey Chair and Professor of Nursing and Director of The Centre for Person-centred Practice Research at Queen Margaret University in Edinburgh. Jan is also Professor at Western University College of Norway (Bergen) and Visiting Professor at University of Maribor, Slovenia.

Ruth Elvish is a Clinical Psychologist and Research Fellow within Pennine Care NHS Foundation Trust and at the University of Manchester, UK.

Reinhard Guss is the Dementia Work Stream Lead for the Faculty of the Psychology of Older People (FPOP) within the British Psychological Society. Reinhard is a qualified Clinical Psychologist and Neuropsychologist working within the National Health Service in the UK.

Julian C. Hughes, based at RICE – The Research Institute for the Care of Older People – is RICE Professor of Old Age Psychiatry at Bristol University, and Honorary Consultant to Royal United Hospitals Bath NHS Foundation Trust and to Avon and Wiltshire Mental Health Partnership NHS Trust in the UK.

John Keady is Professor of Older People's Mental Health Nursing, University of Manchester and the Greater Manchester Mental Health NHS Foundation Trust in the UK.

Keith Oliver is an Alzheimer's Society Ambassador and Dementia Service User Envoy for Kent and Medway Partnership NHS Trust in the UK. He retired from being a head teacher when diagnosed with Alzheimer's at age 55.

Steven R. Sabat is Professor Emeritus of Psychology at Georgetown University in Washington, DC, in the United States.

Claire Surr is Professor of Dementia Studies and Director of the Centre for Dementia Research at Leeds Beckett University in the UK.

Kate Swaffer is Chair, CEO & Co-founder, Dementia Alliance International; Board member, Alzheimer's Disease International; Member, World Dementia Council.

Bob Woods is Emeritus Professor of Clinical Psychology of Older People at Bangor University, Wales, in the UK.

Foreword

It is an honour to write the foreword to this significant update of Tom Kitwood's seminal work. He was a true visionary, casting a picture of a future in which people with dementia such as myself would receive care that respected our personhood. In this book and his prior articles, Kitwood was writing at a time when people with dementia were regarded as lacking insight, and as being little more than physical bodies requiring the basics of care. This was the view that faced me at the time of my diagnosis in 1995, when I was told that I would decline within five years, then require another few years in full-time care until I died. I was a recently divorced mother of three girls aged nine, thirteen and nineteen. There was no hope, only a living death beginning at this moment in the specialist's rooms, when I was labelled with a condition to which was attached an awful stigma of fear of a future 'unbeing'.

Who would I be when I died? Would I still be Christine? Would I still recognize anyone? What would this living death mean for my three young girls and me? But new hope was offered to me by a sympathetic neurologist who gave me the very first anti-dementia medication then available, and refused to deliver the usual script of 'Go home and get your affairs in order.' He offered me some hope, and recognized that each person living with dementia is unique, and that he could not give any reliable prognosis.

Back then, in the early days of the Internet, I was able to find some other people with dementia around the world, and we supported and encouraged one another. I began to speak out about our experiences, first to a national, and then to the international conference in 2001. But I was not believed, regarded as lacking credibility as I did not fit the usual stereotype of people with dementia. Within a few years, more of us were speaking out, and changing the way in which people with dementia were viewed. We needed to describe how we were battling fading recall, language dysfunction, as well as an inability to cope with stress and to plan for the future. As experts in the lived experience, we were trying to express how, within hours or days, our lives could shift from a treacle-like fog to a clear sunny day. On some days or hours we could almost pass for 'normal', and yet on others we are dependent on our families and helpers to guide us through the maze of life. Within these shifting sands of dementia, we need to be seen as people first and foremost, not just a condition that is feared and shunned in our society.

Importantly, Kitwood had the foresight to see that people with dementia were still *people*, and he realized that our care needed to be respectful and not simply a question of showering and feeding us, sitting us up during the day, and putting us to bed at night. He referred to the theological philosopher Martin Buber's work on I–Thou, where the relationship between us should be between an I and a Thou, not an I and an It, whether we have dementia or not. This was central to Kitwood's vision, where the unique personhood of the person with dementia was upheld in a caring relationship, not just our physical needs addressed.

Kitwood foresaw the importance of the recognition of neuroplasticity, which would receive worldwide attention in 2007, with the publication of Norman Doidge's book, *The Brain that Heals Itself*. Kitwood also wrote before the well-known so-called Nun Study of David Snowdon, which showed that the condition of dementia was not necessarily directly related to the neuropathology of the brain when analysed after death. Kitwood foreshadowed these findings when he wrote that dementia was not directly related to damage to the brain, pointing to his central concept that dementia is not just a biological problem, but also a feature of a depersonalizing and disabling psychosocial environment.

Within just 140 pages or so, Kitwood recast the future in a very different light; one in which people with dementia could be heard and their environment improved to support their function. His vision was truly a new way of seeing, in order to bring about significant cultural change; his work has had, and continues to have, an enormous impact.

What we need to remember is that Kitwood was writing before the availability of anti-dementia medication, and before the world began to hear and believe the voices of people with dementia. He needed to find creative ways to see the world from our point of view, and I believe he was successful in doing so and giving us back our 'personhood'. For me, as a person with dementia, he restored my 'self', which I see from my own point of view, where I can say 'I', 'me' and 'my'. I consider that personhood is from the point of view of our carers, which was the only voice available to Kitwood at that time.

I first read Kitwood's work when preparing an article in 2002, and was inspired by his counter-cultural approach. Re-reading his book now, I am again amazed at how he was able to prepare such a succinct work that got to the heart of the need to change the culture of care of people with dementia, as well as support those who care for us – both families and friends, as well as paid workers. His Dementia Care Mapping has spread to many countries, and is having a significant impact on the recognition of the need to improve the culture of care.

The importance of this update is that it recasts his work in the light of the changes that have occurred in the past 20 years, and provides a new vision for the future. The most important of those changes is, of course, the voices of people with dementia, who can describe the type of care that we need. In this regard, Keith Oliver's contribution as a person with dementia is invaluable; he is the expert in the lived experience.

Other changes include language, where, for example, no longer are we victims or sufferers, whose identity has become overwhelmed by and subsumed within our condition. We are people who happen to live with dementia. The advent of communal responses to dementia, such as 'Dementia Friendly Communities', is also important to note, as our relationships are not only I–Thou, but also I–We. We do not want to become isolated through difficulties in coping with our surroundings, so these efforts to adapt our environments and to educate the community as a whole are important.

However, unfortunately, we still face the cost pressures that Kitwood referred to, so that staff-to-client ratios are far from ideal. In addition, the training needed for our carers is not always enough for a true understanding of what dementia feels like, and what can be done to help us. Importantly, where we live geographically can also have a big impact on the type of care we receive, and the type of support our carers need.

This update of Kitwood's ground-breaking work recognizes these ongoing issues, and is very much needed to continue to seek better care for people with dementia, as well as improved support for our families and paid care-workers. The reflective points at the end of each section mean that readers can respond thoughtfully to the contributions, so that this work can be used in teaching, as well as prompt the general readership to think about the future and how best to continue the vision originally set out by Kitwood.

Kitwood saw people with dementia as embodied relational beings, who respond well to I–Thou connections, and to a culture of care that is respectful of each unique individual. There is no typical person with dementia. We all have our own life story, personality and inner resources to draw on as we face the challenges of this condition. I look to a future in which our culture of care for people with dementia, and of support for our carers, continues to improve, shaped and guided by this important revisiting of Kitwood's work.

Indeed, the person must, and will always, come first.

Christine Bryden, PhD
Person with dementia, author and dementia advocate
Adjunct Research Fellow, Public and Contextual Theology Centre,
Charles Sturt University, Australia, April 2018

Editor's preface

It is more than 20 years since *Dementia Reconsidered; the person comes first* by Tom Kitwood was published by Open University Press. It was a seminal text in the field of dementia studies, and is still cited and referenced as core reading on person-centred dementia care. The ideas and theory development in the nine chapters have undoubtedly shaped modern dementia care and research. Tom died unexpectedly at the age of 61, just 12 months after the book was published. He saw *Dementia Reconsidered* as drawing together the key themes that had concerned his academic writing during the decade before. Had he have lived, there is no doubt that Tom would have continued to challenge reductionist paradigms about dementia that still hold sway in a lot of policy, research and practice worldwide. Although Tom has been unable to contribute directly to the ongoing debates around person-centred approaches, he has inspired many scholars who are active in the field. The world is a very different place to 20 years ago and it is now timely to publish an edition that reproduces the original chapters but also provides extra content to update the book to a contemporary level. I have gathered together experts in their respective fields to provide a commentary and critique on each chapter, and update readers to the current status of research, theory and practice in the area. The original text contained a number of photographs of people with dementia, which we have replaced with images from some of the authors and also from Cathy Greenblat, whose photographs have done much to challenge the stereotypical views of people with dementia worldwide. All the people I approached to contribute were unanimous in their commitment to undertake *Dementia Reconsidered, Revisited*.

Tom Kitwood was my mentor and friend. I first heard Tom speak at a conference in 1988 when I was working as the lead NHS clinical psychologist for older people in Birmingham in the UK. At that time, the emotional and psychological needs of people living with dementia were simply not considered. When Tom spoke about 'malignant social psychology' and 'dialectics of dementia', it was as if someone had shone a bright light on the lives of the people that I worked with day in day out. Myself, and many others like me, heard Tom's words and consumed the series of journal articles he produced over the next ten years. We saw for the first time what we could do to actually help people live with their dementia. My PhD research was completed in 1998 with Tom's guidance. The day Tom gave me a copy of *Dementia Reconsidered* and the day he died are memories that will be with me for ever. I was fortunate to have been able to work within the Bradford Dementia Group for many years following his death, trying to remain true to Tom's legacy and helping others around the world to connect with his visionary work.

I, and my fellow contributors, hope that you enjoy reading this book as much as we have enjoyed writing it. It should be of interest to readers who are familiar with the original text, alongside those who may be coming across it for the first time, but who want to ensure they have a contemporary understanding of the issues Kitwood raised. *Dementia Reconsidered, Revisited* is a great way to both honour Tom's memory but also to bring his ideas up to date for the next generation of movers and shakers.

Dawn Brooker

Acknowledgements

We would like to thank the family of the late Professor Tom Kitwood for granting permission for this book to be written. All of us owe them a debt of gratitude. We would also like to acknowledge the contribution of Cathy Greenblat in allowing us to use her beautiful photographs as illustration and to Julia Heron for the cover artwork. We would also like to thank Zuleika Sankey for her help in manuscript preparation.

Introduction

Tom Kitwood

In the world of nature there are some tides that rise dramatically. The sea is a turmoil of gigantic waves; the cliffs tremble and spray flies high into the air. Other tides rise quietly, creeping forward over miles of mud and sand, and causing no obvious disturbance. Although their advance is hardly noticed, they are powerful and persistent nonetheless. It is so too with the tides that change the course of human history.

The rising tide of dementia is of the latter, quiet kind.[1] For many years now prevalence has been slowly but steadily increasing, and this is likely to continue for many years to come. Dementia is primarily a feature of the industrialized societies, where the population profile has undergone huge changes in the last 100 or so years, bringing a far greater proportion of people into the older age range. Many parts of the world that were formerly 'undeveloped' are now going through a similar demographic shift; it is likely that in due course they, too, will face a situation very like our own. The scale of the problem is immense. In the UK alone, most estimates suggest that the total number of people affected is between half and one million. Dementia may prove to be the most significant epidemiological feature of the late twentieth century. Its presence will have profound and lasting effects – for good or ill – on the entire pattern of our political, economic and social life.

How are we to understand dementia, and so develop an appropriate response? Overwhelmingly today it is framed as an 'organic mental disorder', and a medical model – what I shall term the standard paradigm – has held sway. After the great neuropathological investigations of the 1960s it was as if the evidence of organicity was so overwhelming that a 'technical' way of approaching the problem was what was needed: essentially, to elucidate the pathological processes and then find ways of arresting or preventing them. Psychiatry thenceforward tended to deal with dementia in a rather narrow way, often ignoring the larger human issues, and other disciplines allied to medicine followed in its train.

There are many problems with the standard paradigm, as we shall see. The picture that we now have of the nervous system is far more complex than the one on which that paradigm was based. In particular, the brain is now recognized as an organ that is capable of continuing structural adaptation; its circuitry is not static, as in a computer, but dynamic – slowly changing according to environmental demands. Evidence to challenge the standard paradigm comes from care practice, too; it is now clear that the older views about the process of dementia, which were extremely negative and deterministic, were incorrect. A paradigm can be 'saved' almost indefinitely, of course; by subtle redefinitions, by discounting certain pieces of evidence and highlighting others, and even by the suppressing of contradictory views. However, the history of science seems to show that when the anomalies become too glaring there will be some who try to frame the problems in a different way; the time for a new paradigm has come.

The principal aim of this book, then, is to take up this challenge; and present a paradigm in which the person comes first. It accommodates a richer range of evidence than the medical model, and resolves some of its most serious anomalies; also it provides the rationale for an approach to care that looks far more to human than to medical solutions. Many people have found their way, intuitively, to such an approach, and a new culture of dementia care is slowly coming into being.

My own first direct contact with dementia was in 1975. My wife had had a chance meeting with a frail woman in her 70s in the local supermarket, and helped her to choose a painkiller. It turned out that she lived only a mile from where we did, and on that day my wife gave her a lift back home. Gradually Mrs E (as we came to call her) became a friend. We knew that sometimes she felt lonely and sad, but she was excellent company, very hospitable, and she loved children. As time went on we found out a little about her life. She had been a widow for over 10 years, and lived alone. Her council house had once looked out onto fields and farmland; now there was a large estate, notorious for its roughness. During her married life, and for some time after, she had worked as a dressmaker; one room in her house was still set up with the sewing machine. She had no children, and her nearest relative was a niece who lived some 75 miles away. Mrs E was a Catholic, and had been a faithful attender at church; she went less often now, but the priest called in regularly to see her. Occasionally we thought she might not be getting enough to eat; if so, that would be due to neglect or forgetfulness rather than poverty. Sometimes we did an informal 'meals on wheels' service for her, taking her a portion from our family dinner.

The last time I was with Mrs E as the person I had come to know was on Easter Sunday, 1979. She came to lunch with us, and afterwards we were doing the washing up together. It was a bright, cold day, and the daffodils in the garden were shimmering in the breeze. Mrs E and I were both in a jolly mood, and we were singing. One of the songs she chose was by the Seekers; its refrain was 'The carnival is over, we shall never meet again'.

That song turned out to be a tragic premonition, for within a few months Mrs E was in an institution, never to return. It was only later that I pieced together what had happened. Apparently she had become unsafe in her home; at least once she had fallen into the fire. Also she had been seen wandering in the street at night. Members of the church had tried to help, but a social worker was called in, and Mrs E's niece was contacted. One day the niece and her husband called to visit Auntie, as they had often done. They said they would take her out for a drive, but the drive ended up at the local mental hospital, where she was admitted for assessment. After a short time in the hospital Mrs E was put into a Social Services Home. It was a huge building of blackened stone, on a bleak Bradford hillside. When I went to see her I was amazed at the change, and she seemed not to recognize me at all. I didn't stay long; I thought there was no point, when she had so obviously 'gone senile'. To my shame, this was the only time I visited her after she was taken away from her own home. Mrs E died a few months afterwards. I was surprised at how many people came to her funeral.

At the time when I knew Mrs E I was working as an academic psychologist, but I completely failed to apply my professional knowledge to her plight. I simply took for granted the idea that some people 'go senile'; and that when they do, virtually nothing can be done to help them beyond meeting their basic physical needs. It did not even occur to me to use my imagination to try to understand what Mrs E might be experiencing, or to use my creativity to establish a new channel of communication. Like so many other people – then and now – I was completely seduced by the prevailing view: dementia is a 'death that leaves the body behind'.

It was some time later, in 1985, that I began to work with and for people who have dementia. The first initiative was not my own; a psychiatrist and a clinical psychologist invited me to be their academic supervisor. I could offer them general guidance on research methods, and I could give a sympathetic yet critical ear to their ideas, but I had no substantive knowledge of their field. Very soon, however, all that was changed, and I found myself drawn increasingly into their line of work. I joined the Alzheimer's Disease Society, and began to attend the monthly meetings of the local branch. Also I began to help with a small community care scheme in Bradford. I found that I liked people with dementia. I often admired their courage; I felt that I understood something of their predicament, and sometimes I discovered that I could interact with them in what seemed to be a fruitful way. Among my other ventures were helping in carers' support, and beginning to follow up life histories through extended interviews with family members.

As my involvement increased, I met, and came to know as friends, several truly excellent practitioners of care. Initially through them, and then on the basis of my own direct experience, I came to believe that much more could be done to help people with dementia than was commonly assumed. Also, the more I read into the psychiatric literature on dementia, the more sceptical I became of many of the received views. I began to ask myself whether some, at least, of the symptoms that are commonly found might be due more to a failure of understanding and care than to a structural failure of the brain. I discovered that a few people had indeed written along these lines, although their work was generally discounted or neglected.

Coming fresh from other work in psychology, concerned with counselling, psychotherapy and moral development, I was often shocked at the ways in which people with dementia were being demeaned and disregarded. One of my first pieces of research was to document the different ways in which personhood was undermined; I called this, provocatively, the 'malignant social psychology' that surrounds dementia. It was surprising to find that there was virtually no attempt, either in practice or in the literature, to explore the subjectivity of dementia. Furthermore, an examination of interpersonal processes was somehow forbidden, on the utterly spurious ground that we were involved with an 'organic mental disorder'. I wanted to use the phrase 'the social psychology of dementia', and develop it in detail. Ten years ago, however, this seemed almost like a blasphemy. At times I felt very apprehensive – almost guilty – when offering my tentative ideas. When I put forward the concept of 'remerging', which many people have accepted now, it was tantamount to heresy.

As my work developed and deepened, I became increasingly involved with the details of dementia care, particularly drawing on ideas and practices from psychotherapeutic work, where the emphasis is on authentic contact and communication. Many people were making really valuable innovations in care practice, but I was convinced that the full range of possibilities for enhancing well-being had not yet been considered. Also, because much of the good work that was being done did not have a coherent theoretical basis, it lacked general credibility. My colleague Kathleen Bredin and I attempted to bring some of the fragments together. We called the whole approach 'person-centred care', following the example of Rogerian psychotherapy. Some of the basic principles are presented in our

? Christine Bryden ? type or dementia

small book *Person to Person: A Guide to the Care of Those with Failing Mental Powers* (1992c). The theory and its empirical base were set out in some detail in a series of papers, published between 1987 and 1995, all of which are included in the bibliography of this book. Our explorations around this time led to the formation of the Bradford Dementia Group, whose central concern is the development of person-centred care.

One of our main innovations was a new method for evaluating the quality of care in formal settings, which we called Dementia Care Mapping (DCM). It is based on a serious attempt to take the standpoint of the person with dementia, using a combination of empathy and observational skill. The DCM method has proved to be of enormous interest, as witness the fact that the manual has now gone into its seventh edition. The particular strengths of DCM seem to be the way it sheds light on the actual process of care, and the attention that is given to the 'developmental loop' for bringing about improvements. It is thus a powerful challenge – but of a very positive kind – to any organization that is involved in dementia care.

The concept of person-centred care applies to all contexts; it is not simply an issue for formal settings. Throughout the time of my involvement with dementia I have helped in supporting family carers in their near-to-superhuman task. I have been deeply impressed by their courage, humour and sheer determination, and by their ability to give friendship and encouragement to others who are in a similar situation. During the last few years the Bradford Dementia Group has been developing a structured programme for carers' support, with a definite agenda and close attention to process. Recently we have completed the preparation of the materials, and have begun to teach others how to run such a programme for carers in their own locality. Research and development of this kind has been a central feature of our work.

Like many others, I discovered that intense involvement with people who have dementia and their carers makes heavy emotional demands. There is a great deal of anxiety and distress, and at times it feels as if one might sink into a vast morass of unmet need. There were several points at which I felt very despondent, and ready to give up. I believe now that I was beginning to face up to and work through my own fears about ageing and developing dementia. I also came to realize that I had a perverse determination to stay committed to this field of work. These were my first inklings of what, in the Bradford Dementia Group, we now call the 'depth psychology of dementia care': the unconscious defences, compulsions and interpersonal processes that pervade this field of work.

All of the themes I have mentioned thus far are taken up in this book, the plan of which is as follows. We begin by looking at the concept that unifies the whole discussion – that of personhood – and we explore its ethical, social-psychological and neurological significance. Then, in Chapter 2, there is a brief survey of what is known about the nature of dementia and associated conditions. Here we are mainly on standard psychiatric ground, and I expose some of the difficulties and inconsistencies in the kind of medical model that finds its way into simple textbooks. Chapter 3 looks at dementia as it is so often lived out – that is, where the frameworks of support that are truly needed are lacking. I suggest that the process should be conceptualized in dialectical terms; both neurological impairment and social-psychological factors have their part to play in the undermining of persons. The following chapter presents a very contrasting picture, outlining the growth of positive approaches, and illustrating a dialectical interplay in which the social psychology works to offset the process of neurological decline. In Chapter 5 we move onto more subjective ground, and explore what the experience of dementia may be like. This leads on to a discussion of care practice, in Chapter 6, focusing principally on those forms of interaction through which personhood can be sustained. Chapter 7 extends this discussion to the question of how organizations involved in caring function, for good or ill; and in Chapter 8 we look at a number of issues related to the personhood of carers. Finally, in Chapter 9, I examine what is involved in bringing about a radical change in the culture of dementia care, and I come to a cautiously optimistic conclusion.

There is a general, although somewhat undeveloped, hypothesis underpinning much of what I have written about dementia, both in this book and elsewhere. This hypothesis is both psychological and neurological, and can be summarized thus. Contact with dementia or other forms of severe cognitive disability can – and indeed should – take us out of our customary patterns of over-busyness, hypercognitivism and extreme talkativity, into a way of being in which emotion and feeling are given a much larger place. People who have dementia, for whom the life of the emotions is often intense, and without the ordinary forms of inhibition, may have something important to teach the rest of humankind. They are asking us, so to speak, to heal the rift in experience that western culture has engendered, and inviting us to return to aspects of our being that are much older in evolutionary terms: more in tune with the body and its functions, closer to the life of instinct. Most of us live too much – almost literally – from 'the top of our heads' (the outer layers of the neocortex). There is psychological, and hence neurological, work for us to do with and for ourselves, as we work towards a deeper integration and integrity.

My discussion is based, wherever possible, on the findings of research. I am, however, also offering a personal view, derived from my own particular struggle to understand the nature and context of dementia, my own attempt to help in the improvement of care. I make no apology for this, for I would rather reveal something of my own convictions and values than stand back and pretend to be totally objective. I have always worked closely with psychiatrists and others in the biomedical field, and I have tried to develop a model that makes genuine psychiatric sense. My values have come into the open particularly in my emphasis on the moral aspects of personhood, and in opposition to the misuse of drugs, the abuse of power, and those distortions of truth that might be termed 'neuropathic ideology'.

The book contains many small vignettes, descriptions of people and episodes. These vignettes, unless indicated otherwise, come from my own work with people who have dementia, family carers and those employed in dementia care. All of them are true, in that they are based on real events. However, for the sake of confidentiality all names are fictitious, and in some cases other aspects have been disguised or changed.

After a century and more of research into dementia, mainly within the standard paradigm, we have heard just about all that might be cause for dismay. As we now reframe the whole field, and give much greater weight to personal and interpersonal considerations, most of what follows will be good news. We will discover much more about how to enable people who have dementia to fare well, without having to wait for magic bullets or technical fixes. And if we make the venture of genuine and open engagement, we will learn a great deal about ourselves.

Note

1 The image of the rising tide comes from an article by Bernard Ineichen (1987).

1

On being a person

Tom Kitwood

A few months before this book was completed, a day centre was approached by an agency concerned to promote awareness about Alzheimer's disease and similar conditions. Could the day centre provide some photographs of clients, to be used for publicity purposes? Permission was sought and granted; the photographs were duly taken and sent. The agency, however, rejected them, on the ground that the clients did not show the disturbed and agonized characteristics that people with dementia 'ought' to show, and which would be expected to arouse public concern. The failure of the photographic exercise, from the standpoint of the agency, was a measure of the success of the day centre from the standpoint of the clients. Here was a place where men and women with dementia were continuing to live in the world of persons, and not being downgraded into the carriers of an organic brain disease.

Alzheimer victims, dements, elderly mentally infirm – these and similar descriptions devalue the person, and make a unique and sensitive human being into an instance of some category devised for convenience or control. Imagine an old-fashioned weighing scale. Put aspects of personal being into one pan, and aspects of pathology and impairment into the other. In almost all of the conventional thinking that we have inherited, the balance comes down heavily on the latter side. There is no logical ground for this, nor is it an inference drawn from a comprehensive range of empirical data. It is simply a reflection of the values that have prevailed, and of the priorities that were traditionally set in assessment, care practice and research. The time has come to bring the balance down decisively on the other side, and to recognize men and women who have dementia in their full humanity. Our frame of reference should no longer be person-with-DEMENTIA, but PERSON-with-dementia.

This chapter, then, is concerned with personhood: the category itself, the centrality of relationship, the uniqueness of persons, the fact of our embodiment. Rather than emphasize the differences that dementia brings, we will first celebrate our common ground.

The concept of personhood

The term personhood, together with its synonyms and parallels, can be found in three main types of discourse: those of transcendence, those of ethics and those of social psychology. The functions of the term are different in these three contexts, but there is a core of meaning that provides a basic conceptual unity.

Discourses of transcendence make their appeal to a very powerful sense, held in almost every cultural setting, that being-in-itself is sacred, and that life is to be revered. Theistic religions capture something of this in their doctrines of divine creation; in eastern traditions of Christianity, for example, there is the idea that each human being is an 'ikon of God'. Some forms of Buddhism, and other non-theistic spiritual paths, believe in an essential, inner nature: always present, always perfect, and waiting to be discovered through enlightenment. Secular humanism makes no metaphysical assumptions about the essence of our nature, but still often asserts, on the basis of direct experience, that 'the ultimate is personal'.

In the main ethical discourses of western philosophy one primary theme has been the idea that each person has absolute value. We thus have an obligation to treat each other with deep respect; as ends, and never as means towards some other end. The principle of respect for persons, it was argued by Kant and those who followed in his footsteps, requires no theological justification; it is the only assumption on which our life as social beings makes sense. There are parallels to this kind of thinking in the doctrine of human rights, and this has been used rhetorically in many different contexts, including that of dementia (King's Fund 1986). One problem here, however, is that in declarations of rights the person is framed primarily as a separate individual; there is a failure to see human life as interdependent and interconnected.

In social psychology the term personhood has had a rather flexible and varied use. Its primary associations are with self-esteem and its basis; with the place of an individual in a social group; with the performance of given roles; and with the integrity, continuity and stability of the sense of self. Themes such as these have been explored, for example, by Tobin (1991) in his work on later life, and by Barham and Hayward (1991) in their study of ex-mental patients living in the community. Social psychology, as an empirical discipline, seeks to ground its discourses in evidence, even while recognizing that some of this may consist of pointers and allusions. Robust measures such as those valued by the traditional natural sciences usually cannot be obtained, even if an illusion is created that they can.

Thus we arrive at a definition of personhood, as I shall use the term in this book. It is a standing or status that is bestowed upon one human being, by others, in the context of relationship and social being. It implies recognition, respect and trust. Both the according of personhood, and the failure to do so, have consequences that are empirically testable.

The issue of inclusion

As soon as personhood is made into a central category, some crucial questions arise. Who is to be viewed and treated as a person? What are the grounds for inclusion and exclusion, since 'person' is clearly not a mere synonym for 'human being'? Is the concept of personhood absolute, or can it be attenuated?

Such questions have been examined many times, particularly in western moral philosophy. In one of the best-known discussions Quinton (1973) suggests five criteria. The first is consciousness, whose normal accompaniment is consciousness of self. The second is rationality, which in its most developed form includes the capacity for abstract reasoning. The third is agency: being able to form intentions, to consider alternatives, and to direct action accordingly. The fourth is morality, which in its strongest form means living according to principle, and being accountable for one's actions. The fifth is the capacity to form and hold relationships; essential here is the ability to understand and identify with the interests, desires and needs of others. Quinton suggests that each criterion can be taken in a stronger or a weaker sense. We can make the distinction, for example, between someone who has all the capabilities of a moral agent, and someone who does not, but who is nevertheless the proper subject for moral concern.

With the arrival of computers and the creation of systems with artificial intelligence, doubts began to be raised about whether the concept of personhood is still valid (Dennett 1975). The central argument is as follows. In computers we have machines which mimic certain aspects of human mental function. We can (and often do) describe and explain the 'behaviour' of computers as if they were intentional beings, with thoughts, wishes, plans and so on. However, there is no necessity to do this; it is simply an anthropomorphism – a convenient short cut. In fact the behaviour of computers can be completely described and explained in physical terms. It is then argued that the same is possible, in principle, with human beings, although the details are more complex. Thus an intentional frame is not strictly necessary; and the category of personhood, to which it is so strongly tied, becomes redundant.

Behind such debates a vague shadow can be discerned. It is that of the liberal academic of former times: kind, considerate, honest, fair, and above all else an intellectual. Emotion and feeling have only a minor part in the scheme of things; autonomy is given supremacy over relationship and commitment; passion has no place at all. Moreover the problems seem to centre on how to describe and explain, which already presupposes an existential stance of detachment. So long as we stay on this ground the category of personhood is indeed in danger of being undermined, and with it the moral recognition of people with mental impairments. At a popularistic level, matters are more simple. Under the influence of the extreme individualism that has dominated western societies in recent years, criteria such as those set out by Quinton have been reduced to two: autonomy and rationality. Now the shadowy figure in the background is the devotee of 'business culture'. Once this move is made, there is a perfect justification for excluding people with serious disabilities from the 'personhood club'.

Both the mainstream philosophical debate and its popularistic reductions have been radically questioned by Stephen Post, in his book *The Moral Challenge of Alzheimer's Disease* (1995). Here he argues that it has been a grave error to place such great emphasis on autonomy and rational capability; this is part of the imbalance of our cultural tradition. Personhood, he suggests, should be linked far more strongly to feeling, emotion and the ability to live in relationships, and here people with dementia are often highly competent – sometimes more so than their carers.

Post also suggests a principle of *moral solidarity*: a recognition of the essential unity of all human beings, despite whatever differences there may be in their mental capabilities as conventionally determined. Thus we are all, so to speak, in the same boat; and there can be no empirically determined point at which it is justifiable to throw some people into the sea. The radical broadening of moral awareness that Post commends has many applications in the context of dementia: for example to how diagnostic information is handled, to the negotiation of issues such as driving or self-care, and ultimately to the most difficult questions of all, concerning the preservation of life.

Personhood and relationship

There is another approach to the question of what it means to be a person, which gives priority to experience, and relegates analytic discussion to a very minor place. One of its principal exponents was Martin Buber, whose small book *Ich und Du* was first published in 1922, and later appeared in an English translation, with the title *I and Thou*, in 1937. It is significant that this work was written during that very period when the forces of modernization had caused enormous turmoil throughout the world, and in the aftermath of the horrific brutalities of the First World War.

Buber's work centres on a contrast between two ways of being in the world; two ways of living in relationship. The first he terms I–It, and the second I–Thou. In his treatment of Thou he has abstracted one of many meanings; making it so to speak, into a jewel. In older usage it is clear that a person could be addressed as Thou in many forms of 'strong recognition': command, accusation, insult and threat, as well as the special form of intimacy that Buber portrays. Relating in the I–It mode implies coolness, detachment, instrumentality. It is a way of maintaining a safe distance, of avoiding risks; there is no danger of vulnerabilities being exposed. The I–Thou mode, on the other hand, implies going out towards the other; self-disclosure, spontaneity – a journey into uncharted territory. Relationships of the I–It kind can never rise beyond the banal and trivial. Daring to relate to another as Thou may involve anxiety or even suffering, but Buber sees it also as the path to fulfilment and joy. 'The primary word I–Thou can only be spoken with the whole being. The primary word I–It can never be spoken with the whole being' (1937: 2).

Buber's starting point, then, is different from that of western individualism. He does not assume the existence of ready-made monads, and then inquire into their attributes. His central assertion is that relationship is primary; to be a person is to be addressed as Thou. There is no implication here that there are two different kinds of objects in the world: Thous and Its. The difference lies in the manner of relating. Thus it is possible (and, sad to say, all too common) for one human being to engage with another in the I–It mode. Also it is possible, at least to some degree, to engage with a non-human being as Thou. We might think, for example, of a woman in her 80s whose dog is her constant and beloved companion, or of a Japanese man who faithfully attends his bonsai tree each day.

In the English language we have now almost lost the word Thou. Once it was part of everyday speech, corresponding to the life of face-to-face communities. Its traces remain in just a few places still; for example in North country dialects, and in old folk songs such as one about welcoming a guest, which has the heart-warming refrain:

> Draw chair raight up to t'table;
> Stay as long as Thou art able;
> I'm always glad to see a man like Thee.

Among minority groups in Britain, the Quakers were the last to give up the use of Thou in daily conversation, and they did so with regret. Their sense of the sacredness of every person was embedded in their traditional form of speech.

One of the most famous of all Buber's sayings is 'All real living is meeting' (1937: 11). Clearly it is not a matter of committees or business meetings, or even a meeting to plan the management of care. It is not the meeting of one intellectual with another, exchanging their ideas but revealing almost nothing of their feelings. It is not the meeting between a rescuer and a victim, the one intent on helping or 'saving' the other. It is not necessarily the meeting that occurs during a sexual embrace. In the meeting of which Buber speaks there is no ulterior purpose, no hidden agenda. The ideas to be associated with this are openness, tenderness, presence (present-ness), awareness. More than any of these, the word that captures the essence of such meeting is *grace*. Grace implies something not sought or bought, not earned or deserved. It is simply that life has mysteriously revealed itself in the manner of a gift.

For Buber, to become a person also implies the possibility of freedom. 'So long as the heaven of Thou is spread out over me, the wind of causality cowers at my heels, and the whirlwind of fate stays its course' (1937: 9). Here, in poetic language, is a challenge to all determinism, all mechanical theories of action. In that meeting where there is full acceptance, with no attempt to manipulate or utilize, there is a sense of expansiveness and new possibility, as if all chains have been removed. Some might claim that this is simply an illusion, and that no human being can escape from the power of heredity and conditioning. Buber, however, challenges the assumption that there is no freedom by making a direct appeal to the experience of the deepest form of relating. It is here that we gain intuitions of our ability to determine who we are, and to choose the path that we will take. This experience is to be taken far more seriously than any theory that extinguishes the idea of freedom.

Buber's work provides a link between the three types of discourse in which the concept of personhood is found: transcendental, ethical and social-psychological. His account is transcendental, in that he portrays human relationship as the only valid route to what some would describe as an encounter with the divine. His account is ethical, in that it emphasizes so strongly the value of persons. It is not, however, a contribution to analytic debate. For Buber cuts through all argumentation conducted from a detached and intellectualized standpoint, and gives absolute priority to engagement and commitment. Against those who might undermine the concept of personhood through analogies from artificial intelligence, Buber might simply assert that no one has yet engaged with a computer as Thou.

In relation to social psychology, we have here the foundation for an empirical inquiry in which the human being is taken as a person rather than as an object. There is, of course, no way of proving – either through observation or experiment – whether Buber's fundamental assertions are true or false. Any attempt to do so would make them trivial, and statements that appeal through their poetic power would lose their meaning. (It would be equally foolish, for example, to set about verifying the statement 'My love is like a red, red rose, that's newly sprung in June'.) The key point is this. Before any kind of inquiry can get under way in a discipline that draws on evidence, assumptions have to be made. Popper (1959) likened these to stakes, driven into a swamp, so that a stable building can be constructed. These assumptions are metaphysical, beyond the possibility of testing. Thus, in creating a social psychology, we can choose (or not) to accept these particular assumptions, according to whether they help to make sense of everyday experience and whether they correspond to our moral convictions (Kitwood and Bredin 1992a).

To see personhood in relational terms is, I suggest, essential if we are to understand dementia. Even when cognitive impairment is very severe, an I–Thou form of meeting and relating is often possible. There is, however, a very sombre point to consider about contemporary practice. It is that a man or woman could be given the most accurate diagnosis, subjected to the most thorough assessment, provided with a highly detailed care plan and given a place in the most pleasant surroundings – without any meeting of the I–Thou kind ever having taken place.

The psychodynamics of exclusion

Many cultures have shown a tendency to depersonalize those who have some form of serious disability, whether of a physical or a psychological kind. A consensus is created, established in tradition and embedded in social practices, that those affected are not real persons. The rationalizations follow on. If people show bizarre behaviour 'they are possessed by devils'; 'they are being punished for the sins of a former life'; 'the head is rotten'; 'there is a mental disorder whose symptoms are exactly described in the new diagnostic manual'.

Several factors come together to cause this dehumanization. In part, no doubt, it corresponds to characteristics of the culture as a whole; where personhood is widely disregarded, those who are powerless are liable to be particularly devalued. Many societies, including our own, are permeated by an ageism which categorizes older people as incompetent, ugly and burdensome, and which discriminates against them at both a personal and a structural level (Bytheway 1995). Those who have dementia are often subjected to ageism in its most extreme form; and, paradoxically, even people who are affected at a relatively young age are often treated as if they were 'senile'. In financial terms, far too few resources have been allocated to the provision of the necessary services. There is also the fact that very little attention has been given to developing the attitudes and skills that are necessary for good psychological care. In the case of dementia, until very recently this was not even recognized as an issue, with the consequence that many people working in this field have had no proper preparation for their work.

Behind these more obvious reasons, there may be another dynamic which excludes those who have dementia from the world of persons. There seems to be something special about the dementing conditions – almost as if they attract to themselves a particular kind of inhumanity: a social psychology that is malignant in its effects, even when it proceeds from people who are kind and well-intentioned (Kitwood 1990d). This might be seen as a defensive reaction, a response to anxieties held in part at an unconscious level.

The anxieties seem to be of two main kinds. First, and naturally enough, every human being is afraid of becoming frail and highly dependent; these fears are liable to be particularly strong in any society where the sense of community is weak or non-existent. Added to that, there is the fear of a long drawn-out process of dying, and of death itself. Contact with those who are elderly, weak and vulnerable is liable to activate these fears, and threaten our basic sense of security (Stevenson 1989). Second, we carry fears about mental instability. The thought of being insane, deranged, lost forever in confusion, is terrifying. Many people have come close to this at some point, perhaps in times of great stress, or grief, or personal catastrophe, or while suffering from a disease that has affected mental functioning. At the most dreadful end of these experiences lies the realm of 'unbeing', where even the sense of self is undermined.

Dementia in another person has the power to activate fears of both kinds: those concerned with dependence and frailty, and those concerned with going insane. Moreover, there is no real consolation in saying 'It won't happen to me', which can be done with many other anxiety-provoking conditions. Dementia is present in almost every street, and discussed repeatedly in the media. We know also that people from all kinds of background are affected, and that among those over 80 the proportion may be as high as one in five. So in being close to a person with dementia we may be seeing some terrifying anticipation of how we might become.

It is not surprising, then, if sensitivity has caused many people to shrink from such a prospect. Some way has to be found for making the anxieties bearable. The highly defensive tactic is to turn those who have dementia into a different species, not persons in the full sense. The principal problem, then, is not that of changing people with dementia, or of 'managing' their behaviour; it is that of moving beyond our own anxieties and defences, so that true meeting can occur, and life-giving relationships can grow.

The uniqueness of persons

At a commonsensical level it is obvious that each person is profoundly different from all others. It is easy to list some of the dimensions of that difference: culture, gender, temperament, social class, lifestyle, outlook, beliefs, values, commitments, tastes, interests – and so on. Added to this is the matter of personal history. Each person has come to be who they are by a route that is uniquely their own; every stage of the journey has left its mark.

In most of the contexts of everyday life, perhaps this kind of perception will suffice. There are times, however, when it is essential to penetrate the veil of common sense and use theory to develop a deeper understanding. It is not that theory is important in itself, but that it can challenge popular misconceptions; and it helps to generate sensitivity to areas of need, giving caring actions a clearer direction (Kitwood 1997a).

Within conventional psychology the main attempt to make sense of the differences between persons has been through the concept of personality, which may roughly be defined as 'a set of widely generalised dispositions to act in certain kinds of way' (Alston 1976). The concept of personality, in itself, is rich enough to provide many therapeutic insights. However, by far the greatest amount of effort in psychology has been spent in attempts to 'measure' it in terms of a few dimensions (extraversion, neuroticism, and so on), using standard questionnaires – personality inventories, as they are often called. The questions tend to be simplistic and are usually answered through self-report. This approach does have some value, perhaps, in helping to create a general picture, and it has been used in this way in the context of dementia. The main use of personality measurement, however, has been in classifying and selecting people for purposes that were not their own. Psychometric methodology is, essentially, a servant of the I–It mode.

There is another approach within psychology, whose central assumption is that each person is a meaning-maker and an originating source of action (Harré and Secord 1972; Harré 1993). Because of its special interest in everyday life it is sometimes described as being ethogenic, by analogy with the ethological study of animals in their natural habitats. Social life can be considered to consist of a series of episodes, each with certain overriding characteristics (buying a pot plant, sharing a meal, and so on). In each episode the participants make their 'definitions of the situation', usually at a level just below conscious awareness, and then bring more or less ready-made action schemata into play. Interaction occurs as each interprets the meaning of the others' actions. Personality here is viewed as an individual's stock of learned resources for action. It is recognized that one person may have a richer set of resources than another, and in that sense have a more highly developed personality. A full 'personality inventory' would consist of the complete list of such resources, together with the types of situation in which each item is typically deployed.

This view can be taken further by assimilating to it some ideas that are central to depth psychology and psychotherapeutic work. The resources are of two main kinds, which we might term *adaptive* and *experiential*. The first of these consists of learned ways of responding 'appropriately' to other people's demands (both hidden and explicit), to social situations, and to the requirements of given roles. The process of learning is relatively straightforward, and is sometimes portrayed as involving imitation, identification and internalization (Danziger 1978). The second kind of resource relates to a person's capacity to experience what he or she is actually undergoing. Development here occurs primarily when there is an abundance of comfort, pleasure, security and freedom. In Jungian theory

the adaptive resources correspond roughly to the ego, and the experiential resources to the
Self (Jung 1934). The term that I shall use for the latter is 'experiential self'.

In an ideal world, both kinds of personal resource would grow together. The consequence would be an adult who was highly competent in many areas of life, and who had a
well-developed subjectivity. He or she would be 'congruent', in the sense used by Rogers
(1961): that is, there would be a close correspondence between what the person was undergoing, experiencing, and communicating to others. In fact, however, this is very rarely the
case. The development of adaptive resources is often blocked by lack of opportunity, by the
requirements of survival, and sometimes by the naked imposition of power. The growth of
an experiential self is impeded where there is cruelty or a lack of love, or where the demands
of others are overwhelming. Many people have been subjected to some form of childhood
abuse: physical, sexual, emotional, commercial, spiritual. Areas of pain and inner conflict
are hidden away, and the accompanying anxiety is sealed off by psychological defences.
According to the theorists of Transactional Analysis, this is the context in which each person acquires a 'script' – a way of 'getting by' that makes it possible to function in difficult
circumstances (Stewart and Joines 1987). As a result of extreme overadaptation, so Winn-
icott suggested, a person acquires a 'false self', a 'front' that is radically out of touch with
experience and masks an inner chaos (Davis and Wallbridge 1981).

These ideas, which I have sketched here in only the barest outline, can be developed
into a many-sided view or model of personal being. As we shall see, it can shed much light
on the predicament of men and women who have dementia. Where resources have been
lost, we might ask some very searching questions about what has happened and why. If
personhood appears to have been undermined, is any of that a consequence of the ineptitude of others, who have all their cognitive powers intact? If uniqueness has faded into a
grey oblivion, how far is it because those around have not developed the empathy that is
necessary, or their ability to relate in a truly personal way? Thus we are invited to look
carefully at ourselves, and ponder on how we have developed as persons; where we are
indeed strong and capable, but also where we are damaged and deficient. In particular, we
might reflect on whether our own experiential resources are sufficiently well developed for
us to be able to help other people in their need.

Personhood and embodiment

Thus far in this chapter we have looked at issues related to personhood almost totally from
the standpoint of the human sciences. The study of dementia, however, has been dominated
by work in such disciplines as anatomy, physiology, biochemistry, pathology and genetics.
If our account of personhood is to be complete, then, we must find a way of bringing the
discourses of the human and natural sciences together.

There is a long-standing debate within philosophy concerning the problem of how the
mind is related to the body, and to matter itself. The debate first took on a clear form with the
work of Descartes in the seventeenth century, and since that time several distinct positions
have emerged. I am going to set out one of these, drawing to some extent on the work of the
philosopher Donald Davidson (1970), and the brain scientists Steven Rose (1984) and Antonio
Damasio (1995). The starting point is to reject the assumption with which Descartes began:
that there are two fundamentally different substances, matter and mind. Instead, we postu-
late a single (exceedingly complex) reality; it can be termed 'material', so long as it is clear
that 'matter' does not consist of the little solid particles that atoms were once taken to be.

We can never grasp this reality, as it really is, because of the limitations of our nervous system, but we can talk about it in several different ways. Often we use an intentional kind of language, with phrases such as 'I feel happy', 'I believe that you are telling the truth', 'I ought to go and visit my aunt'. Through this kind of language we can describe our feelings, draw up plans, ask people to give reasons for their actions, and so on. Often when we speak and think along these lines we have a sense of freedom, as if we are genuinely making choices, taking decisions, and making things happen in the world.

The natural sciences operate on very different lines. Here the aim is to be rigorously objective, using systematic observation and experiment. Within any one science regularities are discovered, and processes are seen in terms of causal relationships. People who work as scientists sometimes have a sense of absolute determinism. The determinism is actually built in from the start; it is part of the 'grammar'. We know no other way of doing the thing called natural science.

Each type of discourse has its particular uses. One of the greatest and commonest mistakes is to take the descriptions and explanations given in language as if these were the reality itself. Once that is done, many false problems arise; for example, whether or not we really have free will, whether the mind is inside the brain, whether the emotions are merely biochemical, and so on. There are strong reasons for believing that the reality itself, whatever it may be, is far too complex to be caught fully in any of our human nets of language.

Moving on now to the topic of mind and brain, the basic assumption is that any psychological event (such as deciding to go for a walk) or state (such as feeling hungry) is also a brain event or state. It is not that the psychological experience (ψ) is causing the brain activity (**b**) or vice versa; it is simply that some aspect of the true reality is being described in two different ways.

Hence in any individual, $\psi \equiv \mathbf{b}$

The 'equation' simply serves to emphasize the assumption that psychology and neurology are, in truth, inseparable.

It is not known how far experiences which two different individuals describe in the same way have parallel counterparts in brain function; scanning methods which look at brain metabolism do, however, suggest broad similarities (Fischbach 1992).

Now the brain events or states occur within an 'apparatus' that has a structure, an architecture. The key functioning part is a system of around ten thousand million (10^{10}) neurones, with their myriads of branches and connections, or synapses. A synapse is the point at which a 'message' can pass from one neurone to another, thus creating the possibility of very complex 'circuits'. So far as is known, the basic elements of this system, some general features of its development, and most of the 'deeper' forms of circuitry (older in evolutionary terms), are genetically 'given'. On the other hand the elaboration of the whole structure, and particularly the cerebral cortex, is unique to each individual and not pregiven. The elaboration, then, is epigenetic: subject to processes of learning that occur after the genes have had their say. Each human face is unique; so also is each human brain.

It is probable that there are at least two basic types of learning: explicit and implicit (Kandel and Hawkins 1992). The former involves, for example, remembering faces and places, facts and theories. The latter involves acquiring skills that have a strong physical component; for example learning to walk, to swim or to play the piano. In both cases, learning is thought to proceed by stages. First, over a period of minutes or hours, existing neurone circuits are modified, by the strengthening and weakening of synaptic connections that already exist. Then, and much more slowly – over days, weeks and months – new synaptic connections are formed.

> The design of brain circuits continues to change. The circuits are not only receptive to the results of first experiences, but repeatedly pliable and modifiable by continued experience. Some circuits are remodelled over and over throughout the life span, according to the changes that the organism undergoes.
>
> (Damasio 1995: 112)

The brain is a 'plastic' organ. The continuing developmental aspect of its structure can be symbolized as B^d.

In dementia there is usually a loss of neurones and synaptic connections, making it impossible for the brain to carry out its full set of functions (Terry 1992). Some of this occurs slowly, and is a 'normal' part of ageing. It probably arises from the accumulation of errors in the reproduction of biological materials over a long period, and chemical processes such as oxidation. The more serious and rapid losses, however, appear to be the consequence of disease or degenerative processes, and these may be symbolized as B_p (brain pathology). So, very crudely, the situation within an individual can be represented thus:

$$\frac{\psi \equiv \mathbf{b}}{(B^d, B_p)}$$

(Any psychological event or state is also a brain event or state, 'carried' by a brain whose structure has been determined by both developmental and pathological factors.)

If this view is correct in principle, it shows how the issues related to personhood are also those of brain and body. Here, there is one particularly important point to note. It is that the developmental, epigenetic aspects of brain structure have been grossly neglected in recent biomedical research on dementia; moreover, there is scarcely a hint of interest in this topic in contemporary psychiatry and clinical psychology. Yet neuroscience now suggests that there may be very great differences between human beings in the degree to which nerve architecture has developed as a result of learning and experience. It follows that individuals may vary considerably in the extent to which they are able to withstand processes in the brain that destroy synapses, and hence in their resistance to dementia.

In this kind of way we move towards a 'neurology of personhood'. All events in human interaction – great and small – have their counterpart at a neurological level. The sense of freedom which Buber associates with I–Thou relating may correspond to a biochemical environment that is particularly conducive to nerve growth. A malignant social psychology may actually be damaging to nerve tissue. Dementia may be induced in part, by the stresses of life. Thus anyone who envisages the effects of care as being 'purely psychological', independent of what is happening in the nervous system, is perpetuating the error of Descartes in trying to separate mind from body. Maintaining personhood is both a psychological and a neurological task.

Well-being in dementia

Having dementia does not, in itself, entail a loss of personhood. These pictures show people with a high level of well-being, despite the presence of cognitive impairment.

The late Peter Ashley (pictured front right) in 2010 receiving an honorary degree from University of Worcester for services to dementia advocacy.

Copyright: University of Worcester.

A resident in an Australian care home enjoying time with a staff member, a sleepy rabbit, and her own stuffed rabbit, a constant companion.

Copyright: Cathy Greenblat.

On being a person

Commentary by Jan Dewing

This commentary on the opening chapter is undertaken from a point of scholarly respect for Tom Kitwood, his research and contribution to person-centred caring. This does not mean, however, that I will accept everything he says as a given. Further, I want to raise some questions about his assumptions. Kitwood left an unfinished tableau and it is the responsibility of others to take this forward in a way that is fair and just to the ideas he shared. His ideas, as are all ideas, are a product of their time and influenced by his worldview, including his experiences and the culture he was embedded in. It is unfair to treat Kitwood's definition of personhood in a rigid or simplistic way, just as it is unfair to accept it as written in tablet of stone for evermore. A benefit of his definition is that it is written in relatively plain English, and has an instinctive appeal to many people. Yet beneath the surface there are several complex philosophical ideas that need closer examination. Had Kitwood been able to progress his theoretical development further, he would have at least clarified his understanding in the light of critique or even refined and progressed it beyond its current form. Instead, contemporary researchers and scholars have done much to both critique and advance the ideas underpinning Kitwood's notion of person, personhood and also person-centredness. Kitwood, though theoretically active, did not leave a large volume of philosophically based work for those following him to draw on and this has been challenging in terms of trying to isolate the philosophical foundations of his work. At best he had an eclectic approach in which he mixed several philosophical ideas together. Perhaps he was eclectic and less formal in his scholarship as he wanted to bring 'academic' and 'therapeutic' psychology closer together. Indeed, Kitwood can be credited with bringing the notion of personhood to life (i.e. for it to have relevance and meaning) for many people concerned with dementia care. It is, however, worth bearing in mind two important points. First, personhood has been a topic of debate in philosophy for many hundreds of years. Kitwood did not invent it per se; instead he brought it to life in dementia care. Second, he laid the groundwork for much of his ideas and his positioning of them in *Dementia Reconsidered* in an earlier non-dementia specific text, *Concepts in Developmental Psychology. Concern for Others: A New Psychology of Conscience and Morality* (Kitwood 1990a). This is a text that, in my view, is largely and wrongly ignored. Two of the challenges in critiquing and advancing Kitwood's scholarship have been the lack of explicit scholarship and the associated lack of a clear reference audit trail in his work (Dewing 2008). In this commentary, I will offer a critique of the main ideas underpinning Chapter 1, discussing them in the context of related philosophical concepts, and finally consider what the dementia care community needs to address as we move forward with our scholarly, practice-based understandings of person-centredness.

Revisiting core concepts

Many readers of *Dementia Reconsidered* will perhaps recall that the book starts with a chapter on celebrating what Kitwood referred to as 'our common ground' (p. 6). This was unusual at the time, as most books on dementia began with a chapter on the biomedical condition with the text focused on what persons 'suffering' from dementia could no longer do. Further, such chapters mostly presented a negative scenario about dementia, where the experience of those living with dementia was left out entirely or sometimes presented as a 'case study'. Sadly, this often remains the case today, with many textbooks continuing to emphasize abnormality, loss and dependency. Kitwood started his book differently as his intention was to set about challenging readers to examine deeply their values and beliefs, many of which were taken for granted and originating from biomedical science. He wanted readers to take a long, hard look at what and who someone with dementia was, and still is, in terms of humanity. He intended to show that 'they' are 'us' and 'we' are 'them', and any contrived separation was artificial. Kitwood (p. 11) considered the exclusion of persons with dementia from the world of persons as attracting a particular type of inhumanity; he had by then already framed this as malignant social psychology (Kitwood 1990b). Of particular relevance to this chapter is that Kitwood considers the origins of the separation to be from the collective unconscious. There exists, he claimed, a deep-rooted anxiety about, first, ageing and the associated frailty and ultimately a prolonged dying process and, second, about mental instability and moving into a state of 'unbeing' (p. 11). Twenty years on, it can still be argued these two anxieties remain despite much progress in the fields of dementia care and end-of-life care. We can also debate if persons with dementia do move into a state of 'unbeing'. Our values and beliefs and philosophical leaning(s) can assist us to explore this profound concern. For example, it is possible to argue that persons living with dementia do indeed experience an unravelling of identity, which can impact on personhood. One alternative is that it can be argued that persons living with dementia move into a new way of being.

Understanding what a person is, and how we position our definition in relation to what a human being is, must be the starting point for a discussion about what makes a person. In seeking to understand this, we quickly encounter the notion of personhood. Such philosophical and theoretical discussion might appear at first glance to seem far removed from person-centred care. Kitwood makes it clear (p. 7) that a person is not the same as or synonymous with being a human being. A critical question to begin with is to ask why he does this. Given his moral and theological background, it seems more likely he would have opted for the path that claims all human beings are persons by way of some transcendental and non-material means. Taking that route would have significantly reduced the need to have inclusion criteria for personhood. Because he instead highlights the distinction, he then must name and argue criteria that are necessary and sufficient for human beings to be considered as persons. As anyone who has tried to account for this, a criterion-based view of personhood soon becomes fraught with complexities. At the start of Chapter 1, Kitwood (p. 6) stresses that we 'have to recognize men and women who have dementia in their full humanity'. To achieve this, Kitwood argues it is helpful to be concerned with (i) the uniqueness of persons including embodiment, (ii) the category of personhood and (iii) the centrality of [a particular type of] relationship (pp. 6–7, 11). The key features underpinning this are discussed below.

'Personhood' is the central idea to Chapter 1 of the book and Kitwood defines it as 'a standing or status that is bestowed upon one human being, by others, in the context of relationship and social being' (p. 7). There are connections here to the ideas expressed by Buber (1878–1965) and Levinas (1906–1995). For Buber, the I–Thou relationship is between two subjects in a relationship that affirms the 'other' through the act of choosing to relate in a particular way (Jewell 2011). An important point is that the way of relating is not dependent on roles, power or organizational status. This idea suited Kitwood as his intention was to downplay the dementia and to see the person first and foremost. Similarly, he intended that caregivers should see their own personhood and not be constrained or shaped by the culture of the organization or role they were in. To a greater extent it is the former that has received most attention within dementia care and the latter notion has been somewhat reduced in its significance, which in my view has delayed progress. I would contend that person-centredness is primarily about culture, one that holds and enables person-centred care to take place within the overall culture (Dewing and McCormack 2017). Person-centred care requires a person-centred culture to be present and working effectively. Therefore, we will make the most progress when we approach person-centredness as a culture (McCormack and McCance 2017) not just in terms of its being a relationship between individuals.

While Dennett (1976) considers there are seven layers of personhood and Smith (2010) outlines some 30 causal capacities necessary for subjective and objective activity, Kitwood avoided the pitfall of setting out personhood in relation to causal capabilities (for example, cognition, decision making, agency, and so on). Instead, he positioned it as an attribute of moral relationships between human beings. This is often referred to as a relational conceptualization of personhood, according to Buetow (2016). We are helped in our understanding about what Kitwood was hoping to convey when we recognize and appreciate some of the philosophical ideas that he was influenced by. I have already noted the influence of Buber (to whom he devotes two pages); he also cites Descartes (1596–1650) and Kant (1724–1804), as well as contemporaries such as Post (1951–). Kitwood's concern for others was such that he spelled out, specifically for dementia care, the deeper moral implications of actions and inactions people could take in their caring roles. Kitwood, however, departs from Buber's position on personhood, defining it as a gift rather than a moral entitlement. The definition offered here is highly westernized (Callegaro 2013). In contrast, for many Indigenous human beings, such as Australians (McMillan et al. 2010), personhood is connected to community and to country. Similarly, in South Africa there is a word 'ubuntu' (or unhu), meaning 'humanity' or 'humanity towards others'. Ubuntu can be used in a more philosophical sense to mean a belief in a universal bond of sharing that connects all humanity. The connectedness is fundamentally about moral goodness and moral beauty (Ikuenobe 2016). At its core, ubuntu asserts that society, rather than any individuality, gives human beings their humanity or personhood and I think quite effectively captures the essence of Kitwood's definition (i.e. the bestowing of personhood). Eze (2010) suggests that, through recognition of an 'other' in his or her uniqueness and difference, we also validate our own personhood. Interestingly, Eze considers this position as an ideal, although also contends that humanity is a quality we owe to one another.

In the first chapter, Kitwood primarily attempts to consider the ethical, social-psychological and neurological significance of personhood from a westernized perspective – an enormously ambitious aim for the opening chapter. Because of this, there is an oversimplification of complex concepts and a tendency for these to be presented in a linear fashion. Kitwood's definition has several major limitations. For example, he defines personhood as being bestowed or gifted by one human being to another. We might ask: Can, and should, anyone of us bestow personhood on another person? What happens to others and to our own being, should we withhold it? The standing or status is viewed within the context of society and relationship, although the nature or type of relationship is not clarified, other than one that has recognition, respect and trust (p. 7). These attributes are part of a person-centred relationship, but not the totality of it. To go beyond this in the text, in terms of clarifying core concepts, is challenging and requires a large degree of interpretation. For example, Baldwin et al. (2007: 180), inaccurately in my view, argue that Kitwood intends for person-hood to be bestowed by others on the person with dementia and not the other way around. In other words, that this is not a mutual relationship. It may be that focusing too much on the definition is misguided. From my reading of the different sections of the chapter, a number of key concepts, as described below, stand out and seem to be of (more) significance for considering and defining more creatively and inclusively what constitutes personhood.

Unity of all human beings

Post (2000) helpfully refers to this as moral solidarity. He argues for a morality based on what all humans have in common with one another, rather than on what our differences are. Central to his argument is his challenge to the western value of 'hyper-cognition' – in other words, that the most important features are clarity of thought and mind (Post 2006). Partic-ularly at this time, when many countries are highlighting the growing cost to national budgets of ageing populations, it becomes too easy for people with dementia to be 'scapegoated' by wider society because of their disability and decreasing utility. Kitwood suggested that intellectualism and individualism are two significant western cultural factors that have led to people living with dementia being regarded as lesser or non-persons. Intellectualism is underpinned by cognitive capacity and capabilities, and individualism by autonomy and agency (Higgs and Gilleard 2016). The more we include items or categories of intellectual-ism (see, for example, Smith 2010) and attributes associated with individualism (see, for example, Torchia 2008), the further we marginalize and then exclude persons with dementia, and indeed many other persons. Yet Kitwood (1993) reminds us that as we make the effort to discover the person with dementia, we also discover something of who we are. I suggest this can be viewed as a living meeting between two or more persons, in much the way Levinas (1985) proposed.

Inclusion

Kitwood contended that personhood should be conceptualized more broadly, where personal and social relationships and moral solidarity are the foundational principles, not capabili-ties. Therefore, he specifically identified inclusion as a precondition for relationships, and ultimately for personhood. Inclusion here can be thought of as an active process.

Relationship

Buber (1970) proposed two types of ways that people relate to one another: 'I–It' and 'I–Thou'. The I–It way of relating is one in which a person relates to the other in a distanced, non-involved way that does not fully recognize the individuality of the other, and consequently the other becomes less of a person and is even objectified. In contrast, the I–Thou way of relating involves meeting the other person in a genuine human exchange. Kitwood stresses that I–It relating never moves beyond the banal and trivial (p. 9), while in I–Thou relating, there is an authentic engagement and he quotes Buber, who says 'that all real living is meeting' (1937: 11). For Levinas, the first responsibility of philosophy was that of an ethical duty to the other, rather than exploration of knowledge. Levinas maintains that the encounter with others is our primary and privileged responsibility, and it is through this ethical priority that 'I' gets to become me. This line is very similar to that of Buber, although Levinas probably stresses respect and relationship more than mutuality and dialogue as Buber does. Further, Buber's I–Thou relationship is explicitly set up in the image of an I–Thou relationship with a Judeo-Christian God. Kitwood does not reflect on this issue further, either within this chapter or the rest of the book.

Uniqueness of persons

Scruton (2017) considers this as the sense of 'I' and 'me' unique to humans. Kitwood may be drawing on Kant's idea that persons have unique value, often called dignity. Kant conceives of dignity as meaning that persons are both infinitely valuable and irreplaceably valuable. Zagzebski (2001) argues that persons are infinitely valuable in relation to share-able qualities of their human nature, whereas they are irreplaceably valuable because of other aspects of personhood such as personality; and, as Harees (2012) says, are situated within distinctly different self-reflective and imaginative biographies. The uniqueness of persons can therefore be situated within the individual or within a community or culture, within capabilities or within attributes of the relationship between humans. Depending on our values and how we understand the uniqueness of person, it will shape how we facilitate the development of person-centredness, and how we organize, deliver and evaluate person-centred care. We can see in his work how Kitwood considered personality and biography as core to the person coming first.

Embodiment

Kitwood did use this term in his writing of *Dementia Reconsidered*. However, he used it in a very limited way. He referred to it mostly to mean the neurological and mental effects of a condition or experience on the physical body and general health. He did, though, consider sentience in more depth in his writing. Briefly, sentience is the capacity to feel, perceive or experience subjectively and is different from reason (the capability to think in a certain way). Possibly, as a psychologist he tended to privilege the mind and clearly positioned his ideas within a Cartesian model of mind/body duality. By moving away from consciousness and the mind/brain, and beyond the duality to the body and embodiment, we can open up some new possibilities for inclusiveness in how we define personhood. Matthews (2006) nicely emphasizes that our existence (i.e. consciousness) as a person emerges from our bodies not simply from the mind. Kontos and Martin (2013) have further explored 'self-hood' in relation to embodied dimensions and conclude that inclusion of embodiment can encourage innovative care practices. Kontos argues that embodiment disentangles personhood from the cognitive categories upon which it is presumed to depend. Similarly, Lindemann (2014) proposes a view of personhood as the bodily expression of the feelings, thoughts, desires and intentions that constitute a human personality, as recognized by others. Others then respond, in certain ways, to what they see. Because personhood is a social practice, the author argues that others can sustain personhood when we can no longer practise it ourselves.

Moving on

The popularization of Kitwood's definition of personhood has masked his overall purpose, which is a 'moral concern for all others' (Dewing 2008: 10). This moral focus is consistent with his emphasis on relational personhood and therefore on his use of Buber's philosophical ideas (I–Thou). When persons meet in an authentic I–Thou way, they potentially perceive and experience the world differently. In the space of the meeting and living there exists a potential for personhood, of each, to be maintained or enhanced. Kitwood's moral intent is to the removing of any artificial separation among humans. Further, he strongly rejects any criterion based on cognitively derived intelligence, including rationality, and bemoans the minor part emotion and feeling have in the scheme (p. 8) saying:

> People who have dementia, for whom the life of the emotions is often intense, and without the ordinary forms of inhibition, may have something important to teach the rest of humankind.
>
> (p. 5)

It is essential that those of us with intact cognition recognize that life can be and is lived by people like 'me' and 'you' in a different way or ways. Perhaps, when we consider the living through or beyond dementia (Swaffer 2016) we are looking at a radical form of diversity in the evolution of humankind that we need to account for in a united moral and inclusive way. Taylor (2011) says that 'you' and 'I' are fundamentally different from one another in ways that we probably can't express or perceive and appreciate. Central to Taylor's comment is that even if our brains are different, each of us is still as complete as we can be and therefore a *full* human being or person.

It is hard to escape thinking about personhood as not depending on brain or mind consciousness, memory, self-hood along with ideas of decision making, agency and autonomy. Yet this is exactly what we need to do in order to open up new representations of personhood for people living with dementia. Human beings with dementia are persons, in both fundamentally the same way and yet, at the same time, in different ways than they were before. Based on the discussion in this chapter we perhaps need to re-begin our re-considerations of personhood by including these concepts:

- A body consciousness
- Moral entitlement not a gift
- Dignity
- Always being open to difference, diversity and becoming.

As we move forward, the explorations we have must be inclusive of persons living with or beyond dementia (Swaffer 2016) – at present many persons living with dementia are still (kept) on the periphery of these scholarly discussions. Each time a new definition of personhood is released we, intentionally or unintentionally, position personhood within philosophy that is either a moral or a metaphysical category (Higgs and Gilleard 2016). While the nature of personal identity and 'self' occupies metaphysics, in moral philosophy the term is con-cerned more with the moral standing of persons. Both psychiatry and psychology have approached personhood and dementia in metaphysical terms, while the law and theology, on the other hand, have been more involved with moral considerations of personhood as 'a foundational concept in many systems of ethics' (Higgs and Gilleard 2016).

Summary

Revisiting Kitwood's ideas and his definition 20 years on, I conclude that he did advance the theory of person-centred dementia care and also influenced the development of person-centredness more broadly within the UK countries and beyond. It remains the case that Kitwood presented a definition of personhood that continues to be influential, despite its theoretical inconsistencies. The premise that personhood can be an optional gift is not a robust notion, even if it is the way it can happen in the real world. Maybe it is time we stopped searching for some special definition of personhood for human beings living with dementia and, in the desire to achieve unity and inclusion, instead perhaps look, alongside persons living with dementia, to more general considerations of personhood that capture our shared humanity, whatever way is our individual or collective being in the world.

Reflection points

- How would you summarize the progression of philosophical ideas since Kitwood's defi-nition emerged?
- What might the next 10–20 years bring in terms of challenging our ideas on human-based personhood?
- How would you argue the call for a universal definition of personhood that is inclusive of persons living with dementia (but not specific to people with dementia)?

2

Dementia as a psychiatric category

Tom Kitwood

A person who has dementia is involved in two kinds of change, going on side by side. First, there is the gradually advancing failure of mental powers such as memory, reasoning and comprehension. Much here can be attributed directly to the brain being less efficient; its function has declined, and usually there is degeneration in its actual structure. Second, there are changes in the social-psychological environment – in patterns of relationship and interaction:

> George, who used to be extremely polite and kind, shows great confusion at times, and on occasion says things that his former friends find offensive. Some of these friends do not know how to deal with George's apparent rudeness and unpredictability, and so begin to behave differently towards him; he now has to find ways of coping with their changed behaviour . . . and so on.

It is impossible, of course, to distinguish clearly between the two kinds of change – the one neurological and the other social-psychological. There can be no doubt, however, that the dementing process, as it actually occurs, is a consequence of them both.

The scientific disciplines related to psychiatry have devoted intense and detailed attention to the first kind of change, while subjecting the second to almost total neglect. As a result there has been much progress in elucidating the neuropathology, biochemistry and genetics of dementia, and several very promising lines of research are being pursued. When, however, those who work in these fields attempt to provide a larger picture, complete with causal hypotheses, they are less successful. The framework they have created, which I have termed 'the standard paradigm' (Kitwood 1989) has several major anomalies, both empirical and conceptual; and at times it falls into blatant reductionism. It is easy to find individual pieces of research convincing, and then be seduced into accepting the paradigm as a whole.

The purpose of this chapter is to summarize some of the significant research, and to point to the genuine advances of psychiatry in this field. At the same time I shall expose some of the weaknesses of the standard paradigm. Chapters 3, 4 and 6 will explore the social psychology of dementia. My hope, then, is that the three chapters taken together will provide a more complete picture of the process of dementia than the one which is commonly offered. This will not only have theoretical value, but also help us to see more clearly what dementia care involves.

Some definitional issues

It is now generally agreed that the term dementia should be used in a broad descriptive way, to point to a clinically identified condition; it refers to the whole person and not to the brain (see, for example, Hart and Semple 1990). One of the most widely accepted definitions was produced by a working party of neuroscientists and doctors in the USA in 1984:

> Dementia is the decline in memory and other cognitive functions in comparison with the patient's previous level of function as determined by a history of decline in performance and by abnormalities noted from clinical examination and neuropsychological tests.

> A diagnosis of dementia cannot be made when consciousness is impaired or when other clinical abnormalities prevent adequate evaluation of mental state. Dementia is a diagnosis based on behaviour and cannot be determined by brain scan, EEG or other laboratory instruments, although specific causes of dementia may be identified by these means.

> (McKhann et al. 1984)

The clearest indication of dementia, then, is that an individual's cognitive performance has gone down from an earlier level. As a rough and ready guide, dementia is more likely to be present if a person shows a decline in memory and at least one other main cognitive function; for example comprehension, judgement or planning. Some degree of loss of memory function, when it occurs alone, may be relatively benign (Kral 1962; Burns and Forstl 1994). An initial diagnosis of probable dementia still leaves open the question of what physiological and pathological processes may be involved. The primary dementias are those which are clearly associated with damage to brain tissue; the secondary dementias are those associated with other pathologies or physiological disturbances.

In general discussion dementia is said to be *mild* if a person still retains the ability to manage independently; *moderate* if some help is needed in the ordinary tasks of living; and *severe* if continual help and support are required. At a more technical level, various attempts have been made to define the degree of dementia in terms of stages. One of the most thoroughly worked out of these is that produced by Barry Reisburg and his colleagues. Here dementia is envisaged as involving seven stages of 'global deterioration', culminating in a state of extreme dependence and loss of psychomotor skills (Reisberg et al. 1982). Schemes such as this are helpful in focusing attention on what may be the precise nature of a person's disabilities. They can be misleading, however, in that they often seem to have bought in to a simple neurological determinism, while neglecting the social psychology. Also, like many schemes that incline to structuralism, in looking at general characteristics they easily obscure the uniqueness of persons.

At a popular level, the definitional issues have been clouded by what might be termed the 'alzheimerization' of dementia. Twenty-five years ago the name of Alois Alzheimer was known only to a small handful of specialists, and the main dementias of old age were often labelled as senility. Today Alzheimer has become a household word; there are Alzheimer's disease societies in many countries; and there is a world-wide federation – Alzheimer International.

No additional data were needed to convert senility into Alzheimer's disease, nor was there a shift of scientific paradigm. The change came about as a result of several pragmatic decisions, made in the attempt to attract funding for research in neuroscience, and following the conspicuous success of lobbying for heart disease and cancer (Fox 1989). In the early

1970s in the USA, Alzheimer's disease was taken from being a term for the pathology associated with an early-onset form of dementia, and applied to dementia as a whole. Moreover, it was declared to be the fourth largest cause of death in the USA (thereby confounding 'dying with' and 'dying from' a dementing condition). This renaming proved extremely popular all over the world. Perhaps it took away some of the stigma associated with going senile, and implied that there was a medical condition for which a cure might one day be found. In terms of nomenclature, however, we now have the rather unsatisfactory situation where 'Alzheimer's disease' has two different meanings. In ordinary speech, it is a general term to replace senility; and in biomedical science and psychiatry, it is a technical term for a broad category of pathology.

Neuropathology and dementia

The study of human nervous tissue has been a continuing project throughout the twentieth century. Even at the time when Alzheimer carried out his famous investigations in 1907, the microscopic examination of thin slices of brain, duly 'fixed' and stained, was an established technique (Berrios and Freeman 1991). Detailed work on brain structure gained momentum in the 1960s, with major investigations such as those carried out in Britain by the Newcastle Group (Blessed et al. 1968; Tomlinson et al. 1968, 1970). We now have a highly complex picture of the different kinds of disease and degenerative process that are associated with dementia. The three main categories that have come to be accepted are Alzheimer type, vascular type and 'mixed' – where the former two are found together.

Alzheimer type pathology

Three features mark out this category. First, there is a general loss of neurones, and hence of synaptic connections; in certain regions of the cortex as much as 40 per cent of all neurones may have been lost when dementia is severe. Second, there is an overall atrophy of the brain, shown as a shrinkage of the outer volume and an enlargement of the inner ventricles which were occupied by cerebro-spinal fluid. Third, there are certain signs of the degeneration of cell structure, which become visible at a microscopic level. The best-known signs are neuritic plaques and neurofibrillary tangles, though these are not the only ones. Recently, for example, Lewy bodies, which have been recognized for some time in the brains of people who died with Parkinson's disease, have been given much attention, and some authorities now prefer to make a separate category of Lewy body disease to mark instances where this is a dominant feature (Shergill and Katona 1996).

Although there are no clear age-related differences in Alzheimer type pathology, many workers have drawn attention to the heterogeneity of the condition (Boller et al. 1992). One possible explanation is that a single disease process gives rise to diverse outcomes in different individuals. Another, and more likely, explanation is that Alzheimer's disease (in the technical sense) is an umbrella term, in fact covering several different pathological processes that still remain to be differentiated.

Vascular pathology

This category includes all cases in which dementia is associated with cerebrovascular disease, and hence a lowered supply of blood to areas of the brain. Research has shown that there are several main forms of vascular pathology according to which parts of the brain are affected, and which types of blood vessel are failing in their function (O'Brien 1994). Occlusion may have occurred in larger or smaller arteries, or in capillary blood vessels, through deposits of amyloid material very similar to that found in the neuritic plaque. The more common forms of vascular dementia involve damage to the grey matter. In some cases, however, it is the white matter that is mainly affected; these conditions, which include that known as Binswanger's disease, have been given the general label of leukoariosis. Multi-infarct dementia is the term given to those conditions where the vascular damage seems to have taken a form very similar to that of a succession of tiny strokes. In most instances, as with Alzheimer's disease, vascular pathology is associated with cerebral atrophy. Specific regions where damage has occurred due to infarction may be detectable through scanning.

The term vascular dementia, then, covers a wide spectrum. At one end are conditions that could also be classified as minor strokes, while at the other the damage is more generalized, associated with a clinical picture which closely resembles that of Alzheimer's disease. Where vascular pathology is present in brain tissue, there is almost always a more general problem with the cardiovascular system.

'Mixed' pathology

Since the foundational studies in neuropathology of the 1960s it has been recognized that the brains of some persons who died with dementia contain the signs of both Alzheimer type and vascular pathologies. There are difficulties, however, in ascertaining the extent to which either type has actually contributed to the failure of brain function; this is especially the case with vascular pathology, since it is known that some brains are able to tolerate a considerable amount of damage due to this cause. Not surprisingly, then, estimates of the proportion of brains in the 'mixed' category have varied widely, from 4 to 23 per cent (O'Brien 1994). As a rough generalization, the older a person with Alzheimer's disease is at the point of death, the more likely it is that the brain will also show signs of vascular pathology.

Beyond the three main categories, there are many other causes of damage to brain structure: degenerative (e.g. Pick's disease, frontal lobe pathology), infective (e.g. Creutzfeldt-Jakob disease, meningitis, neurosyphilis, AIDS-related dementia), toxic (e.g. alcohol-related brain damage, poisoning by metals such as lead, cadmium or mercury, or by neuroactive organic compounds). For recent discussions of neurotoxins, whose significance may have been seriously underestimated, see Purdey (1994) and Holden (1996). Finally, there is the loss of neurones as a result of gross brain damage, whether through a single major head injury or through repeated smaller injuries as in boxing.

A distinction has been made between dementias of the cortical type, where the main pathology was believed to be in the cerebral cortex, and those of the subcortical type, associated with damage in the deeper (subcortical) regions. The three most common forms of dementia are, according to this classification, in the former category. The main items in the latter are dementia associated with Parkinson's disease, Huntington's disease, Wilson's disease, progressive supranuclear palsy and multiple sclerosis (Miller and Morris 1993). The cortical–subcortical distinction, however, is misleading, since most dementias are associated with pathology in both cortical and subcortical regions. Indeed, one of the keys to unravelling the mystery of Alzheimer's disease may lie in the damage to those neurones

Table 2.1 Distribution of pathologies associated with dementia (older view)

Type of pathology	%
Alzheimer	50
Vascular	10–15
Mixed	10–15
Other	to 100

Table 2.2 Distribution of pathology associated with dementia (Lewy body pathology differentiated)

Type of pathology	%
Alzheimer	50
Lewy body	20
Vascular	10
Mixed (the three types above)	10
Other	10

which have their cell bodies in the brain stem and mid-brain, and which project into the cerebral cortex (Hart and Semple 1990; Jobst 1994).

There is considerable variation in research findings on the relative proportions of the different types of pathology. Older data typically presented a pattern of the type shown in Table 2.1 (Albeit 1982). More recent figures, which separate out Lewy body disease as a distinct category, are shown in Table 2.2 (McKeith 1995).

Neuropathology and dementia: in more detail

Simple descriptions of neuropathology, especially if backed by photographic evidence, tend to convey the impression that the 'organic' basis of dementia is a simple and clear-cut matter. In fact this is very far from being the case.

All the common forms of neuropathology that are associated with the main dementias are also found in the brains of people who have no cognitive impairment. Even some degree of cerebral atrophy, as measured by computed topography (CT scanning), is found in a small proportion of 'normal' persons (Jacoby and Levy 1980; Burns et al. 1991). Clearly, then, there is no possibility of Alzheimer's or vascular dementia meeting the key criterion of a classical disease: that distinct pathological features should be present in all cases where the symptoms appear, and in none of the cases where they do not. Matters are made even more problematic when we take into account the lack of strong and consistent correlations between the degree of dementia, as measured in the living person, and the extent of neuropathology found post mortem. The correlations are especially weak with the neuritic plaque, which is rather widely distributed in the grey matter (Kitwood 1987; Nagy et al. 1995). It is thus doubtful whether either of the main primary dementias even meet the more modest criteria of a syndrome: that there should be a consistent association between symptoms and biological markers of some kind (Terry 1992).

The greatest difficulties arise in accounting for those people who have been found to meet clinical or neuropsychological criteria for dementia, but whose brains are found, post mortem, to have no neuropathology beyond what is normal for their age group. In different studies this proportion varies, the highest reported figure being 34 per cent (Homer et al. 1988). One way of saving the situation is to suggest that the original diagnosis was incorrect, and to create a category of 'pseudodementia', where mental impairment is said to be functional (Arie 1983). The difficulty with this move, however, is that it casts doubt on the whole diagnostic procedure, since it was clearly incapable of differentiating between true and 'pseudo' cases.

Even at the neuropathological level there is no clear criterion to provide a 'gold standard' for dementia. As we have seen, several markers of the degeneration of nerve tissue are visible when brain slices are examined microscopically, and signs of general atrophy can be observed through scanning. Since there is a continuum between those who do have dementia and those who do not, it is necessary to state which markers are to be taken as relevant, in which brain locations; and then, arbitrarily, to specify the minimum intensity that defines a particular disease. More than 10 years ago, attempts were made to define such criteria, but these have not been consistently followed (Hart and Semple 1990: 42–5). Recently it has even been suggested that the cut-off points should now be adjusted, to accommodate new genetic data (Roses 1995). Thus the idea that the true diagnosis of all cases will become clear once the brain is examined post mortem is certainly not correct.

Within biomedical research two main hypotheses have been put forward to explain the correlational anomalies. The better known and older view is that there may be a threshold effect; that is, there comes a point where the loss of neurones (or, more accurately, synaptic connections) in key areas of the brain is so great that normal function is impaired, and dementia ensues (Blessed et al. 1968). Recently, however, another hypothesis has been advanced: that the key difference lies in the rate of loss of neurones. Kim Jobst and his colleagues, who have been engaged in one of the world's largest prospective studies, present evidence from their scanning work that the rate of atrophy in the medial temporal lobe is about 10 times faster in people who have Alzheimer's disease than it is in controls (Jobst 1994). The suggestion is that the brain undergoes a kind of catastrophic change, although why this should occur remains mysterious. Many people have suggested that psychological factors such as stress, or depressive reactions to loss, may be involved. At last evidence to support the stress hypothesis is beginning to appear (O'Dwyer and Orrell 1994).

Diagnosing dementia

Making a diagnosis of dementia in any individual case – and even more, getting an idea of the associated pathology – is a very difficult task. It is notorious that GPs, clinical psychologists, psychiatrists and neurologists tend to differ in their opinions. Much depends, of course, on the kind of evidence that is considered, and in particular how much weight is given to problems of memory. Many simple psychological methods, such as the use of the Mini-Mental State Examination (Folstein et al. 1975), or the Abbreviated Mental Test (Jitapunkel et al. 1991), simply provide a rough estimate of performance at a particular point in time. These have no way of taking into account a person's previous levels, related to their education and the skills that they developed. To some extent this criticism is true also of the more elaborate test procedures, such as the CAMDEX (Roth et al. 1988). Tests which focus on long-term decline, on the other hand, generally have to depend on retrospective accounts given by relatives. Here many kinds of distortion, for example related to their idealization of the past or their anxieties about the present, may occur (Jorm et al. 1991). A general problem in making a diagnosis of dementia is the fact that depression, which may be moderate to severe in some 5 to 10 per cent of all older persons, is often associated with some degree of cognitive impairment (Hart and Semple 1990: 100–6). Among those who have been institutionalized for a long time, and labelled as having dementia, there may well be a considerable number whose basic difficulties arise from a depression that has never been recognized or treated.

So the general diagnosis of dementia is never absolutely clear, whether it is based on clinical judgement or psychological testing. The existing methods are at their best in identifying conditions that are treatable. In relation to differential diagnosis within primary degenerative dementia, too, there are many difficulties. One area where some progress has been made, however, is in identifying multi-infarct conditions. A set of 13 indicators, of which the best known are abrupt onset, stepwise decline, a history of strokes, focal neurological symptoms and relatively little obvious personality change, can be combined to give an 'ischaemic score', which has some association with this form of vascular pathology as identified with post mortem (Swanwick et al. 1995). Caution, however, is required. A high ischaemic score does not necessarily indicate a vascular dementia, because there is no clear way of knowing how far the vascular damage may be causing impairment to brain function. On the other hand, a low score strongly indicates that the dementia is not associated with cerebrovascular pathology.

The more common forms of brain scanning, notably CT, can show some structural changes clearly, such as general atrophy, small regions affected by infarction, or the presence of a tumour. In relation to Alzheimer type pathology, however, general methods for using scanning to help in diagnosis are only just beginning to be developed. Diagnostic accuracy seems to be at its best if the two main types of scanning are combined: those which provide data on brain structure, and those which provide data on some aspect of brain metabolism (Jobst 1995; Alzheimer's Disease Society 1996). This, however, is a very expensive procedure, and is likely to be used mainly in research rather than general diagnostic practice.

In relation to diagnosis, there is now a greater openness on all sides: it is becoming acceptable for a person to be told his or her diagnosis, and then to receive help in accepting its implications. In part this is a consequence of better diagnostic methods, and in part because the stigma surrounding dementia is gradually being dispersed. In the parallel case of cancer, diagnosis used to be covered over by secrecy, but the norms have radically changed. There can be no doubt that this has been beneficial, and it may even have contributed to the greater frequency of cure. We do not know what may be the effect with dementia; at the very least, it is likely to secure in many people a more honest and considered commitment to a different, and more realistic pattern of life.

The study of prevalence

Popular literature on dementia often conveys the impression that prevalence figures are well-established, although in fact this is far from being the case. The many surveys that have been carried out over the last 30 or so years show very wide variation. Overall prevalence figures for those in the over 65 age group in individual societies vary from around 2 to 20 per cent. With mild dementia the range is even greater; the lowest figure being 3 per cent and the highest 64 per cent (Ineichen 1987; Hart and Semple 1990). A consensus is growing that the total prevalence in industrialized societies may be around 7 per cent, and that in the UK the total number of people with a clearly recognizable dementia may be approaching 700,000 (Alzheimer's Disease Society 1996). It is extremely difficult to make estimates of world prevalence; the figure of 15 million that is sometimes quoted rests on a very poor empirical foundation.

The anomalies in prevalence data can be partly explained in simple empiricist terms (Ineichen 1987). Samples have generally been small, typically numbering a few hundred persons in an entire survey. Refusal rates tend to be rather high, in some cases of the order of 20 per cent. Community surveys usually leave out people who are already in long-stay care. Studies based on medical and social services cannot take accurate account of people who are outside their range.

There are also many problems related to the rather rough-and-ready diagnostic tests that are involved in prevalence studies. Clinical judgements, even at the best of times, have to take many aspects of a person's state into account, and involve implicit decisions about how to weigh cognitive and non-cognitive factors. The standard tests that are the most reliable focus exclusively on cognitive impairments (Blessed et al. 1991). Tests of short-term memory are particularly easy to administer, but tend to give higher prevalence figures than tests that are multifaceted, partly because they blur the boundaries between dementia and simple memory impairment. The translation of tests from one language or another often involves hidden cultural bias. Virtually all prevalence research is based on 'snapshots', and takes no account of the actual course of dementia in individual cases.

Prevalence is clearly age-related. One meta-analysis (a statistical combination of separate studies) suggests that overall prevalence may double about every six years of the lifespan (Ritchie et al. 1992). Among those who are over 85 years old, around 15 per cent might be expected to have dementia. There appear to be small prevalence differences according to sex, with the possibility that Alzheimer pathology is more common among women, and vascular pathology among men. This difference may itself have an age-relation. The likelihood of a person developing Alzheimer's disease may peak at some point in the mid-80s, whereas that of developing a vascular-related dementia continues to increase with age; here men are at somewhat greater risk (Skaog et al. 1993).

There have been very few rigorous cross-cultural or cross-societal studies of prevalence. Perhaps the best that has been carried out thus far is a comparison of New York and London, using exactly the same criteria and even crossing over the researchers part-way through the study (Gurland et al. 1983). Higher prevalence rates were found in New York than in London, for all ages and all degrees of severity. Within any one society, some research has suggested that there may be lower prevalence rates among people who have higher levels of education, and those who are in the higher socio-economic categories (Orrell 1995). With research findings such as these, it is easy to rush to simplistic interpretations. General epidemiology suggests that most illness is education and class-related; in other words, it is situated in the context of social inequality. It is by no means clear that there is anything specific here about dementia, since many of the risk factors are likely to have a greater relevance to those who are relatively poor, and have experienced more dangerous or disabling occupations.

Depression and dementia

The relation between these two conditions appears increasingly complex as research advances. Just as the term dementia covers a wide range of symptoms, so also does the term depression (Ames et al. 1990). In part this is an artefactual problem, arising from the way in which diagnostic categories have been created. Both depression and dementia involve neurochemical changes, and some forms of depression may be associated with damage to nerve structure at a subcortical level (Forstl et al. 1993).

The common symptoms of depression are well known: a lowered mood, lethargy, loss of interest in life, a lack of self-confidence and self-esteem. Among those who have a reasonably clear diagnosis of primary dementia, it has been estimated that around one-third show evidence of depression at some point, and in about a third of these the condition may be severe. About a quarter of all those who show depression in dementia have had a previous episode of depression, and for some people a depressive reaction may be a direct precursor of the onset of dementia (Carpenter and Strauss 1995).

Fairly severe depression in older people is often accompanied by a decline in cognitive abilities. In some instances, indeed, these changes may be more obvious than the disturbances of mood that are typically associated with depression. It was this that led to the creation of the category pseudodementia (Arie 1983), now more commonly termed depression induced cognitive impairment (Rabins and Pearlson 1994). Consequently it is possible that many people have been misdiagnosed as having a primary degenerative dementia, when in fact their condition might have been open to the treatments available for depression.

Of course the only evidence that a condition is one of this kind rather than a 'true' dementia, is that a person fully recovers the cognitive abilities that were lost. Often, however, clues can be gathered from the pattern of daily activity. People who are depressed tend to be very low and confused in the morning, but to improve in mood and performance towards the evening. Those who have dementia, on the other hand, are often at their best in the early part of the day, and tend to fade as the day goes on.

To some extent depression in dementia can be explained in psychological terms, as we will explore further in Chapter 5. Dementia may be experienced as a form of bereavement; it means having to face two kinds of loss simultaneously – the loss of mental powers, and the loss of a familiar way of life. Some research also suggests that the general prevalence of depression is very high in residential settings, and here people with dementia are no exception (Harrison et al. 1990). Depressive reactions are common in the aftermath of a clear diagnosis, especially as the terms dementia and Alzheimer's disease still carry such fearful connotations.

A psychological approach to the problem of depression in dementia may, however, not be adequate to the whole picture. Much depression is, no doubt, related to brain function (or more precisely, neurochemical imbalance). Here there can be a reasonable expectation that some people will recover, with human support. There is also a growing opinion that much help can be gained from the careful use of anti-depressant medication. However, where depression is associated with permanent damage to nerve tissue, it may not be amenable to treatment. Some of those who are affected in this way may never recover from the depressed state, and so will need particularly skilled and supportive care. Here caregivers should realize that even their best efforts may bring few positive changes, and thus that the rewards they are likely to receive, in the form of recognition or gratitude, may be very limited.

Even this brief discussion of the relationship between depression and dementia reveals how problematic is an old-fashioned 'medical model', with its assumption that the diagnostic categories are in some way real. There is an arbitrariness in supposing that a person 'has' one condition, dementia, onto which another, depression, is overlaid. It would be closer to the truth to recognize that there is a wide range of structural changes in nerve tissue, both cortical and subcortical, that deficits may be possible in any combination of up to about

40 different neurotransmitters, and that some degree of neuronal repair can occur. The traditional division that psychiatry has made between 'organic' and 'functional' disorders cannot be sustained. As knowledge advances further, medical science will need to look for more detailed and subtle forms of classification.

Psychotic complications

It is widely agreed today that dementia in itself should not be regarded as a form of psychosis, as this term is commonly used. Many people go through the entire course of a dementing condition without showing any of the symptoms that are commonly associated with a psychotic disturbance: for example hearing voices, having delusions, or gross confusion over personal identity. The situation is not, however, a simple one, for two main reasons.

First, some people who have a history of psychosis from earlier in their lives go on to develop a dementing condition also (Burns et al. 1990). The three forms of disturbance most emphasized in psychiatry are schizophrenia, manic-depressive disorder, and late paraphrenia (identified primarily by paranoid delusions). In such instances the disabilities accompanying dementia will be compounded by the psychotic symptoms, which themselves may become accentuated. From a psychological standpoint, we can understand why this may be so. Many people who have psychotic disturbances without dementia still retain insight; they can recognize that their experience is strange in some way. With dementia they may lose their understanding and so be more deeply confused and destabilized.

Second, in some instances of primary dementia a person may undergo disturbances of a kind very similar to those found in the psychoses. Some people have dramatic swings of mood, and around one-fifth have hallucinations or delusions; the delusion of theft is an example. A degree of paranoia is relatively common as mental powers fail and familiar sources of security are no longer available. Here it is particularly difficult to know how much to attribute directly to neurological factors, and how much is actually induced by the inadequacies of care.

Does personality change?

No one doubts that some abilities are lost during the course of dementia, and that patterns of mood and behaviour are altered. The controversial question is how the evidence should be interpreted.

Psychometric methods register the commonly observed phenomena as change in personality; there is no option, since the basic definitions require it. One study using the NEO-PI, for example, found higher levels of anxiety, more introversion and less conscientiousness as the process of dementia continued (Mills and Coleman 1994). Many relatives and friends speak of change in the personality of the one they are caring for, or even suggest that the person whom they once knew and loved is no longer there. Here too they are resting on an implicit trait theory, and seeing the changes in that light.

From an ethogenic standpoint, as we have seen, many of the changes that are observed can be interpreted in a more differentiated way, as a loss of resources and a breakdown of psychological defences (pp. 12–13). Thus someone who had been extremely self-controlled might show episodes of rage, or someone who had learned how to endure prolonged sexual deprivation might now appear to be shockingly disinhibited and lustful. The suggestion here is of a general continuity of personality during the course of dementia, with some characteristics that were always present now appearing in an exaggerated form. This view is certainly held by some who have had long experience of care work, for example Janet Bell and Iain McGregor (1995). In the course of the carers' support work of the Bradford Dementia Group we have found that those who are well supported only very rarely suggest that their relative has acquired a different personality, or 'disappeared'. Perhaps they have found ways of maintaining relationship and communication, and can deal more accurately with their own feelings of loss and bewilderment. Some who are in a less favourable situation may be coping with their changed experience by using the defence of projection.

There is one main exception to the view that personality patterns continue in dementia. This is in those cases where it is clearly established that there has been a substantial loss of neurones in the frontal lobes of the brain. It is well known in neurology that people whose frontal lobes have received gross damage tend to undergo drastic deterioration, for example, becoming 'unreliable', 'shiftless' or 'dishonest' (to use the highly judgemental terms of everyday speech), whereas previously they had shown a 'strong' and 'upright' character (Damasio 1995: 20–33).

In assessing a person with dementia, however, great caution is needed here. A highly controversial diagnostic category, frontal lobe dementia (FLD) has been created, whose alleged symptoms include personal neglect, lack of initiative, and a flattening of the emotions without there necessarily being evidence of cognitive decline (Neary et al. 1994). It is all too easy to attribute certain kinds of behaviour change to frontal lobe damage, without any direct neurological evidence. Also, while clear forms of nerve degeneration have been found in the frontal lobes of some brains post mortem, the correlation of these with the supposed symptoms of FLD in the living person is not strong. If a person's behaviour is strange, or if an apathetic mood has supervened, the first task should be to look to the social psychology. The imputation of FLD, or talk of frontal lobe involvement, can easily become a rationalization of uncare.

The genetics of Alzheimer's disease

This topic has received a great deal of attention in the last few years, as techniques for genetic research have rapidly advanced. There has been relatively little interest, however, in genetic aspects of vascular dementia, perhaps because this topic is seen as part of the larger issue of cardiovascular disease. A brief survey of the genetics of AD has been provided by Andrea Capstick (1995); findings reported since that date do not radically change the picture she presents (see also Alzheimer's Disease Society 1996).

In relation to genetics, it is generally held that there are two main categories of Alzheimer's disease. The first is very rare, affecting perhaps only a few thousand families worldwide. Here, it is claimed, there is a 'genetics of inevitability'; that is, an individual who inherits one copy of the 'faulty' gene from a parent is said to be certain to develop AD, provided he or she lives long enough. The genes that are implicated are on chromosomes 21, 14, and 1. The age of onset of dementia is early, and in the case of chromosome 14 is typically around 40–45. The claim of 'genetic inevitability' may not be so robust as it is assumed to be, however, for the following reason. In order to demonstrate true genetic causation it would have to be shown that the 'faulty' gene is present in every person who does develop the disease, and that it is not present in every person who does not (a very large sample would suffice). Scientists are on strong ground with the first condition, but usually have not established the second. Thus the logic of their position is scarcely more robust than that of the assertion: 'All sparrows that fly have beaks. Therefore a beak is what enables a sparrow to fly.'

In the second category there is what might be called a 'genetics of probability'. The claim here is that if an individual has a certain variant of a gene, or a combination of variants, he or she has a greater than normal likelihood of developing AD, or developing it at a particular age. The genetically controlled production of a certain protein (apolipoprotein E, or Apo E) is thought to be implicated in the development of AD mainly among people in the 60-plus age range (Roses et al. 1994). The gene is located on chromosome 19. There are three forms of the gene (alleles: E2, E3, and E4). So, since each individual inherits two genes, one from each parent, there are six combinations: E2/E2, E2/E3, etc. Combinations containing E4 appear to be associated with a greater probability of AD. (Incidentally, combinations with E2 are highly associated with cardiovascular disorder.)

Strictly speaking, it is meaningless to talk of an individual as having a probability X per cent of developing a genetically related condition. A central question still remains. What distinguishes those who do from those who do not develop a condition, considering that they all have the relevant genetic combination? Here many of the answers are likely to be epigenetic; that is, related to the way each individual develops, given a particular genetic endowment. In general, the gene has been accorded a causal power that goes far beyond the evidence; it is, after all, simply a template on the basis of which proteins are assembled. The dynamics of cell function must be explained in other, and far more complex ways.

The new genetic discoveries present huge ethical problems, as Harry Cayton, executive director of the English Alzheimer's Disease Society, has shown (Cayton 1995). Perhaps the most crucial questions relate to predictive genetic testing, and how to counsel those for whom genetic issues are a source of great anxiety. The problems are made more difficult because genetic science has been primarily concerned with identifying maladaptive gene combinations. The links between basic genetic discoveries and effective treatments, however, have been far less well explored. Here it would be necessary to have detailed knowledge of how genes interact, and a much better understanding of epigenetic c factors. Huntington's disease, which has been known for many years to have a strong genetic basis, provides a very sobering example; no 'genetic cures' have appeared as yet. Media reports often imply that as soon as a genetic basis for some disease is found, a cure will soon be on the way. This, however, is a fallacy (*Economist* 1996), and it plays dangerously on unrealistic hopes for miracle cures.

Physical conditions that enhance dementia

There is a wide range of conditions related to physical health which can cause dementia-like confusion (Allardyce 1996a). When primary dementia is present, these tend to enhance the symptoms, and can lead to false estimates of a person's genuine impairments. Ideally, then, a diagnosis should be considered provisional until all problems of physical health have been identified and, where possible, treated.[1]

Among these conditions the best-known are the so-called toxic confusional states that accompany or follow acute infections such as pneumonia. Their presence is easy to identify, because there is obvious 'clouding of consciousness', of which the extreme example is delirium. There are also the consequences of chronic or low-grade infections, such as those of the urinary system; these are more readily overlooked. Another relatively common problem is hormonal imbalance, especially a lowered level of thyroid function (Allardyce 1996c).

Diabetes may compound dementia, especially in that it causes a general drain on health (Allardyce 1996b). Confusion can be related to inadequate nutrition, in some instances caused by the simple fact that a person may not have been taking a balanced diet. A deficiency in vitamin B_{12} is sometimes associated with dementia, although it is not clear whether this is a cause or an accompaniment. It is commonly believed that chronic constipation can add to confusion, perhaps because toxic material that would normally be eliminated is being reabsorbed; also, of course, severe constipation can be a source of great discomfort.

Any form of impairment to the senses is likely to enhance the symptoms of dementia. A person is likely, as a result, to be less in contact with his or her environment and – an even more serious matter – less in communication with other people. Of all the sensory impairments, probably deafness is the one that adds most of the disabilities already present. A deaf person with dementia can appear to be 'normal' in most respects, and so not in need of extra attention; yet the truth may be that he or she is radically cut off from the social world, and thus deprived of personhood.

The effect of physical pain, arising from some condition that in itself does not cause confusion, should also be taken into account. Anyone who has been through a period of prolonged physical pain can testify to the way in which coping with the pain becomes a major preoccupation, sapping vitality and causing much distraction from everyday concerns. Human support and understanding can greatly relieve the feeling of pain; loneliness and anxiety can make it very much worse. It must be extremely difficult for a person to cope with pain when they have no way of understanding its cause, and perhaps no means of communicating clearly to others what they are feeling. Two of the most common sources of pain among people with dementia are arthritis and angina. There is also the possibility that a person may be harbouring a tumour that has never been diagnosed.

Beyond the problems related directly to physical health, it may be that a person who has had a major operation is confused because of the lingering presence of general anaesthetics in the body. Also it is now becoming widely recognized that some people may be suffering from the effect of a long-term build-up of drugs, giving rise to the condition that has been called 'iatrogenic drug-related chronic confusional state' (Absher and Cummings 1994). Some people receive represcriptions for a long time, without the whole pattern of their medication being reviewed. That is why many geriatricians, in making a first assessment, take a person off all but life-saving medication, and then seek to identify what is really needed. Among the drugs that add to confusion are most anti-psychotics, some anti-Parkinsonian compounds, the anti-epileptics and all tranquillizers. The opinion is growing that the latter have been far too much used in the so-called treatment of dementia. Drugs of the benzodiazepine group (such as Valium), when used over a long period, may actually be dementogenic (Coleman 1988).

Dementia, then, is always embedded in the general health picture of each individual. Earlier in life, illnesses tend to be relatively clear-cut, and often can be treated medically as separate entities. In later life, however, the pattern of illness tends much more towards being one of several chronic conditions, without clear boundaries and often without the prospect of complete cure. It is vital, then, that close attention be given to all aspects of the physical well-being of a person who has dementia. In the eagerness to provide person-centred care, there can be a danger of neglecting this issue. The particular trap to avoid is that of treating some problem as if it has psychological causes, and hence looking only to psychological solutions, when the major underlying problem is one related to physical health.

A paradigm in disarray

The brain is an exceedingly complex organ, in health and in disease. The fact that so much is now known about it testifies to the skill, ingenuity and sheer dedication of research workers in diverse fields, many of whom have given years of their lives to their investigations.

The whole conceptual framework of biomedical research into dementia, however, is far from adequate to the problem field. As Kuhn (1966) might have put it, it is a paradigm in disarray. The general hypothesis, on which it rests, may be expressed as follows:

factor or factors X $\longrightarrow$ neuropathic change $\longrightarrow$ dementia

The hypothesis is only rarely set out in this form, but close inspection of many research articles makes it clear that this is the 'generative grammar'. The hypothesis sometimes comes to the surface in an explicit form when researchers try to explain their work to a wider audience. For example,

> Alzheimer's disease is a physical condition. The mental and emotional symptoms are a direct result of a set of catastrophic changes in the brain that lead to the death of brain cells. This degeneration is irreversible.
>
> (Alzheimer's Disease Society 1996)

It is necessary to have a paradigm in order to focus attention on particular problems. This paradigm, however, does not provide a sound basis for the general explanation of dementia – Alzheimer's or any other type. It is logically flawed, and it does not easily accommodate the full range of evidence. There are three particularly problematic features.

The first concerns ideas about the so-called 'organic' base of dementia, which are generally far too narrow. As we have seen, the simple idea that neuropathology causes dementia is unsound. There can be substantial neuropathology without dementia – and there can be dementia without significant neuropathology, as every serious worker in the field now knows. The standard paradigm takes no account of the way in which brain function is translated into brain structure; it ignores those aspects of nerve architecture that are developmental, and thus closely related to a person's experiences and defences. We cannot even be sure that the origin of Alzheimer's disease lies exclusively in the neurones. Another possibility – and one that has been grossly neglected – is that it lies in the neuroglia: those cells which are far more numerous than the neurones, and whose function is to provide repair, maintenance and immunity. To use an analogy, suppose a car engine had failed, and small pieces of metal were found in the sump, and examination clearly showed that these came from broken piston rings. It does not follow that the root cause of the trouble is a fault in the piston rings. The basic problem might have been with the oil pump, and hence with the lubrication.

The second problematic feature concerns the theory of causation. The standard paradigm often works with a simple linear idea, along the lines of a billiard cue setting one ball in motion, and this colliding into another, causing it to move as well, and so on. Within the standard paradigm, the ultimate cause is assumed to be genetic. A view of causation that works for billiard balls, and even for Newtonian atoms, will not suffice for biological systems. There is a sense in which genes do not 'cause' anything; they are simply a background on which other causes operate. A paper pattern does not cause the making of a dress. At the very least we need that view of causation that looks for the set of interacting conditions – all necessary but none sufficient in themselves – that are required for an event to occur. If a group of engineers were seeking to understand the collapse of a bridge, this is the kind of framework they would use. Moreover, they would find their explanation partly in general principles, such as the statics of structures or the chemistry of steel, and partly in conjunctural factors such as the density of the traffic, and speed and direction of the wind. It is along these lines that we are likely to move towards a sound explanation of dementia in any particular case.

The third problematic feature of the standard paradigm is this. Neuropathic processes generally proceed relatively slowly, especially in people of an advanced age. Their typical timespan is a matter of years. Dementia, however, sometimes advances extremely fast. Even over a few months a person can deteriorate from a state of coping almost normally to being drastically 'demented'. The adverse changes that often follow hospitalization or going into residential care are well known. Clearly, more than simple neuropathology is needed to explain these changes, and yet the standard paradigm has almost nothing to offer. We need a framework that can incorporate personal experience and social psychology, and so, concomitantly, brain function. Similar issues arise, and with even greater force, around the phenomenon of 'rementing', or recovery of some of the powers that had, apparently, been lost. Here the standard paradigm is impotent; it can only suggest that the case couldn't have been one of true dementia.

A different paradigm is possible along the lines that I set out at the end of Chapter 1 and summarized in the simple formula

$$\frac{\psi \equiv b}{(B^d, B_p)}$$

With this as the 'generative grammar', we can remain true to neuroscience, and yet be true to the person as well. The science of genetics is respected, but not genetic hype. There is a place for neuropathology, but not for neuropathic ideology. The view of causation is not linear, but multiple and interactional. Both general theory and intense particularism go hand in hand.

Note

1   I acknowledge with gratitude the advice given by Dr John Wattis, both in the preparation of this section and the chapter as a whole.

Dementia as a psychiatric category

Commentary by Julian C. Hughes

I bought my copy of *Dementia Reconsidered* in 1998, one year after it had been published and, sadly, in the same year that Tom Kitwood died. I was a senior registrar in old age psychiatry at the time. In other words, I was completing my higher training and was reading avidly. Kitwood was an inspiration. Along with the papers that I had read by Steve Sabat and Rom Harré (Sabat and Harré 1992, 1994) and, later, Sabat's own seminal work, *The Experience of Alzheimer's Disease* (Sabat 2001), Kitwood helped me in ways of thinking that have shaped the rest of my clinical and academic career. At the time I read Kitwood, I was also completing my PhD thesis, which later formed the basis of *Thinking Through Dementia* (Hughes 2011). Several sections of that work discuss Kitwood and the references include seven of Kitwood's works, including *Dementia Reconsidered*, a book to which I have often returned for inspiration and with pleasure.

Interestingly, however, Chapter 2, on which I now write a commentary, is the one with which I had the most problems: it annoyed me! I remember this to be the case and it is confirmed by my pencilled annotations from the time. You might say this is unsurprising, for Chapter 2 is critical of what is described as 'the standard paradigm', which is linked by implication to psychiatry. Since psychiatry was the field to which I was intending to devote my career, no wonder I was defensive and critical on its behalf. Re-reading Chapter 2, I see that Kitwood went to some lengths to make plain that he respected the work of psychiatrists, other clinicians and basic scientists. His complaint was, I would suggest, that they did not see the whole picture.

Concerning the neuropathology, biochemistry and genetics of dementia, for instance, he wrote: 'The framework they have created . . . has several major anomalies, both empirical and conceptual' (Kitwood 1997: 24); and at times, he says, the standard paradigm they use 'falls into blatant reductionism' (p. 24). There is an antipathy to psychiatry, which is apparent elsewhere and reaches its apotheosis in the final sentence of the book: 'And here, in comparison to conventional psychiatry, we may find an immeasurably richer conception of the healing of the mind' (p. 170). So now I approach Chapter 2 again to ask what is wrong with it and what is right?

What's wrong with Chapter 2?

It seems almost peevish to point out faults in Kitwood's work. But he did get things wrong, he did make assertions without good evidence and he did put forward some poor arguments. Let me give a few examples.

He cites Homer et al. (1988) and says that they report that 34 per cent of the people they reviewed met the clinical or neuropsychological criteria for dementia but had no pathology in their brains post mortem. The authors do say in their abstract that, of the 27 patients they considered, 'The clinical diagnosis made during life was not supported by the findings at necropsy in 11 cases' (Homer et al. 1988). This might seem to be worse than Kitwood suggested: that, actually, 41 per cent did not have pathology. But the authors are not saying there was no pathology, just that the clinical diagnosis was wrong in comparison with the pathological diagnosis. In fact, in just one of the people they reviewed did they find no brain pathology, which would make the proportion only 3.7 per cent. Reading this paper, I have not been able to find where Kitwood derives his figure of 34 per cent. This seems, therefore, to be an error, for which we must forgive him. His broader point – that clinical presentations and neuropathology do not always square – still stands.

But I would make another point about Homer et al. (1988), which is that it is a good example of clinicians and scientists working together to try to improve their diagnostic rates and to understand, with humility and honesty, what is happening to their patients. The final section of Kitwood's Chapter 2 is entitled 'A paradigm in disarray', whereas Homer et al. (1988) might be regarded as an example of a paradigm working appropriately for the betterment of humanity.

Here are some examples of assertions made without good evidence: 'Making a diagnosis of dementia in any individual case . . . is a very difficult task. It is notorious that GPs, clinical psychologists, psychiatrists and neurologists tend to differ in their opinions' (p. 29). On the contrary, it is often very easy to make a diagnosis of dementia, even if the exact type of dementia is less clear. Making an early diagnosis of dementia (when only slight symptoms are in evidence) can be more problematic. I am not at all sure that professionals 'tend' to have different opinions, even if it is true that people do sometimes have different opinions. The impression Kitwood is creating anticipates his final suggestion that the paradigm is 'in disarray'.

He states: 'So the general diagnosis of dementia is *never* absolutely clear . . .' (p. 30, emphasis added). This is clearly an overstatement. It would be better had he said it is 'sometimes not' absolutely clear. One has to ask why Kitwood makes such an overstatement. Shortly before this he wrote: 'Among those who have been institutionalized for a long time, and labelled as having dementia, there may well be a considerable number whose basic difficulties arise from a depression that has never been recognized or treated' (p. 30). As with the other statements above, there are no references to support this assertion. But even slight analysis renders it suspect: '. . . there may well be . . .' can be attached to all sorts of claims. *There may well be* a kernel of truth attached to some of the assertions of certain political leaders, but we might still wish to condemn many of them. Depression is undoubtedly a problem for many people. Depression in the context of dementia is a hot and complicated topic, which fine minds are considering (Morimoto et al. 2017), but Kitwood's assertion suggests 'disarray' – institutions full of people with clinical depression having been incorrectly diagnosed as having dementia. Once again, the standard paradigm, the inability ever to make a clear diagnosis, the misdiagnosis rates, all conspire to create havoc, disarray and human suffering. So, if not completely true, why paint such a picture, unless it sets up what is to come: Kitwood's salvific person-centred, psychosocial dementia care? The portrayal of disarray in this chapter is a rhetorical device in anticipation of the salvation that ensues.

Finally, then, what of poor arguments? The pathological hallmarks of the main dementias can be found in people without cognitive impairment. 'Clearly, then, there is no possibility,' says Kitwood, 'of Alzheimer's or vascular dementia meeting the key criterion of a classical disease: that distinct pathological features should be present in all cases where the symptoms appear, and in none of the cases where they do not' (p. 28). Well, but Kitwood's move here is to stipulate the definition of a 'classical disease'. There are two points, at least, to be made.

First, I might have wear and tear of my joints and yet experience no symptoms. Does this mean that osteoarthritis is not a 'classical disease'? Moreover, some people have debilitating chest pain, similar in all respects to cardiac pain, but no evidence of cardiac pathology. Do they, therefore, not have a disease? (They would be aggrieved to be told this!)

Second, must we accept the definition as it has been stipulated? Is it not the case that what counts as a disease is also culturally and historically determined? Attention deficit hyperactivity disorder (ADHD) might be an example. And does not Kitwood's 'key criterion' rather rule out most mental health conditions being diseases? What is the distinct pathology of depression or of post-traumatic stress disorder, for instance? In any case, if we said to the relative of a person with obvious advanced Alzheimer's disease or vascular dementia that their relative did not have a 'classical disease', I am not sure they would know what to make of this. If this is not a disease, they might say, then what is?

When Kitwood talks about the paradigm being in disarray, he says, 'the simple idea that neuropathology causes dementia is unsound' (p. 37). This is because there can be neuropathology without dementia and dementia without significant neuropathology. But the fact that *sometimes* there is neuropathology without dementia, does not entail that dementia is *never* caused by neuropathology; and the fact that *sometimes* there is dementia without significant pathology does not entail that there is *never* pathology in dementia. Kitwood suggests that this 'simple idea' (the standard paradigm) is 'logically flawed' (p. 37), but the erroneous logic is to think that because X *sometimes* does not entail Y, it *never* does.

We should also note that what Kitwood calls the *unsound* 'simple idea that neuropathology causes dementia' has proved quite useful. In a seminal paper published 20 years before I bought my copy of *Dementia Reconsidered*, Elaine Perry and her Newcastle colleagues demonstrated that there was 'a close relation between changes in the cholinergic system and Alzheimer's dementia' (Perry et al. 1978). Neuropathology – and in particular deficits in the neurotransmitter acetylcholine, which increased in parallel with Alzheimer's pathology – were linked with the symptoms of dementia. In the same year that Kitwood's book appeared, the first cholinesterase inhibitor (i.e. a drug that boosts the presence of acetylcholine, counteracting the deficit Perry and her colleagues had detected) was licensed for use in the UK. No one with any sense would suggest that these drugs (donepezil, rivastigmine or galantamine) or memantine (a different class of drug that was to follow) have anything but a modest effect. Nevertheless, they can maintain or improve cognition and functional abilities (Kurz and Lautenschlager 2017) in much the way that the 'unsound' standard paradigm suggests they might. The standard paradigm has furnished us with treatments that are valued by people living with dementia and by their carers.

What's right with Chapter 2?

Much that Kitwood says is still correct. Large sections of the chapter are devoted to setting the scene by describing the current state of play in terms of the main dementias. In a sense this is mundane, but it is largely accurate. Things have moved on of course. For instance, albeit Kitwood mentions it, the separate status of dementia with Lewy bodies (DLB) would now be given more prominence (McKeith 2017). Much more work has been done on the links between depression and dementia, and on how to treat depression in dementia (Morimoto et al. 2017) – areas of concern for Kitwood. He would also have been much exercised, as many of us have been (Hughes 2006; Hughes 2011: 256), by the emergence of mild cognitive impairment (MCI) as a diagnostic entity. Kitwood was certainly correct to highlight (p. 26) the heterogeneity not only of dementia but also of Alzheimer's itself (Richards and Brayne 2010). If the chapter were to be rewritten today, I think the empirical study of non-pharmacological treatments of dementia (Livingston and Cooper 2017) – likely to have been inspired by Kitwood's work – would receive greater attention in this chapter as well as elsewhere in the book.

There are things, which Kitwood says with great clarity, that remain important and maybe more so today: 'In general, the gene has been accorded a causal power that goes far beyond the evidence; it is, after all, simply a template on the basis of which proteins are assembled. The dynamics of cell function must be explained in other, and far more complex ways' (p. 35). He also wisely emphasizes the importance of the person's physical health: 'Dementia . . . is always embedded in the general health picture of each individual . . . In the eagerness to provide person-centred care, there can be a danger of neglecting this issue' (p. 36).

In summary, if Chapter 2 is largely mundane, it is (as always with Kitwood's work) clearly written, at times trenchant, elegant and controversial. It serves a purpose: there is something wrong with the disease model of dementia, even if it has brought some benefits. Kitwood, like many others, refers to the 'medical model', but I think there are reasons to doubt that this is a suitable label for what he is complaining about (Hughes 2011: 121), because most medical people involved in the care of those living with dementia are prone by nature and training to take a broader view. Whereas, the disease model (according to my lights) can infect that broader view and is reductionist in the manner that worried Kitwood.

The uplands

If Chapter 2 remains a little annoying, Kitwood can be forgiven, for this was really preparatory work in anticipation of his positive message, which recurs from Chapter 1 in this chapter's final paragraph. It is the broader view of the person who lives with dementia. The uplands, which Kitwood's work inhabits, provide a clearer perspective of what it is to be a human being in the world. Mind and brain, development and pathology, genes and the environment must all be seen together. I would wish to broaden Kitwood's social constructionist definition of 'personhood' (p. 7), and characterize the person as a situated embodied agent (Hughes 2011), but for the same purpose: to encourage the broader view – the human person perspective (Hughes 2011: 223–250) – which cannot be contained. We, *qua* human beings, cannot be pinned down. And, thus, understanding the person living with dementia requires intellect, knowledge, skill, experience, imagination, creativity, and so on. There is no reason why psychiatry, at its best, cannot provide the necessary perspective. Only, however, if it shares Kitwood's vision.

Points for reflection

- As Kitwood suggests, we need a broad view of dementia and of what it is for a person to live with dementia, but that breadth of vision needs to incorporate the biology *as much as* the psychology and sociology (as well as the ethics, law, spirituality and so forth) that surround dementia.

- We should watch out for stipulative definitions: we can stipulate that a classical disease must have 'X' (in this case, that dementia requires specific pathology, which must not be present where there is no disease), but what is it that justifies our stipulations? Actually, it is often values. Diagnoses reflect value judgements. Kitwood, I think, would have liked this idea, but perhaps it would have led him to change some of his arguments.

- We should consider what the 'medical model' *really* is and how it is different from the 'disease model'.

3

How personhood is undermined

Tom Kitwood

Most of the topics covered in the previous chapter are familiar ones in the psychiatry and clinical psychology of dementia. In my discussion of them I have stayed mainly on accepted ground, drawing on a small sample of the vast body of relevant research. The criticisms that I have made have very largely been directed at the 'standard paradigm', the whole framework into which research findings are usually incorporated; and I have pointed mainly to its internal inconsistencies.

If, now, we bring in all those considerations of personhood that were explored in Chapter 1, we can identify another major inadequacy. Essentially the paradigm frames the problems surrounding dementia in a technical way, as an electronics expert might with a computer whose hardware is faulty, or a mechanic with a car that has broken down. Neither from the standard paradigm, nor from the majority of the research that is affiliated to it, do we get any sense of the real persons, in the diversity of their backgrounds, personalities and ordinary lives, who develop a dementing condition. Furthermore, the standard paradigm has nothing to say about how to care effectively for a person who has dementia. It leaves the caring process vague, opaque, untheoretized, and implies that nothing will get much better until the medical breakthroughs come. Implicitly, then, the standard paradigm feeds into an extremely negative and deterministic view, which can be summed up in the popular image of 'the death that leaves the body behind', and in the headline of an article that appeared a few years ago in a popular magazine, 'Alzheimer's: No cure, no help, no hope'.

If we stay close to mundane reality, and explore how people with dementia live out their lives from day to day, in their own homes and in the settings where formal care is provided, we get a very different picture (Kitwood 1990b). It is clear that many social, or societal, factors are involved: culture, locality, social class, education, financial resources, the availability or absence of support and services. Also, at the interpersonal or social-psychological level, much depends on how far a person with dementia is enabled to retain intact relationships, to use his or her abilities, to experience variety and enjoyment. From the vantage-point of the standard paradigm, these things are externalities, separate from the advancing process of disease. According to the paradigm that I am suggesting, they are also part of the whole process – actually incorporated into the dementing condition, for good or ill (Kitwood 1994a).

A story of our time

Here, in outline, is an account of the process of dementia in an older woman, covering a period of eight or so years in all. I have used it in the form presented here on training courses, as a way of raising awareness of the broader context of the dementing conditions.

Margaret B. died in March 1995, at the age of 89, in Bank Top Nursing Home. The first episode that really convinced her husband Brian that something was seriously wrong occurred in the summer of 1987, while they were on holiday in Spain, staying in a large hotel. One morning when she was collecting her breakfast in the dining room she got completely lost; she could not find Brian, or their table. When he found her she was very upset and frightened, and apparently had no idea where she was. She seemed to lose confidence from this point forward, becoming increasingly anxious and confused. Margaret had shown some signs of forgetfulness before this time; for example, she had difficulty remembering the names of their six grandchildren. She had also made a few odd mistakes, such as coming home from the supermarket with cat food, despite the fact that their last cat had died several years before. Brian had simply passed off these things as part of growing older; after all, he and his wife were both approaching 80.

Margaret had always been a very conscientious person, loyal to her husband and family. She had worked part-time for a while, but mainly her life had centred on the home. Brian was a strong and upright man, highly efficient and organized. He was respected in the community, although few people knew him well. He had been a very strict father to their three children, and he had always had a rather formal manner with his wife. As a couple, Margaret and Brian 'kept themselves to themselves'. They had no close friends. Their daughter Susan had emigrated, and both of their two sons had settled in distant places.

After the episode in Spain, life for Brian and Margaret became more and more difficult, although neither of them understood what was happening. Brian found himself resenting Margaret's unreliability, and to his shame he became openly critical of her mistakes. When she showed signs of anxiety or sadness, he often told her to 'pull herself together'. Sometimes she came close to him, pleading with him to hold her and help her to feel safe; usually he pushed her away, or suggested that she go and sit down while he got on with his various jobs. On a few occasions he became really angry with her, which was very unlike how he had usually been. One afternoon she wandered away from home, and when Brian returned she was nowhere to be found. The police picked her up in a distant part of town. He was furious about this, telling her it was a disgrace to the family and all they stood for. From this point forward he felt it was necessary to lock her in the house whenever he went out.

Although Brian knew a little about Alzheimer's disease from television, and things he had read, he did not consciously connect this knowledge with Margaret's behaviour. It was only in 1990, when Susan came on a visit from Australia, that the realization dawned. Susan was a nurse. She immediately recognized the signs of dementia, and insisted that her mother was taken to the doctor. Margaret was given a provisional diagnosis of Alzheimer's disease, and the doctor suggested that Brian should do the best he could to look after Margaret at home.

Brian's response was dramatic. He quickly absorbed all the information about Alzheimer's disease he could lay his hands on, and set about looking after Margaret in the most efficient way. He took over all the housework and cooking. If she hovered around him while he was doing his tasks, he made her return to the sitting room. When he went shopping, he went alone. As soon as Margaret began to have problems with continence, he obtained help from the advisory service, and did all that was necessary to avoid unpleasant accidents. When she developed problems with sleeping, he took her to the doctor, who prescribed some night sedation. Although the task of looking after Margaret was extremely tiring, Brian was determined to play his part well.

By late 1991 Brian knew that it was all getting too much for him. He was becoming increasingly tired and irritable; Margaret was more and more bewildered and tearful. Brian called in the social services. After Margaret's assessment it was decided that she should go to a day centre. This gave Brian some relief, although Margaret was often very upset before going, and sometimes seemed extremely confused on her return. He never went with her to the centre, but kept in touch with the manager by telephone.

A new crisis developed in mid-1992. Brian's health was deteriorating; he had developed angina. Margaret was extremely confused and agitated; her medication was increased. The day centre manager stated that Margaret was no longer an appropriate client because her dementia was too severe. The district nurses who came in to help get Margaret to bed were usually in a hurry, and they talked to each other continually while they gave her a bath and put her to bed. This seemed to make Margaret very upset. One evening she bit one of the nurses on the arm, which caused great distress. For Brian, this was the last straw. After talking things through with the social worker, he came to the conclusion that Margaret would have to go into full-time residential care. He felt extremely guilty and uneasy at the prospect.

Brian had heard that The Gables was a good home. He rang the manager, who immediately offered a place for Margaret. One day in November Brian told Margaret that they were going out for a ride in the car, although he did not say where they were going. This was how she entered residential care. As Margaret was very anxious and tearful, the manager suggested that Brian should not visit for several days, to give time for her to get used to her new home.

Unfortunately, Margaret did not settle in The Gables. Her distress and agitation caused great annoyance to other residents; she would not stay in bed at night. Brian usually visited her three times each week, but soon she appeared not to recognize him and often ignored him. One evening one of the residents shouted very abusively at Margaret, and Margaret hit her in the face, causing severe bruises. The family of this resident immediately lodged a complaint, and insisted on an inquiry.

Two days later Margaret was taken to a psychiatric assessment ward, where she spent six weeks. She was given heavy tranquillizing medication. After this she was placed in Bank Top Nursing Home, which had a wing entirely for people with dementia.

At Bank Top, Margaret remained under sedation. Her life consisted of being got up in the morning, having her breakfast, and then being put in a chair. Here she sat for hours on end, half awake, half asleep, and occasionally wandering around. Around 8.00 p.m. each day she was put to bed. Within four months she had lost the use of her legs.

She was becoming very thin, and often left her food. Only one member of staff realized that Margaret was often eager to eat, but needed prompting about actually doing it. Brian's visits became less and less frequent; he saw little point in coming. The two sons did not come at all. For the very last part of her life Margaret spent longer and longer periods lying on her bed. She was fed, mainly with liquid food. One morning it was found that she had died.

Although this narrative taken as a whole is a fiction, each element of it is based on events that have actually happened. Also, while The Gables and Bank Top Nursing Home have no existence in reality, they both epitomize the poorer quality kind of place where people are taken in for residential care. The story of Margaret and Brian is typical of how dementia has been lived out in recent years in Britain, and it has close parallels in other industrialized countries. Several people have said to me, after I have used it in training work, that it almost exactly describes a case they know, or even what has happened in their own family.

If we follow the development of any person's dementing condition closely, again and again we will come to see how social and interpersonal factors come into play, either adding to the difficulties directly arising from neurological impairment, or helping to lessen their effects. In the light of this it is extremely difficult to hold to the view suggested by the standard paradigm: that the mental and emotional symptoms are a direct result of a catastrophic series of changes in the brain that lead to the death of brain cells – and nothing more than that. This narrow conception of the ill-being that dementia often entails can easily divert attention away from the inadequacy of our social arrangements, and it has led to a gross imbalance in research. Insofar as it has done this, it might be regarded as a 'neuropathic ideology' – a body of opinion that systematically distorts the truth.

In moral terms, it is clear even from the brief account given here that there were many points at which Margaret was not treated fully as a person. She needed comfort in her anxiety, but Brian was unable to give it. She pleaded for encouragement and reassurance when her self-confidence was failing, but she met criticism or anger. She wanted a 'way of life', a continuity with her past, but her role as the homemaker was totally stripped away. The day centre was unable to provide her with occupation within her range of capability, and it failed to offer her the kind of company with which she could feel at ease. Neither The Gables nor Bank Top had developed the skills among staff that would enable them to provide effective psychological care for residents with dementia. Margaret's 'behaviour problems' were never explored in a sympathetic way, or traced back to their roots; eventually they were controlled by medication, but at the cost of suppressing much of what enabled her still to be a person, and possibly of adding further damage to her nervous system.

In a case such as this one might be tempted to blame the main carer, but it would be both psychologically inept and morally blind to do so. Those who have this role take on, almost single-handed, a colossal task. The weight of evidence from anthropology is that no individual was ever 'designed' for such an onerous commitment; human beings emerged through evolution as a highly social species, where burdens are carried by a group. Even in those rare instances in industrial societies where the care is genuinely shared by several members of the family, the situation is far less fraught and strained.

Brian, in the story, was left to live out the consequence of the tendency of our kind of society to force into isolation people who are under pressure. Furthermore, he had received no preparation, practical or psychological, for his new role. He was the product of his own upbringing, with its many limitations, and of his own attempts to measure up to the common standards of how to be a man. At many points his own needs were not met, and when the situation became really difficult he received no support. Where 'community care' was available, it consisted mainly of *ad hoc* interventions, and when the situation became really difficult it proved completely inadequate. Some of the things Brian did to Margaret fell far short of true respect for her personhood, but what about his personhood too? Locking his wife in the house when he went out might be considered deeply immoral, but perhaps it was the 'least bad' thing that he could do in the circumstances. As Margaret's dementia grew worse, no one helped Brian with his feelings of anger, inadequacy and guilt; no one enabled him to come to terms with his own tragic predicament.

So this story of one person's dementia is much more than that of an advancing neurological illness. It is absurdly reductionistic to suggest, as some have done, that 'everything in the end comes down to what is going on in individual brain cells'. In very many cases, we find that the process of dementia is also the story of a tragic inadequacy in our culture, our economy, our traditional views about gender, our medical system and our general way of life. In engaging with people who are in Brian's position we should take great care not to be judgemental; it is probable that they already carry a very heavy burden of guilt feelings. The fault lies in the context, and at a systemic level – it is the culmination of a long historical process. That whole context needs radical improvement – through a change in the culture of care. But that is a task that has, until very recently, been almost totally neglected.

The problematic inheritance

If the story of Margaret and Brian is typical, it points to a disastrous incompetence within contemporary societies. At this point in history it is certainly not convenient for any government to take the 'rising tide' of dementia seriously; it has such momentous implications for health services and social care, and it points to an immense educational deficit. In broad cultural terms also, we are still largely unprepared for the new situation, where there is a vast new field of moral responsibility. This general ineptitude at a societal level goes back for many centuries; Europe never had a golden age of compassion and enlightenment. I wish now to give a very brief sketch of the history of institutional and social 'care'. This is significant in itself, for it puts our present predicament into a historical context. Also it shows how great are the problems in the way of cultural change.

In the late Middle Ages, and throughout the social upheavals of the fourteenth, fifteenth and sixteenth centuries, virtually no organized provision was made for the more vulnerable members of society (Tuchman 1979). For the greater part they were dependent on individual acts of charity, and a few religious bodies provided a modicum of refuge. During the seventeenth century, society in its 'modern' form was coming into being, with many of the nation states virtually as we know them today, developing their economic interests throughout the globe. If the new form of society, more centrally governed, and oriented to property, trade and empire was to function 'efficiently', it needed to get rid of obvious chaos and disorder. During this period many institutions of confinement were built, and large numbers of the misfits of society – beggars, tramps, criminals, dissidents, the mad, the disabled and the flagrantly immoral – were taken off the streets (Foucault 1967). Some were forced into menial labour. Those who were deranged were locked away, and in many respects treated like animals in the worst kind of zoo. The docile were generally left to their own devices, while the violent were kept in chains. Generally there was no relief at all from squalor and disease, and no constructive attempt to help or cure. This is the image that we have of bedlam, which was of course a real place of confinement.

One of the great innovators in medicine, Samuel Hahnemann, writing in 1810, had the following to say about the treatment of those suffering mental distress.

> The hardhearted mindlessness of physicians in many institutions of this kind is astounding . . . they have the inhumanity to torment these most pathetic patients with violent beatings and other agonising tortures. By this unconscionable and disgraceful behaviour they debase themselves far below the level of prison guards, who carry out such punishments on criminals only because it is their duty. These people, on the other hand, humiliated by feelings of their own medical ineptitude, seem to vent their spite at the presumed incurability of mental and emotional diseases by displaying cruelty to the pathetic, innocent sufferers themselves.
>
> (Hahnemann 1983: 152)

Hahnemann's comments signify a new and growing concern about the dreadful conditions in the institutions. A slow process of reform got under way during the nineteenth century, and eventually a system of inspection was established. At best the new style of regime was designed to bring about a kind of 'moral education', with a firm but kindly discipline. In some ways it was like the method of behaviour modification, using a system of rewards and punishments. These reforms were an advance, but there was still an intense misogyny, and a tendency towards victim-blaming (Ussher 1991). Although a sociological awareness was growing, and many improvements were made in the conditions of work in mines and factories, the application to mental distress lagged some way behind. Only little recognition was given to the conditions in society that had led some people to become deviant, violent or insane. As the century drew to a close the numbers in the institutions increased enormously. Many of the asylums built around the late nineteenth century had space for 1000 inmates. The majority of these places are still standing today, a memorial to the enormous social malaise of the great age of industrialism, and to its overweening paternalism.

As medical science advanced, at times with spectacular success, a new way of viewing abnormal behaviour was gaining ground. Much that had previously been regarded as some kind of moral inadequacy or congenital deficit was reframed as a disease condition. The paradigm case for this was syphilis, where there was an incontrovertible relationship between severe mental disorder and organic pathology. The existence of the neurone in grey matter was clearly established. This was the time when psychiatry, in the highly medicalized form that we know it today, was born. The hope of many of the new practitioners was that in due course the pathological process underlying every mental disorder would be uncovered. The first scientific investigations of the brains of people who had died with dementia – including the work of Alzheimer himself – were part of this general project (Berrios and Freeman 1991). The ideas of Freud and the early psychoanalysts formed, in a sense, a counter-culture; unconscious mental processes were postulated as the underlying cause of some forms of mental disturbance, rather than organic disease.

Much, no doubt, has been gained from this process of medicalization. Far better diagnosis is available; we are beginning to understand the neurophysiological and neuropathological substrates of mental processes; there are now treatments that can bring rapid relief from some very distressing symptoms. Medical approaches in psychiatry have, however, brought their own problems, as we have already seen: simplistic views of organicity, research led not so much by theory as by available technique, and exaggerated hopes that science will deliver wonder-cures. Often personhood has been disregarded, particularly when the 'patients' cannot easily speak in support of their own interests. It has become all too easy to ignore the suffering of a fellow human being, and see instead a merely biological problem, to be solved by some kind of technical intervention.

Now, of course, many of the old institutions have closed or are closing, with the attempt to provide 'community care'. A very clear account of the background to this process, and of its implications for the future, has been given by Elaine Murphy (1991) in her book *After the Asylums*. There were many good reasons for making the change to care in the community. The warehousing of people with very varied mental disorders could be brought to an end; many people might be enabled to live in a virtually normal way; smaller residential units, locally based, could provide a better quality of life, with more continuity and richer human contact. There was also the potential for developing a more person-centred and ethically responsible form of social service (Stevenson and Parsloe 1993).

The first moves in this direction were made in Britain well over 20 years ago. When the rapid changes were brought about, however, following the NHS and Community Care Act of 1990, the promise was not fulfilled. A large part of the motive was economic, for the state had been shedding its responsibilities for welfare whenever it could. One of the key ideas was to create a 'mixed economy of care', in which market forces would have free reign, but this, of course, was specious in the extreme. When conditions approximate a true market, the consumers have sound knowledge of what it is they are buying, and there is a considerable choice. The idea is that competition creates pressures both to raise quality and to keep prices low. Conditions such as these can never be fulfilled when a human service is being delivered, as was shown many years ago by Richard Titmuss (1969). In particular, people do not know clearly what they need and can be easily deceived by 'experts' who act for economic motives; also with an issue such as dementia, they have no idea how matters will develop, or for how long. The nonsense is made even greater when a public sector, eager to keep costs low, is one of the major purchasers.

So it cannot be concluded that the move to community care will necessarily be an improvement, from a person-centred point of view. We will lurch and stagger from one dire situation to another, so long as there is insufficient funding for all the necessary social services. The crisis over dementia care is still developing, but there are ominous signs in what has happened to many ex-mental patients now living 'in the community'. They are being subjected to severe discrimination and deprivation (Barham and Hayward 1991). Gradually they are becoming the new outcasts of society, having a place similar to that of lepers in a former age.

Dementia is a relatively late comer on this historical scene, largely because the demographic shift to bring a general ageing of the population is so recent. The 'back wards' of the asylums, occupied by older people in varying states of confusion, agitation and depression are typically a feature of the period since the end of the Second World War. It is now widely acknowledged that the provision made for them was generally far below an acceptable standard, and much is being done to bring about improvements in the quality of care. The attempt to enable people to live for longer in their own homes, and then if need be, to move to smaller residential units, undoubtedly gives the opportunity for doing something far better than in the past.

All, however, is not well, as the story of Margaret and Brian makes clear. The darker possibility is that many people with dementia will continue to stay at home – for economic reasons – long beyond the point when it is consistent either with their well-being or that of their carers. Those who live alone may face an even more dreadful prospect: that of being imprisoned in terrifying loneliness and personal danger, as they await their 'packages of care'. As for the new residential units, we cannot assume that they will be an improvement. It is possible that many will be looked after in a way that is similar to that of the old institutions, only now subject to the corrupting pressures of the cash nexus. There is also the likelihood that drugs will be used very intensively, not so much for the genuine relief of symptoms as for behaviour control and cost-cutting.

Care practice, then, whether in institutions or in 'the community', contains the residues of at least four depersonalizing traditions: bestialization, the attribution of moral deficit, warehousing, and the unnecessary use of a medical model. Among all fields, provision for people who have dementia is perhaps the most affected, because gross underresourcing is compounded by fear, defence and a pervasive ageism.

Malignant social psychology

If we come close to the details of how life is lived, hour by hour and minute by minute, we can see many processes that work towards the undermining of people who have dementia. Consider the following vignette, written by an experienced care practitioner, looking back to the early days of her work in 1984.

> In this residential home the 'babies', as people with dementia were often called, were given their lunch before the other residents were served in the dining room. For all residents, mealtimes were highlights in their day. After feeding Mrs G her lunch in her own room, I went along to the 'ward' to see if any assistance was needed there. This was a large room with four beds, four chairs and four commodes; it was home to four ladies with dementia. As I entered, the door was wide open; all four ladies were sitting on their commodes, and the smell of faeces permeated the air. There were no curtains or partitions to screen the ladies from one another or anyone else walking past. My colleagues Sandra and Mary were feeding two of the ladies, and talking about the night out they had just spent together. Sandra was feeding Mrs T. As soon as there appeared a little room in her mouth, more food was inserted. Her cheeks were bulging with food she hadn't had a chance to swallow. Mrs T started to gag; food began to spill from her mouth; then she coughed, and sprayed Sandra with half-chewed food. Sandra proceeded to clean herself up, while leaving Mrs T with food debris all over her clothes and exposed thighs. Sandra berated Mrs T for being a 'filthy old woman'. She then commented to Mary that she hoped if ever she 'got like that' someone would shoot her. 'After all', Sandra said, 'if it was a dog it would have been put down by now'. Neither lady received the remainder of her lunch. To my offer of help, Sandra and Mary told me I was too late; they had finished; and why had it taken me so long to feed one lady? They had fed two each. We left the room, leaving the door open; all four ladies were still sitting on their commodes.[1]

When we consider that horrifying episodes of this kind were typical, not exceptional, within the 'old culture of care', it is impossible to hold the view that all of the personal deterioration associated with dementia comes about as a result of a neurological process that has its own autonomous dynamic. The conclusion reached by Michael Meacher (1972) in his famous study of residential homes, seems nearer to the mark; for he suggested that the social psychology and general arrangements were virtually sufficient in themselves to 'drive people demented'.

In other fields a recognition of this kind of process has been developed into a 'social model of disability', or more accurately, disablement; that is, the attitudes and actions of other people, combined with their neglect, actively disempower those who have some kind of 'difference', overlooking their attempts at action and denying them a voice (Makin 1995). Gradually it has been perceived that similar processes are at work around people who have dementia (e.g. Gwilliam and Gilliard 1996).

Almost as soon as I became involved with dementia, I was strongly aware of these depersonalizing tendencies; I decided to make them a topic of research. My method involved a simple form of critical incident technique; essentially, making brief notes on episodes as soon as possible after they had been observed, and then attempting to classify them (Kitwood 1990a). The term which I gave for these episodes was 'malignant social psychology'. The strong word malignant signifies something very harmful, symptomatic of a care environment that is deeply damaging to personhood, possibly even undermining physical well-being. The effect of the psychosocial environment on health is just beginning to be understood, particularly with the study of stress and the genesis of conditions such as cancer (see, for example, Cooper 1984; Ader et al. 1991). The term malignant does not, however, imply evil intent on the part of caregivers; most of their work is done with kindness and good intent. The malignancy is part of our cultural inheritance.

My original list contained ten elements:

1   *Treachery* – using forms of deception in order to distract or manipulate a person, or force them into compliance.

2   *Disempowerment* – not allowing a person to use the abilities that they do have; failing to help them to complete actions that they have initiated.

3   *Infantilization* – treating a person very patronizingly (or 'matronizingly'), as an insensitive parent might treat a very young child.

4   *Intimidation* – inducing fear in a person, through the use of threats or physical power.

5   *Labelling* – using a category such as dementia, or 'organic mental disorder', as the main basis for interacting with a person and for explaining their behaviour.

6   *Stigmatization* – treating a person as if they were a diseased object, an alien or an outcast.

7   *Outpacing* – providing information, presenting choices, etc., at a rate too fast for a person to understand; putting them under pressure to do things more rapidly than they can bear.

8   *Invalidation* – failing to acknowledge the subjective reality of a person's experience, and especially what they are feeling.

9   *Banishment* – sending a person away, or excluding them – physically or psychologically.

10   *Objectification* – treating a person as if they were a lump of dead matter: to be pushed, lifted, filled, pumped or drained, without proper reference to the fact that they are sentient beings.

Since the time of my first study of malignant social psychology I have added seven further elements to the list:

11 *Ignoring* – carrying on (in conversation or action) in the presence of a person as if they were not there.

12 *Imposition* – forcing a person to do something, overriding desire or denying the possibility of choice on their part.

13 *Withholding* – [r]efusing to give asked-for attention, or to meet an evident need.

14 *Accusation* – blaming a person for actions or failures of action that arise from their lack of ability, or their misunderstanding of the situation.

15 *Disruption* – intruding suddenly or disturbingly upon a person's action or reflection; crudely breaking their frame of reference.

16 *Mockery* – making fun of a person's 'strange' actions or remarks; teasing, humiliating, making jokes at their expense.

17 *Disparagement* – telling a person that they are incompetent, useless, worthless, etc., giving them messages that are damaging to their self-esteem.

Some of the more common aspects of malignant social psychology in formal care settings have been operationalized in the observational method of Dementia Care Mapping (Kitwood and Bredin 1992b; Kitwood 1997c). This has brought the whole concept into an arena where it can be observed systematically, and even crudely quantified.

Since illustrations of each of the first ten items have already been published, these will not be repeated here (see Kitwood 1990a; Kitwood and Bredin 1992c). I will simply give one example from my recent experience.

> The scene is the 'Alzheimer Unit' of an American nursing home. A young male care assistant is pushing a woman of about 75 years old across the room. She is protesting and resisting, but without words. Gradually he manoeuvres her towards a bean-bag chair, and manages to get her down into it. The chair is very low on the floor; it supports her back, but provides no way in which she can rest her head. She has not got the strength to get up out of it. She looks up at me, and suddenly expresses herself with perfect clarity; 'It's cruel mental torture. They're doing it to me all the time'.

This tiny episode contains elements of disempowerment, intimidation, invalidation, banishment, objectification, imposition and withholding. The care assistant was acting under instruction, and he was doing his work as kindly as he knew how. The home had taken to using bean-bag chairs as a way of preventing residents from moving around, but it could still claim, in technical terms, that it was not using physical restraint. The reader might return at this point to the vignette on page 51, and see how many elements of malignant social psychology he or she can identify there.

Processes of this kind are present in many contexts besides that of dementia: in childcare and schooling, for example, and in the treatment of mental 'patients' in hospital and in the community. The malignancy tends to increase in proportion to three factors: fear, anonymity and the differential of power. Dementia is an extreme example. At times, perhaps, people who are affected simply pick up the main messages through non-verbal channels, and experience the malignancy as a weird and oppressive force.

Ideas similar to those that I have put forward are to be found in the work of Goffman (1974), who looked at the social-psychological processes to which patients were subjected in mental hospitals, focusing particularly on stigmatization. His research, however, did not involve dementia. The idea of malignant social psychology has also been corroborated in some more recent work. Steven Sabat and Rom Harre (1992), for example, explore how people with dementia can be deprived of their 'social selves'. Essentially others who are close refuse to take up the roles complementary to the one the person with dementia wishes to occupy, thus obstructing creative interaction. The idea of stigma has been taken forward into the context of family caregiving in a study by Nancy Blum (1991). She charts how carers at first associate themselves with the person who has dementia, accepting a 'courtesy stigma', doing all they can to cover up the disabilities and to minimize adverse consequences. After a time, however, some carers change their allegiance and begin to convey information to an increasingly wide circle of people, leaving the one who has the stigma to bear it alone. One example that Blum gives is of a man with dementia who starts to talk in the street with a stranger; his wife aligns with the stranger and makes signs to him that her husband is 'crazy'.

Another study by the same author looks at the way deception is used in 'managing' people who have dementia, and identifies four different kinds of deceptive practice (Blum 1994). The first is 'going along' with (factually incorrect) ideas. The second is 'not telling'; for example, transferring a person from their own home into residential care without any prior preparation, and implying that they are simply going on an outing. The third is 'little white lies'; such as telling a man who tends to wander that the doctor has ordered him not to do so. The fourth is 'tricks'; for example, deliberately disabling the car, and then claiming that the person with dementia cannot use it because it is in need of repair. Blum also notes that while much deception is on a one-to-one basis, there is also a good deal of collusion, where two or more people agree together on a deceptive practice; the person with dementia is left in the position of being 'ex-colluded', to use Goffman's phrase. Although Blum's study is small-scale, the implication is that in the American 'Alzheimer culture' (at least) deceptive practices are widely taken for granted, almost with a kind of cynicism; and they are actually encouraged by some professionals, such as support group leaders. There is no hint of recognition here that there might be other ways of dealing with difficulties, through recognizing what a person is needing, and trying to meet that need.

Thus far we have looked at the malignant social psychology in an active sense. There is also the fact of sheer neglect. Evidence from many studies shows that people with dementia who are in residential care typically spend very long periods without any human contact (e.g. Woods and Britton 1977; Clarke and Bowling 1990; Kitwood and Bredin 1992b; Ward et al. 1992; Barnett 1995). In the worst care settings, this may even be as much as 80 per cent of the day. Tessa Perrin (1997), in very detailed work using Dementia Care Mapping, involving nine settings with observation periods of around seven hours in each case, found that people with very severe dementia were severely deprived of human contact; and that much of the interaction that did occur was extremely brief and superficial.

Malignant social psychology is, perhaps, the most glaringly bad part of the care traditions that we have inherited. Fortunately, it is relatively easy to sensitize staff in formal care settings to its presence, and to reduce it greatly through a series of short training sessions. It is noteworthy that the type of episode that seems to be most resistant to elimination is 'talking about a person (not unkindly) in their presence'. This is a mild example of item 11 – ignoring.

The dialectics of dementia

At the level of theory, there is a strong case for bringing the story of advancing neuropathology and that of the social psychology surrounding dementia into a single frame. It is consistent with neuroscientific findings thus far to suppose that the immediate cause of dementia, in all cases, is a lack of that well-functioning interneuronal circuitry through which a person might process the contemporary events of his or her life. Moving beyond the conventional view, however, there are four possible ways in which the circuitry may be lacking.

1   It has never been formed. The person has not been able to adapt, psychologically, to his or her present life situation (which in some instances is equivalent to saying that the appropriate neuronal circuitry has not been developed).

2   The necessary circuitry exists, but it has been deactivated or bypassed. Possibly this is what occurs in some instances of extreme psychological defence, for example after sudden and traumatic loss.

3   The structure of the circuitry exists, but the synapses are not functioning well; there is a neurochemical deficit or imbalance. A depressed mood, for example, may simply be associated with neurochemical changes.

4   The relevant circuitry did exist, or at least the potential to develop it; but a pathological or degenerative process has supervened.

This general hypothesis accommodates the essential unity of brain and mind. It assumes that all events in a person's experience, whether or not they are registered in consciousness, have their counterpart in brain activity, and envisages aspects of personality and biography as being slowly incorporated into brain structure. Ideally, then, a person will be neurologically 'up to date', having neuronal structures relevant to the present situation. Where this is not the case, the background causes may be related to a pathology that has its own dynamic; but also, they may be related to psychological factors, which initially have their counterpart in neurochemistry and, eventually, in the way brain circuitry fails to develop, or is destroyed.

We can thus view the process of dementia as involving a continuing interplay between those factors that pertain to neuropathology *per se*, and those which are social-psychological. The nature of that interplay is dialectical (Kitwood 1990a). Originally the term dialectic referred to a type of argument or disputation. One proposition or thesis would be brought forward, and then be countered by another – an antithesis. Out of the discussion a new position (a synthesis) would emerge, containing elements from both of the original contributions. Then yet another proposition would be brought into the discussion – and so on. Much later, this idea was used as an analogy for certain kinds of process. For example, the state of traffic on the roads might be viewed as the outcome of a dialectical interplay between two main variables. The first is road capacity, and the second is the number of vehicles. When road capacity is enlarged, traffic density increases; when traffic density increases, pressure builds up to enlarge road capacity; this is the story of the M25. In a dialectical process a steady state is never reached. Furthermore, no monocausal theory could predict a later state of affairs.

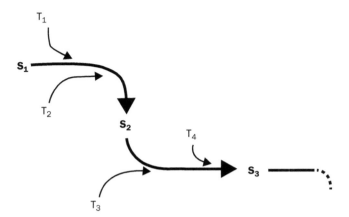

Figure 3.1

The general nature of a dialectical process is illustrated in Figure 3.1.

The 'dialectics of dementia' portrays a person as moving through a succession of states, each of which involves both brain function (in the terms of pp. 13–15, $\psi \equiv \mathbf{b}$) and brain structure in both its developmental and pathological aspects (B^d, B_p). Each state can be symbolized as

$$\frac{\psi \equiv \mathbf{b}}{(B^d, B_p)}$$

As a person moves from one state to another there may be alterations in any of the components. Some changes in brain structure may indeed be caused by a process that has its own (non-psychological) dynamic; other changes, however, are consequent upon experience. A malignant social-psychological environment might retard the development of new circuitry, or even accelerate the advance of neurological degeneration.

All of this can be roughly summarized as

$$\frac{\psi \equiv \mathbf{b}}{(B^d, B_p)} \Big) -$$

A small fragment of the dialectical process has the form shown in Figure 3.2.

The whole of the dementing process, as classically described, might be regarded as an 'involutionary spiral', in which personhood is gradually undermined. This idea was suggested originally by Barnes et al. (1973), though its full implications were generally disregarded. In the case of Margaret, the form of the spiral is shown in Figure 3.3.

The general nature of the process, as a dialectical interplay between neurological impairment (NI) and malignant social psychology (MSP), is common to all persons who go though the classical dementing process. The contribution made by NI will vary from one individual to another; there are some cases where, undoubtedly, the advance of neuropathology is particularly disabling and distressing in its direct effects. There are differences between persons, too, in many details: the order of events, the balance between

Figure 3.2

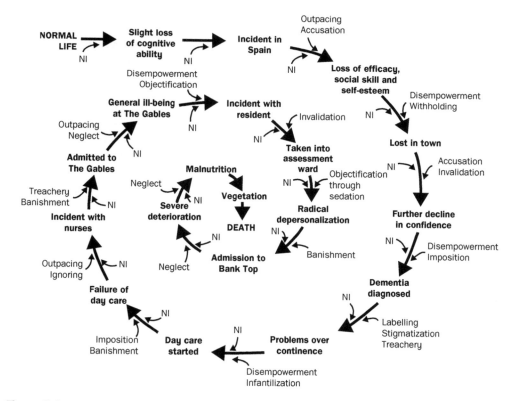

Figure 3.3

NI and MSP in causation, the content of MSP, and the overall rate at which the process moves forward. In some instances of multi-infarct dementia different states can be clearly identified; a person may stay on a plateau for a period, go through a fairly rapid decline, then attain a further stability, and so on. Where the pathology is of the Alzheimer type, however, generally the stages are infinitesimal; a scheme such as that shown in Figure 3.3 is simply an illustrative convenience.

This dialectical framework has the potential for explaining most of the more serious anomalies that the standard paradigm cannot accommodate. A fully reversible 'pseudomentia', perhaps of the depressive kind, is one that solely involves $\psi \equiv \mathbf{b}$; neurochemical deficits are sufficient to prevent the effective functioning of synapses. The categorical distinction between depression and dementia collapses, because both conditions involve neurochemical deficits, and both may or may not be accompanied by structural changes. Environmental variations, such as those found in the London/New York study (see page 31) do not necessarily have to be explained in physical terms (different genetic mixes, environmental toxins, etc.). It is possible that New York is simply a more stressful place to live than London, especially for older people who are vulnerable, and that the stresses of life may be dementogenic. Prevalence variations among people from different educational backgrounds might be accounted for in terms of overall health and lifestyle, or even, as some have suggested, through the simple idea that 'if you don't use it, you lose it'. Another possibility, however, is that the more immediate causal factor is self-esteem, a global state affecting both feeling and cognition; educational differences would then turn out to be only indirect markers.

Even if the kind of approach that I am advocating is correct in principle – and consistent with neuroscience – it must be admitted that we are very far from having the means to corroborate it in fine detail. Neither the methods of neurological nor of social psychological inquiry are sufficiently well developed as yet. However, the person-centred paradigm is open to falsification, as I shall show later in this book, and in that sense it meets Popper's (1959) criterion of scientificity.

In this chapter we have considered the dialectical process almost entirely in negative terms, where both neurological impairment and social psychology work together in the undermining of personhood. There is, however, another possibility: that in which the social psychology is of a more positive and enabling kind, offsetting the effects of neuropathology and even promoting some degree of structural regeneration in the neurones that remain. This is the topic to which we will now turn.

Note

1 The person who supplied this vignette wishes to remain anonymous.

How personhood is undermined

Commentary by Steven R. Sabat

In Chapter 3, Kitwood provided a compelling exploration of how interpersonal interactions can lead to the unwitting undermining of the personhood of people living with dementia. Appropriately, he called these interactions 'malignant social psychology', for these social interactions assault the feelings of self-worth of and depersonalize people living with dementia. It is sad that, even more than a decade after Kitwood's book was published, malignant social psychology was still documented in psycho-geriatric wards in the UK (Kelly 2010). In my own work during the past decade with people living with dementia, I have observed numerous instances of such interactions on the part of formal and informal care partners as well as striking improvements in the demeanour of people living with dementia when they are not subjected to malignant social psychology. The fact that Kitwood identified these interactions 20 years ago has not yet resulted in their eradication, which itself would be a significant non-pharmacological way to improve the lives of those living with dementia. Clearly, we do not generally treat people deemed healthy in such ways or seek to harm those diagnosed with dementia, so what is it that gives us permission, as it were, to act in these ways? This is one of the questions raised and examined in the years since Kitwood's book was published and it is an important question to address for a number of compelling reasons. If we can understand the rather unique, often unspoken, logic that seems to allow those deemed healthy to treat people diagnosed in ways that they would never treat those not diagnosed, we can begin to:

- Unearth the corrective measures that will prevent the occurrence of malignant social psychology
- Eliminate a tremendous source of unnecessary anguish for those living with dementia, and thereby
- Improve their lives as well those of their care partners without the use of drugs.

In this commentary, I should like to discuss some of what we have learned in this regard since *Dementia Reconsidered* was first published.

Foundational precursors of malignant social psychology

Among the interpersonal dynamics that inspire malignant social psychology is what I have termed *malignant positioning* (Sabat 2003, 2004). Positioning itself is the way in which people take for themselves, impose on others, reject or accept social positions. Through these positions, we define another individual's moral and personal attributes including their rights and, thereby, define our own rights and duties towards that individual. Malignant positioning entails a focus primarily on a person's dysfunctional attributes that arise, in the case of people with dementia, due to brain injury resulting from disease. That is, healthy others pay attention to these troublesome attributes almost to the exclusion of valued, intact strengths still possessed and displayed by the person diagnosed, whose 'spoiled identity' (Goffman 1963) has now become 'dementia patient' or 'burdensome patient' or 'demented patient', or some variation thereupon. Once this focus is established, there then follows the creation of storylines about those diagnosed that emphasize dysfunction even where it may not exist at all. For example, Benjamin (1999: 124) commented on a study done by Toseland et al. (1997) on the effectiveness of validation therapy: '. . . nurses reported that patients receiving validation therapy were less physically and verbally aggressive, less depressed, but more non-physically aggressive in terms of increased wandering, pacing, and repetitive movement'. In this case, the authors clearly interpreted walking about and pacing as being 'non-physically aggressive', even though there is no evidence whatsoever given for how such actions could possibly be indicative of aggression of any kind. In addition, walking about is seen through a lens emphasizing dysfunction and thereby called 'wandering', connoting pathology. People diagnosed with dementia wander, but the same people in healthier days walked. Once a person is diagnosed, he or she seemingly cannot take a walk (a healthy activity), but must wander (something pathological) instead. Finally, repetitive movements are somehow understood as being aggressive because people diagnosed are understood to engage in 'irrational hostility'. Someone sitting in a movie theatre and moving his or her leg repeatedly may be annoying to someone nearby, but the action itself is hardly aggressive in any way. Yet, when a person is seen principally in terms of the diagnosis and its related dysfunction, even neutral actions are often viewed within the storyline of defect and labelled as being pathological, thereby validating the storyline.

Once malignant positioning is established, people can lose their right to be treated with the same common courtesy and respect they have enjoyed throughout decades of adult life. Thus, Gen. U, a nursing home resident, is awakened in the early morning by a care worker and told it's time to take a shower. Gen. U says repeatedly that he does not wish to take a shower at that time and so the care worker tries to pull him out of bed forcibly. Gen. U resists and, in the process of this struggle, hits the care worker. Gen. U is then described as being 'unco-operative and combative' rather than simply exercising his right as an adult human being not to be pulled out of bed by someone he hardly knows and who insists that he do something (take a shower) that he does not wish to do at that moment. The care worker's job takes precedence over the rights of the resident because the resident has a diagnosis of dementia and the resident's desire not to take a shower at that moment is not respected. Indeed, the resident seems to have lost his right to decide not to take a shower at that particular time. Gen. U was positioned as someone whose desire in this case was itself an instance of dysfunction rather than something akin to, 'Look, I'm half asleep and I don't like having someone insisting that I have to get into a shower now, and I like even less having that person put his hands on me, trying to yank me out of my bed as if I were a sack of potatoes.' Gen. U's righteous indignation at being accosted physically was interpreted as 'unco-operative and combative', thereby fitting the prevailing storyline of dysfunction. Indeed, he was positioned in a way such that he was incapable of having a normal adult response to a situation that would arouse consternation, to say the least, in anyone. Instead, given his being 'combative', he was prescribed a type of anti-psychotic drug expressly contraindicated for people with dementia by the manufacturer.

Thus, to be seen principally in terms of the dysfunctions entailed in a diagnosis of dementia is the basis of malignant positioning. This means that one's positive, valued intact personal attributes are virtually ignored, or interpreted as a type of dysfunction (righteous indignation is seen as irrational hostility), leading to the deprivation of one's rights to be treated with common courtesy as a human being, which in turn serves as the springboard to what Kitwood called 'malignant social psychology'.

There are still other factors that contribute to the undermining of personhood and these include the incorrect belief that people with dementia cannot make new memories, that they have 'memory loss'. It is often said by care partners that their loved one who is diagnosed with dementia 'won't remember it anyway' so, in a sense, it's okay to discuss his or her problems openly in the person's presence or treat the person in other ways that conform to 'malignant social psychology'. This belief stems from a pervasive, incorrect concept of memory functions, specifically from the mistaken notion that (i) a particular form of retrieval from memory, *recall*, is the one and only way to remember and (ii) a failure to recall something means a failure to remember. These notions are incorrect for a number of reasons, one of which is the existence of *implicit memory*, which is a change in a person's actions that occurs due to an experience that he or she *doesn't recall* having had. The experimental literature on this phenomenon in people with dementia actually pre-dated *Dementia Reconsidered* (for example, Butters et al. 1990; Knopman 1991; Gabrieli et al. 1993; Deweer et al. 1994; Monti et al. 1994). Even though its demonstration in everyday life by people with dementia was reported more recently (Sabat 2006), its exis-tence and meaning have yet to penetrate the awareness of the general public, many health professionals and innumerable voluntary organizations around the world that are set up to help people living with dementia. People with dementia can, in fact, learn new things, make new friends, and make long-term memories of those who treat them kindly as well as those who treat them badly. For example, a person with dementia can make a long-term memory that a particular person was kind even though the ability to *recall the exact details involved* in that experience is not intact. Long-term implicit memories can be made. If care partners are unaware of this fact and believe instead that the person they are supporting cannot make new memories (due to their obvious recall dysfunction – they cannot recall what they had for breakfast, or that they already had breakfast, for example), they assume that the anger shown presently by the diagnosed person towards someone who has treated him or her badly days earlier is 'irrational hostility' rather than 'righteous indignation'.

Another example of social dynamics that can lead to the undermining of personhood is found in the contribution of Hydén (2018), who discusses a phenomenon occurring in con-versations involving persons with dementia who have word-finding problems. In trying to provide support for the person diagnosed, the otherwise healthy person may 'take over' and provide the word or phrase or name that the former is having difficulty recalling. This *micro-management*, as Hydén calls it, can be another form of malignant social psychology that is done with the best of intentions, but can easily serve unwittingly to position the person diagnosed as being unable to converse or, perhaps, a less than capable partner in conversation. This, then, can easily lead the person diagnosed to experience failure, feel inadequate and/or burdensome, and to withdraw entirely from speaking. Often, this occurs because the healthy partner in conversation is unable to tolerate long pauses in the conversation – pauses that the diagnosed person needs in order to recall the word or words he or she wishes to say. It is not uncommon to find people intolerant of protracted silence during a conversation, for they feel the need to 'fill the unforgiving minute', in Kipling's words, with chatter. This situation is a variation on what Kitwood called *outpacing*, a form of malignant social psychology. When provided with patience in conversation, in which rather long pauses are met with a non-anxious presence on the part of the healthy interlocutor, however, people with severe word-finding problems do not withdraw at all (Sabat 2001) for they have permission, as it were, to use as much time as they require. Under these conditions, it is possible also to encourage the speaker who has word-finding problems to use gestures, to act out in bodily fashion using their hands, arms, eyes, to convey their thoughts. Hydén (2018) discusses embodied communication in detail, and Sabat and Cagigas (1997) provided a case study of successful extra-linguistic communication in a person with Alzheimer's disease. Giving the person with dementia as much time as he or she requires to communicate with words or with a combination of words and gestures can be of great value to the communicative process, help the person diagnosed to feel respected and capable and engaged by others, and thereby avoid feeling depersonalized, burdensome and lacking still more in self-worth. Of course, this all requires that the person diagnosed with dementia is positioned initially as a person (i) possessing the desire and need to communicate, (ii) whose utterances, even if difficult at first to decipher, are themselves attempts to communicate something of import, and (iii) who needs and would benefit from having a willing partner to facilitate the communicative process.

Finally, malignant social psychology can be avoided if the person diagnosed is positioned as (i) having intact selfhood, (ii) possessing the ability for creative expression and (iii) one whose actions are driven by the meaning of situations, thus demonstrating semiotic behaviour. Selfhood and semiotic behaviour have been shown to be intact in the verbal discourse of people with dementia in the moderate to severe stages (Sabat 2001) as well as in embodied expressions (Kontos 2005; Hughes 2014). Likewise, creative expression has been shown to exist, with appropriate facilitation (Sauer et al. 2014; Killick 2016). Therefore, a diagnosis of dementia does not, by definition, strip people of the ability to act meaningfully, to be sensitive to the way others treat them, to show concern and care for others, to make new long-term memories and act upon them. That is, people diagnosed with dementia share a great deal with those not diagnosed (Indicators of Relative Well-Being, in Kitwood's terms), and ought to be positioned and treated accordingly. One rather compelling recent example of positioning and treating people living with dementia in positive ways is the important, searching exploration of 'Truth Telling' (Mental Health Foundation 2016) in communicating with people diagnosed.

Malignant social psychology still exists; it reflects misinformed thinking about and the resulting malignant positioning of people living with dementia, and hurts not only those diagnosed, but their carers as well. There is still much room for improvement in our psychosocial treatment of people living with dementia and it behoves us to effect such improvements for the benefit of all concerned.

Reflection points

- How does a purely biomedical understanding of dementia, including what is contained in the DSM-V (called a neurocognitive disorder), contribute to malignant positioning and malignant social psychology?

- How must our understanding of people living with dementia change such that malignant positioning and malignant social psychology can be eliminated?

- Can professionals create what Buber called 'I–Thou' relationships with people with dementia?

4

Personhood maintained

Tom Kitwood

Although the picture of dementia presented in the previous chapter was strongly marked by degradation and pain, it was not the deterministic one summed up in the phrase 'Alzheimer's: No cure, no help, no hope'. In every case societal and social-psychological aspects are involved in some way, and I have suggested that they should be regarded as integral to the process of decline. So it is important to look in detail at how factors which are within human control might serve to enhance the personhood of those who have dementia, offsetting the consequences of neurological impairment.

The best care settings have, of course, been working along these lines, and often with remarkable success. Some practitioners, however, cannot give a clear account of what they are doing; there is a kind of double-think. At one level they hold to the official theory, a popular rendering of the standard paradigm; in practice they don't believe in it, preferring a more positive view. Progress will occur much faster if there is a clear theoretical frame; good care needs to find a voice.

This chapter offers a review and appraisal of the more optimistic and person-centred approaches that have been developing. We will trace their growth, and survey some of the evidence that points to better outcomes. In the final section we will return to the theme of the dialectics of dementia, and place the findings within the framework of a person-centred paradigm.

A growing concern

In moving away from the negativity of the past, improvements have been brought about in almost every aspect of the lives of people with dementia: in diagnosis, assessment, care planning, patterns for living, occupations, diet, medical treatment, the use of technology, the physical design of care environments. There has also been a considerable transfer of knowledge and expertise from other fields, such as learning disability, psychotherapy and the hospice movement. Among the reviews of positive approaches, by far the most comprehensive in Britain is that of Holden and Woods (1995); other valuable sources are Woods (1995), Hunter (1997), Marshall (1997), and the two volumes edited by Jones and Miesen (1992, 1994). The very brief account that is given in this section, and the subsequent summary of research evidence, owes something to each of these sources. Here we will focus attention on three of the most central topics: conceptions of the person with dementia, improvements in care practice, and developments in community care.

The person with dementia

There was a time before the standard paradigm was established, when psychiatrists and other investigators were relatively open to exploring how personal factors might be involved in dementia. Some of this earlier work is reviewed by Gilhooly (1984), and in one of my own articles (Kitwood 1988). The figure who stands as a pioneer is the American psychiatrist David Rothschild. His view was that neuropathology alone cannot account for the manifestation of primary dementia, and that (as in the parallel case of stroke) psychological aspects are always involved (Rothschild 1937; Rothschild and Sharpe 1944). Among other significant studies are some which suggest that psychological defence processes such as denial are implicated in dementia (e.g. Morgan 1965), and some which look at the role of personality in aetiology and presentation (e.g. Gillespie 1963; Oakley 1965). The significance of these writings lies not so much in their substantive findings as in the breadth and humanity of their approach.

In more recent times, we can discern a general movement towards a recognition of the personhood of men and women with dementia. During the 1970s a few workers were opening up psychological approaches, and thus implicitly taking a stand against the prevailing negativity and determinism (e.g. Woods and Britton 1977). A major landmark in Britain was the document *Living Well into Old Age*, published by the King's Fund (1986). Here it is plainly stated that those with dementia have the same value, the same needs and the same rights as everyone else; they are to be brought fully into the arena of moral concern. After this it became more acceptable to give attention to the psychology and real life of people with dementia, as the work of Mary Marshall (1988) and Christopher Gilleard (1984) clearly shows.

In my own work on dementia I have tried to develop a view of personhood that meets at least four main criteria. It must reveal our moral obligations; it must be valid in terms of a psychology that focuses on experience, action and spirituality; it must illuminate care practice; and it must be fully compatible with the well-corroborated findings of neuroscience. This book, in its entirety, will show how far that project is successful.

Care practice

The first clear attempt at providing positive intervention came from methods of reality orientation (RO) that had been developed in the 1950s, and used in the rehabilitation of men traumatized by war. When RO was introduced into work with confused older people its good effects, in the form of renewed vitality and hopefulness, were clearly visible (Taulbee and Folsom 1966). As the method was amplified it included the senses, human relationships and general awareness (Holden and Woods 1988); it was certainly not the narrowly cognitive technique portrayed in caricatures. Whatever may have been its weaknesses, RO did recognize the personhood of men and women with dementia, expressing the belief that it was worth taking the trouble to try to bring them back into a 'normal' way of life.

In the early 1960s, a few years after RO had taken hold, Naomi Feil developed the approach which she named validation therapy (VT) (Feil 1982, 1993). Here there was a dramatic shift towards the feelings and emotions, and a realization that there might be genuinely therapeutic psychological outcomes in dementia. As with RO, it is easy to parody Feil's work, particularly as the theoretical frame that she provides is not strong (Kitwood 1994c). Nevertheless, the introduction of VT marked a big step forward, affirming that the experience of people with dementia should be taken with the utmost seriousness.

These insights were taken even further in the approach which Graham Stokes and Fiona Goudie (1989) termed resolution therapy, with its emphasis on empathy and communication, and on responding to present need.

Another major contribution was the introduction of reminiscence, following the work of Robert Butler (1963) and the subsequent research of Peter Coleman (1986). Although primary dementia involves major losses in cognitive ability, it was well known that long-term memory often remains relatively intact. Various kinds of individual and group reminiscence work were possible, often using aids such as music, photographs, or household equipment (Woods et al. 1992; Mills and Coleman 1994). As reminiscence work developed it became clear that it was much more than a matter of revisiting the past. Often, it seems, memories provide metaphorical resources for people to talk about their present situation in a way that they can handle (Barnett 1996; Cheston 1996). Laura Sutton (1995) has gone even further, and developed a theory of reminiscence as interpersonal communication, with a radical critique of simplistic ideas of memory as factual recall.

Alongside reminiscence work, it came to be recognized that there were many ways in which biographical knowledge could be incorporated into care planning and practice (Gibson 1991, 1994; Murphy et al. 1994). Care settings began to consult with family members about how to provide activities which would match a person's former tastes and interests, and the idea of having some kind of life history book, complete with photographs, became part of best practice. In dementia the sense of identity based on having a life-story to tell may eventually fade, as Marie Mills (1995) has shown. When it does, biographical knowledge about a person becomes essential if that identity is still to be held in place.

Following the evident success of practices such as these, many ways of enriching the lives of people with dementia have been explored: for example, the use of music, dance, drama and graphic art. One of the most significant of the recent additions to this array is the development of methods for providing human contact and pleasurable stimulation to the senses, bypassing cognition almost entirely; these include massage, relaxation and aromatherapy. The combined use of light, sound and pleasant aromas has been packaged as 'Snoezelen', and many care settings now have a special room set up for this purpose (Benson 1994; Threadgold 1995). A great deal of work has also been done in developing activities suited for different degrees of cognitive impairment. Here, in keeping with their extrovert cultural tradition, the Americans have made many excellent innovations (e.g. Funnemark 1995). In Britain many of the most creative ideas to date have been collected together by Carol Archibald (1990, 1993).

As the concern to provide good care has grown, it has been increasingly recognized that there is a need for quality standards and for sound methods of evaluation. Several observational methods for evaluating the actual process of care have now been developed, and are in widespread use, for example Dementia Care Mapping (Kitwood and Bredin 1992b) and the Quality of Interaction Schedule (Dean et al. 1993). A review of available methods has been written by Dawn Brooker (1995). It is now possible to devise integrated strategies for evaluation and quality improvement, giving staff clear and usable feedback on the progress of their work (Kitwood and Woods 1996).

Community care

This, in strategic terms, is the top priority, because around 80 per cent of all people with dementia are still living in their own homes; a substantial proportion – around 30 per cent of these – are living alone (Ely et al. 1996). Social services are only slowly adapting to the new situation, and face many problems through being grossly underresourced. New skills are required, particularly around issues of care management, and there is a huge need for training at all levels (Chapman and Marshall 1996). Despite the difficulties, many promising innovations have been made.

Day care has developed in a very short time from being a type of 'minding', mainly to provide relief for hard-pressed carers, into a highly skilled and specialized form of practice. In the best settings there is very thorough assessment, and care is planned to meet each individual's personal and rehabilitative needs. Much more is known now about how to provide good day care for younger people with dementia. A relatively new idea is the provision of 'informal' day care where two or three people with dementia spend their day in the home of a trained volunteer. Increasing use is being made of befriending services, where a visitor spends a period with the person with dementia in their own home.

In several countries there have been moves towards providing smaller residential settings that are fully part of the local community. In Sweden, for example, experiments have been tried where people have flats close together, in an ordinary block, with a small input of continuing care (Annerstedt 1987). Several forms of small group living have been devised, with the aim of maximizing independence and cooperation, while at the same time providing the necessary background of care. The Domus project in Britain has been developed with particular attention to the need for people to feel in control of their lives (Murphy et al. 1994). The number of people with dementia in sheltered housing is growing, and some providers are taking steps to enable them to remain in their flats, if at all possible, rather than move into residential care (Petre 1995). In these and many other ways we are beginning to realize how much scope there is for providing a meaningful way of life in dementia, and how stilted was the older binary division between formal and informal care.

Much progress has been made in providing support for carers, and so, indirectly, helping the people they are looking after. Several different models for carers' support have been explored, some more 'educational' and some more 'therapeutic' (see Miller and Morris 1993: 133–53). One promising innovation has been the development of a structured programme of group support for carers, lasting around 15 weeks, working as the borderline between education, empowerment and group therapy. Each group that completes the programme then continues to meet, without the facilitator present (Bruce 1995, 1996).

Finally, mention must be made of the development of counselling and group therapy for people who have dementia, especially in the period after they have received diagnosis. We are even seeing the first mutual support groups run by people with dementia for one another – a thing that would have been inconceivable 10 years ago. The progress that has been made in these areas is due in large part to a greater openness about dementia, and a shedding of some of the stigma, following the lead set in the United States. Despite the 'disease' label, dementia is beginning to be depathologized and accepted as part of the human condition.

Evidence for a positive view: a case study

A series in the *Journal of Dementia Care* presents accounts of good effects associated with (and almost certainly resulting from) person-centred care (Kitwood 1995c). Each one shows how a deteriorating situation was turned around, or how well-being was maintained, in the face of cognitive disability, and thus points to a dialectical process very different from that described in Chapter 3. The following story describes the last part of the life of a woman with dementia, after she had moved into sheltered housing.

When Bessy moved into Flower Court, from a village a few miles away, she was already showing early signs of memory problems that were obvious to her close family. Her daughter lived near the scheme and had applied for a flat for her mother so that she could give her extra help.

Two years later, when I first met Bessy, her dementia had increased considerably. However, she appeared to have a very high level of well-being. During my visit to her flat she made no real conversation but constantly laughed and made happy fragmented comments. This impression was confirmed by the warden. According to her reports Bessy always showed a considerable amount of humour, frequently initiated social contact with others and was usually relaxed.

When Bessy first moved into the scheme the situation was not as happy as I found it. During her first few months in Flower Court she had often been aggressive, and indeed physically violent, towards people who came into conflict with her. For example, she always refused to be undressed for bed, and if encouraged she would hit out. Her neighbours were afraid of the aggressive outbursts. As a consequence they tended to avoid Bessy, which severely restricted her social life.

In addition a problem of a different kind was occurring. At a similar time every day Bessy would attempt to leave the scheme and search for a bus back to the village where she had previously lived. In sheltered housing, tenants tend to be active enough to come and go as they please, and there are no care staff to look out for them. Therefore as Bessy's dementia developed it was a growing concern that she would be lost and/or injured if this continued.

Luckily for Bessy, she and Janet the warden had 'clicked' on their first meeting and over time became strongly bonded to one another. A number of behaviours on Bessy's part confirmed her attachment. For example, she had learned Janet's name straight away and always used it – 'to my surprise' said Janet. If Bessy hurt herself she would search out Janet to help her. On one such occasion she fell and badly hurt her knee and yet still managed to walk to Janet's office, saying to her, 'Save me.'

Janet was committed to exploring possibilities to lessen Bessy's afternoon disappearances, her aggression and consequent stigmatization by other tenants. So she arranged to discuss the situation with Bessy's daughter. What emerged from their conversation was a rich picture of Bessy's previous life. Before her husband had died, the couple had spent their life as publicans. Apparently Bessy had been extremely extrovert and outgoing – she loved company, jokes, dressing up for work and having a firm routine to her life. Obviously due to such a lifestyle Bessy had also needed to be able to protect herself when threatened, even if this was by just appearing aggressive.

Janet had used this personal information to form a few ideas of ways in which she might lessen Bessy's problems; for example, Bessy refused to undress for bed, becoming aggressive if pushed. Some creative thinking around Bessy's previous love of dressing-up eased the problem. The warden allowed Bessy to sleep in the clothes she had worn during the day. The next morning when the home help would visit Bessy, she would get out lots of outfits and comment, 'It's like C&A in here, let's try on some clothes.' Bessy would then happily try on different things until she was in a new, clean outfit each day.

Turning her attention to Bessy's increasingly dangerous wandering and searching, Janet thought of the boredom she must now be experiencing after such a busy and routine filled life. As a start Janet began to take Bessy with her when she took and picked up her children from school. This gave a very regular format to her day. At exactly the same time each morning and afternoon Bessy would go on what she called 'an out-ing', meeting other people as she went, which encouraged her sociable nature. With a little encouragement tenants accepted that Bessy would come to some social events in the communal lounge, and a few would pick her up from her flat. Bessy 'had a wonder-ful time', according to Janet, at these social events. She loved to sing and when tenants walked her back to her flat they would have to sing with her all the way.

Thus the scheme had arrived at the situation I found. Bessy was happy and relaxed, strongly attached to Janet. Her initial aggression had lessened considerably without ever using medication. Other tenants had grown to like Bessy and actively helped her to join in events.

Before my most recent visit to Flower Court, Bessy had a serious fall and was subse-quently admitted to a geriatric ward. Three weeks later she died while still in hospital. Until the end of her time in Flower Court she had remained closely bonded to Janet and well liked by other tenants. On the day of her funeral half of the tenants of the scheme attended and paid their respects – an indication of how well thought of she had been.

(Petre, *Journal of Dementia Care* 4(1), Hawker Publications Ltd, 1996)

This story shows, incontrovertibly, some of the effects of person-centred care. The ground of Bessy's well-being, in her widowhood, was the close attachment she had formed with Janet, the warden. Janet also provided a structure for Bessy's day, and helped her to recover enough confidence to recreate her former outgoing pattern of life. As other tenants became involved, a 'virtuous circle' was set in motion. Tracy Petre, who carried out the research, was able to give Bessy an informal Mini-Mental State Examination about a year before she died. Her score was 1 (out of a maximum of 30); this, as well as informal observation, suggests very severe cognitive impairment.

Single examples, of course, cannot be used to prove a general case. They can merely illustrate particular points, and highlight areas where evidence needs to be gathered systematically. That project, as I have suggested, is still only in its infancy, but considerable progress has already been made, as we shall see in the following section.

Evidence for a more positive view: experience and research

Although research related to the everyday life of people with dementia has been far less generously funded than in the biomedical field, there is now a small but substantial body of evidence which suggests that cases such as that of Bessy are not exceptional. They are part of the emerging new picture of dementia, which will almost certainly look very dif-ferent from the one to which we have been accustomed.

First, and possibly of greatest significance (even though it does not take the form of structured research), is the experience of a now considerable number of people who have committed themselves to the delivery of person-centred care. Janet Bell and Iain McGregor, for example, have written a number of articles which describe life in the specialist residential home which they set up. They consistently report that the majority of their residents do not end up in vegetation; a significant number stabilize and maintain relatively high levels of well-being despite having very severe cognitive impairments (Bell and McGregor 1995). Many of their residents, at the point of admission, had been written off as hopeless in other settings, and the home has always provided some places for people of a younger age, for whom dementia is often particularly devastating. Similar accounts are beginning to appear from many quarters, in some cases supported by systematically collected data (e.g. Mills 1997).

Research evidence is beginning to point in a similar direction. Andrew Sixmith and colleagues (1993) for example made a study of 'homely homes', where the care was of very high quality. Here they found clear examples of 'rementing', or measurable recovery of powers that had apparently been lost; a degree of cognitive decline often ensued, but it was far slower than that which has been typically expected when people with dementia are in long-stay care. A study of residential care by Ann Netten (1993) found that positive features were significantly correlated with three intermediate outcome measures: orientation to place, lower social disturbance and lower levels of apathy. The evaluation of the Domus project (see p. 67) also showed very promising results. As compared to more traditional settings there was more interaction, and of higher quality, a decrease in depression, and a lower rate of general decline (Murphy et al. 1994). Research carried out by Bradford Dementia Group involved a detailed cross-sectional study of 224 persons with dementia, in 26 residential homes and 51 sheltered housing schemes – the majority owned by two non-profit-making organizations. Unexpectedly high levels of well-being were found, suggesting that a transformation of the life of people with dementia is already under way (Kitwood et al. 1995).

There have now been many studies to explore the efficacy of particular interventions. In the case of reality orientation and validation therapy the research evidence is somewhat ambiguous (Holden and Woods 1995), although the positive experience of practitioners is not to be lightly dismissed. In their review Holden and Woods report short-term beneficial effects from several other types of intervention: for example music, visits by children, the introduction of pets and relaxation programmes. Among research published since their review went to press is a study by Helen Nairn (1995), who found markedly positive changes over a nine month period as a result of introducing an activities programme into a long-stay hospital ward.

A particularly thorough piece of research has been recently completed by Tessa Perrin (1997). Her work focused entirely on people with very severe dementia, all of whom would be in the final stage of 'global deterioration' as judged by a stage scheme such as that of Reisburg (see p. 25). Fourteen different types of occupational intervention were explored, and 29 people were included in the study, which involved around 200 hours of minutely detailed observation. Positive effects were observed in around 60 per cent of the instances, and there were only six people from whom no positive response could be elicited. This study is both poignant and revealing, because many of those involved in it had had to endure years of the 'old culture' of care. Despite this, and despite extreme cognitive impairment and physical dependency, in most cases the potential for personhood still remained.

There is a body of research originating from a medically-oriented group in Sweden which adds an important dimension to this positive picture. This is a series of investigations of the effects of 'integrity-promoting care', involving, for example, high levels of individual attention, carefully planned activities, close personal support, and the opportunity to participate in general decision making. In one controlled study over two months, and in another which made observations after three and six months, significant positive changes were found in both psychological and neurochemical variables (Karlsson et al. 1988; Brane et al. 1989). This research provides the first clear evidence that care practice can have neurological consequences, and the authors hypothesize that the psychosocial environment actually affected neuronal growth. Research of this kind is still in its infancy, and these studies are marred by the use of the method of lumbar puncture for obtaining neuro-chemical data. There is an urgent need for non-invasive ways of monitoring the structure and function of the nervous system in dementia, without removing a person from his or her own familiar setting.

Another line of inquiry which may prove to be significant, in neurological terms, is the study of those short-lived episodes of apparent lucidity and clear communication that people with dementia sometimes show, particularly when near to the point of death. Until recently this topic has been known only through hearsay, but now it has been made a subject for detailed research (Thorpe 1996). If 'spontaneous intermittent remissions' do indeed occur, some of the most cherished tenets of the standard paradigm are challenged. The implication is that even a brain which is carrying severe pathology may have more reserve and flexibility than is commonly assured.

The study of 'rementing' has been taken a step further by work with people who are still living in their own homes. Jackie Pool (forthcoming) for example, has followed up 73 people for whom she provided very detailed assessment and an individual programme of rehabilitation, with an average contact level of six sessions per person. In 22 instances there was a measured improvement in both well-being and cognitive performance, and in another nine an improvement in well-being alone.

Many individual case studies have now been carried out, showing in detail how good care practice is associated with well-being. The story of Bessy given in the previous section is typical of this genre. One of the pioneers of this kind of work was Faith Gibson, who devoted particular attention to people who were severely deteriorated and disturbed. In effect she was using a kind of 'methodology of the worst case'; its logical force is that if positive effects are found even in these cases, it is highly probable that they will also be found in those who are less severely affected. One of the people in her study was a woman aged 86, who had been in residential care for five years; she was isolated, agitated, and had lost most of her ability to communicate. The staff knew little about her past, and had labelled her (for obvious reasons) as 'the stripper'. After a thorough assessment, a programme of person-centred care was designed. This included making visits to her sister, outings to a garden centre and to the place of her childhood, giving her the opportunity to take part in some housework, and giving more attention to her appearance. Many positive changes were observed, and the team concluded that about three-quarters of all the interventions had brought clear benefit (Gibson 1991). Another of Gibson's case studies is presented in the series in the *Journal of Dementia Care*, to which I have already referred on page 58 (Gibson et al. 1995).

Most of the research reviewed above has been concerned with relatively short-term changes – over days, weeks or months. I have made one small attempt to enlarge the picture by obtaining data concerning outcomes in the longer term – over several years (Kitwood 1995b). This study collected retrospective evidence from 10 persons involved in the provision of residential care, representing six distinct and geographically separate settings. The accumulated data show relatively positive long-term outcomes in 43 persons. In 27 of these there were even signs of the emergence of positive characteristics that had not been strongly in evidence before the dementia developed; examples are the growth of trust, affection and assertiveness. This small study might be taken as a marker for much more detailed, and preferably prospective, research (see also p. 117). My estimate was that currently we might expect to see clear positive outcomes in around 5 to 10 per cent of all cases, where the quality of care is good by present standards. If the general position that I have set out has substantial truth, we would expect the proportion to increase considerably as the quality of care improves. This will be one of the most important of all tests of the validity of the person-centred paradigm.

The evidence for a more optimistic view of dementia, a little of which I have summarized here, is very fragmentary as yet. Some research designs may not have been well chosen, and many studies are marred by the use of rather insensitive techniques of measurement. In the case of qualitative data one must, of course, be particularly cautious; there is a very understandable tendency for people to see what they are hoping for, and to ignore evidence to the contrary – especially when they are strongly committed to a cause. Nevertheless, the general inference to be drawn from the research to date is how much has been achieved through interventions that are only relatively modest; if improvements were consistent, and throughout the entire context of dementia, we might reasonably expect to see much more than this. We are very far from having reached the limits that are genuinely set by the structural state of the brain.

When neurological impairment is extreme

In a case such as that of Bessy, as indeed the others reported in the series in the *Journal of Dementia Care*, it might be objected that although there were major problems with cognition, the more general consequences of neuropathology might have been relatively benign. One way of exploring this is to consider those cases where a person had to face the most devastating kind of neurological damage – an extreme form of the 'methodology of the worst case'. In so doing it may be possible to get a sense of both the power and the limits of a person-centred approach. The following account was prepared by Errollyn Bruce, Linda Fox and myself, from our support work with carers in Bradford.

> Brenda Baker's really serious health problems began when she was in her early 50s, while she was working in the textiles industry. First she had difficulties with balance; she kept falling off her stool at work for no apparent reason. Then her handwriting and other manual skills deteriorated. Treatment with thyroxin did nothing to relieve these symptoms, and she was invalided out of work with a diagnosis of ataxia – an impairment of motor nerve function originating in the cerebellum. When Brenda was 55, her husband Duncan left his job as an HGV driver so that he could look after her. Within the following year Brenda began to show clear signs of dementia, and by the time she was 57 she had lost her speech. Eventually she was referred to a neurologist, who confirmed the diagnosis. Later Duncan recalled how the neurologist had dismissed her case saying, 'Sorry, Mr Baker, there's nothing we can do'. Duncan had experienced this as cold and heartless, giving him no encouragement in the difficult task he was to undertake.

Brenda showed frequent signs of severe agitation. Her balance was now very poor, and she had many falls. Often she would keep her eyes shut for hours at a time, and when in this state she refused to eat or cooperate. She fought dressing and undressing – in fact everything that Duncan had to do for her. She suffered from frequent urine infections and chest problems; these illnesses made her even more agitated, and brought greater problems with sleeping and eating. Despite her difficulties with balance she was very active, and was constantly exploring her surroundings with her mouth and hands, without any sense of danger. On one occasion she burned her hands through clinging to a radiator when she was at day care; on another her thumb was split through being trapped in the door of a taxi, causing severe pain and a serious infection.

Duncan loved Brenda deeply, and he remained loyal and devoted to her as her disabilities increased, and as they moved on from one crisis to another. He kept a photo of their wedding day in his wallet, which he sometimes brought out when he was talking about Brenda. The photo showed a beautiful and happy woman, and a couple who looked very much at ease with each other. Brenda's deterioration caused Duncan great distress. At times he was able to reveal this, and allow himself to break down in tears. He was determined to look after Brenda, if it was humanly possible, until the end of her life.

Around this time Brenda showed few signs of pleasure, and frequently her face carried an expression of deep despair. At day care she would often stand at the window, gazing out; everything about her seemed to express her yearning to be away from all this, perhaps to be out in the open air. Duncan said that on her good days she appeared to find some pleasure – or at least less distress – in shopping expeditions, and in walks in the park near their home.

Duncan felt that he was being put under pressure to place Brenda in long-stay care, and he avoided contact with the professionals who advised this most forcefully. Various members of the family and numerous other people told him, 'She'd be better off in a home'; one acquaintance even said, 'She'd be better off dead'. Duncan's conviction remained that he should look after her in their own home, with some help from their daughter. He believed that Brenda had been grossly neglected when she was in hospital after one of her accidents. Also, in his view, the space and greater freedom in residential homes were outweighed by the lack of staff time to watch her properly. He was also against 'pumping tablets down her', and he felt that this was more likely if Brenda was put into formal care.

Although he was strongly committed to caring, for a long time Duncan seemed to be under the spell of the extremely negative and deterministic opinions he had received from the professionals. About some new event he would often say, 'This is the ataxia, isn't it?' and he would ask, 'Is this the worst case of dementia you have ever seen?' (perhaps reflecting an opinion that had actually been given to him). Gradually, though, as he shared his difficulties with others in a support group, he came to value more highly his own work as a carer. In particular, the nearest that Brenda came to a sense of relaxation and comfort was when he was holding her closely, in the intimacy of their own home. Duncan slowly acquired a new confidence, and some relief from his own severe stress.

During the last months of Brenda's life Duncan described them as 'living on a knife-edge'. Brenda stayed at home, but also went most days to a residential home. Brenda was losing weight; she suffered from bouts of diarrhoea, and infections from sores and rubbing became more frequent. She was losing her ability to swallow, which made it very hard for her to take sufficient fluids. Her walking deteriorated to the point where two people were needed to take her out. She began to be active in the early hours. Duncan would be woken by the sound of her scrabbling furiously with her hands, and then she would lie rigidly, staring into space. He found these moments very unnerving, but he could not tell if Brenda herself was distressed. One problem followed another. Duncan was in a state of high anxiety, but still he held on. One summer morning Brenda suffered a major heart attack, and died in his arms.

Simply in neurological terms, it would be hard to find a more terrible case; the professionals themselves conveyed this message to Duncan. Brenda had to face not only the rapid failing of her mental powers at an early age, but a devastating breakdown of motor control as a result of disease in her cerebellum, and a great deal of physical pain. She was on the threshold of a radical loss of personhood after her time in hospital. If at this point Duncan had heeded the advice to place her in long-stay care, it is almost certain that she would have undergone a drastic deterioration. Duncan, however, emerged from the profoundly negative view that had been foisted upon him, and was able to give Brenda much of the comfort and reassurance that she so desperately needed. Brenda, for her part, was able to hold on to Duncan; she remained in a living relationship with him, and it was in the safety of that relationship that she died.

It should be said, in passing, that this story does not entail the conclusion that residential care should be avoided at all costs. In this case Duncan had made a clear judgement; he would not be able to find a long-stay setting that would meet Brenda's extreme and difficult needs. Also he had estimated that his own strength, though failing, had a good chance of outlasting her fairly short life expectancy, with the help and support he had gathered around him. Circumstances were to prove him right.

The dialectics of dementia: a second look

As the brief survey given in this chapter has shown, there is good ground for holding the view that dementia does not entail, as a necessary consequence, a radical disintegration of the person. There may, of course, be some instances where the neurological damage is so devastating that even the most excellent care cannot enable personhood to remain intact, but we cannot know whether that is so until good quality care has been in place for several years. In the meantime we can be certain that good care has vast potential for offsetting the deterioration that is normally attributed to dementia. We are only at the end of the beginning.

The standard paradigm, insofar as I have represented it correctly, does not tell us the truth about dementia. 'Alzheimer's: No cure, no help, no hope' is a false proposition; the 'death that leaves the body behind' is a misleading image. Two fallacies were involved in the more traditional view, and it is important to recognize them clearly. The first was to make premature inductive generalizations: that is, to draw broad conclusions from too few, and too narrow, a range of cases. The second was to create the illusion of a natural history of dementia, by making social and psychological factors into mere externalities. If the cause of the whole downward process of dementia is attributed to disease processes in the brain, we are no longer in the realm of science, but of neuropathic ideology.

Throughout the greater part of biomedical research – especially studies of neuropathology, brain biochemistry, scanning and drug trials – a crucial variable has been missing. It is the nature of the social psychology, whose major component is the quality of care. Imagine, for a moment, a group of investigators (natural philosophers, as they would be called) at the very threshold of the scientific age. They are studying the rate at which steel balls fall through various liquids. After many years of research they have refined their methods of inquiry. The timing devices are extremely accurate; the shapes and densities of the balls have been thoroughly standardized; the liquids are rigorously pure. A breakthrough is declared to be imminent. The evidence is collected with the utmost care, but some important truth seems to be still concealed, as patterns in the data begin to form and then mysteriously disappear. We can see it now; of course no account was taken of the temperature, which has a large effect on the viscosity of all liquids. Something like this has happened with research based on the standard paradigm; no wonder it is in disarray. It will remain so, I suggest, until the missing variable of social psychology is properly included.

The dialectical view which I set out towards the end of Chapter 3 enables us to begin to give a theoretical account of the effects of person-centred care. This time, however, there is a dialectic in the stronger sense, for the two main tendencies are mutually opposed.

In the best contexts of care each advance in neurological impairment (NI), which has the potential to be deeply damaging if the social psychology is not helpful, is compensated for by positive person work (PPW). The nature of this work will be explored in detail in Chapter 6; suffice to say here that it consists of interactions that meet psychological need. The greater the degree of NI, the more PPW is provided. This is the very opposite of what has traditionally happened, where people are subjected to increasing neglect as their mental powers fail. The form of the dialectical process is illustrated in Figure 4.1.

This process cannot be realized in its entirety; we are looking at an ideal that lies far beyond our present skill and knowledge. In terms of the psycho-neurological formula I have used at several points, we can be sure that each episode of person-enhancing interaction has its concomitants and consequences in neurochemistry ($\psi \equiv \mathbf{b}$). It is beginning to look as if the effects are stronger than this, involving brain structure as well, perhaps slowing

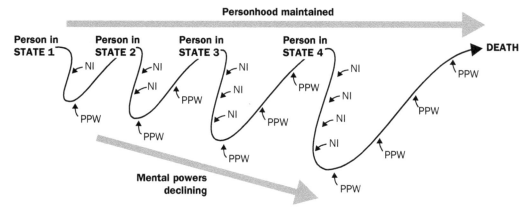

Figure 4.1

down the pathological processes and enhancing growth in the neurones that remain. Thus the whole effect can be summed up as

$$\frac{\psi \equiv \mathbf{b}}{(B^d, B_p)} \longrightarrow -$$

In developmental terms, it is almost a reversal of what happened in the earliest part of life. As an infant responds to others, processes that are at first interpersonal become 'internalized' – part of the individual psyche. At the same time the central nervous system is growing and maturing, holding the fruit of experience in place. In dementia many aspects of the psyche that had, for a long time, been individual and 'internal', are again made over to the interpersonal milieu. Memory may have faded, but something of the past is known; identity remains intact, because others hold it in place; thoughts may have disappeared, but there are still interpersonal processes; feelings are expressed and meet a validating response; and if there is a spirituality, it will most likely be of the kind that Buber describes, where the divine is encountered in the depth of I–Thou relating.

The process of dementia, then, begins to look very different from the 'death that leaves the body behind', when we take into account the possibilities that are opened up by person-centred care. For some people high levels of relative well-being may be a realistic expectation throughout the entire course. Even when the ravages inflicted by neuropathology are at their most severe, at least some of the hopelessness and fear can be mitigated. Dementia will always have a deeply tragic aspect, both for those who are affected and for those who are close to them. There is, however, a vast difference between a tragedy, in which persons are actively involved and morally committed, and a blind and hopeless submission to fate.

Maintaining personhood

When the physical needs have been met, this is the central task of dementia care. It involves enabling choice, the use of abilities, the expression of feelings, and living in the context of relationship.

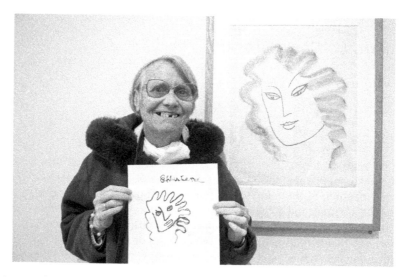

As the last step of a visit to the Matisse Museum in Nice, participants were given sketching materials and invited to try to reproduce the artist's technique. Christiane was very proud of her results, with good reason.

Copyright: Cathy Greenblat.

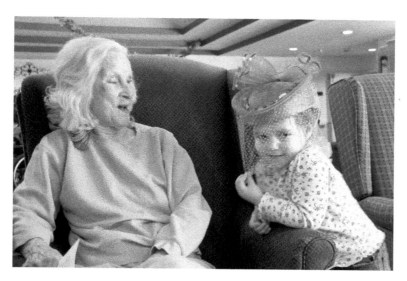

At the end of a special luncheon for six residents of the Kingwood Silverado care community, Lois charmed Sabrina, the daughter of a staff member, by placing her hat on Sabrina's head.

Copyright: Cathy Greenblat.

Personhood maintained

Commentary by Dawn Brooker

In this chapter Kitwood turns his attention to the emerging evidence that a more positive view could actually help people to maintain their sense of personhood. Given the paucity of dementia care research in the mid-1990s, this is a chapter of hope and ideas rather than of hard evidence. At the time Kitwood was writing, there were no academic journals that focused on psychosocial aspects of dementia. It was difficult to get research on dementia care accepted into mainstream psychiatry, psychology or sociology journals. There was no Internet to disseminate good practice. Good practice in the field spread through word of mouth and by getting to know people who shared this passion. It is interesting that Kitwood uses the full names of many of the people whose work he cites, rather than the academic tradition of surname only. These were people he spoke with rather than people whose work he simply read. He brought the academic and practice world together, challenging the idea that evidence in this area was generated only by formal research. The ideas around person-hood developed from discussions and the sharing of 'case studies'. In this chapter, he draws extensively on articles published in the *Journal of Dementia Care*, founded in late 1993. Kitwood wrote an article in the first issue entitled 'Discover the person, not the disease'. Those words set the tone and purpose of the journal, which was not peer reviewed but acted as a vehicle for sharing ideas on person-centred dementia care. It continues to do so today, and there are now similar publications in Australia and Germany.

Writing this commentary 20 years on, the challenge I find is that there is now so much evidence about the centrality of person-centred care in dementia, and the types of interventions and service models that support it, that it is difficult to summarize it in such a short space. Kitwood pointed to a number of areas (reality orientation, validation, reminiscence, the arts, sensory interventions) that had already emerged as having potential to maintain personhood. The evidence base for these has continued to develop. Reality orientation formed the basis of Cognitive Stimulation Therapy (CST), for which there is now a robust evidence base (Spector et al. 2003; Spector et al. 2010; Orrell et al. 2014) for its benefits for cognitive performance, language function and quality of life. Evidence-based clinical guidelines in the UK have recommended CST for those with mild to moderate dementia for over a decade now (NICE 2006, 2018). Naomi Feil has continued to provide training worldwide in validation therapy. While there is still little in the way of published research on effectiveness, the principles within validation therapy have influenced many practitioners and therapists over the years engaged in emotion-oriented practice (Finnema et al. 2017). Any-one who doubts the ability to connect emotionally with a person in the advanced stage of dementia has only to watch the film of Feil working with Gladys Wilson (Memory Bridge 2007) to see the power of validating emotions. Reminiscence and life-story work now forms the basis for multiple interventions and ways of working with people living with dementia at all stages (Kaiser and Eley 2016), and incorporates care planning tools, memory boxes, musical playlists, nostalgia for sports, films, objects and environments, all of which can help to maintain identity, enjoyment and relationships. Reminiscence also has a role to play in the arts and creative activities that Kitwood also referred to in this chapter, such as music, dance and drama. Indeed many museums, heritage centres, art galleries and cine-mas now have programmes of work specifically tailored to people affected by dementia (Mittelman and Epstein 2009; Camic et al. 2014). The arts and creative approaches, though, have now moved beyond using their media just for reminiscence, recognizing that taking part or becoming involved in creative activity can help people to express themselves and (re)connect with their supporters in a multitude of ways (Basting et al. 2016). Systematic reviews and evidence syntheses of research into arts and music interventions are emerging (e.g. Beard 2011; McDermott et al. 2013; Dowlen et al. 2017), with some controlled trials into music interventions (such as Särkämö et al. 2013) showing positive benefits against a range of cognitive, emotional and social measures. Sensory stimulation, aromatherapy and massage are now a more common feature of dementia care than when Kitwood was writing. Again, the research evidence of effectiveness for specific sensory interventions is not strong (for example, Forrester et al. 2014), however researching the impact of such complex interventions with people with such wide-ranging needs is not straightforward and it is per-haps not surprising that the outcomes of controlled trials have led to varied results. These gentle ways of reaching people, particularly in more advanced dementia, certainly appear to have positive outcomes for some people. These approaches have been integrated into larger programmes of engaging with people living with advanced dementia, such as Namaste Care (Simard 2013).

In this chapter and in others, however, Kitwood underlines that it is not just making progress on those individual 'interventions' that can help maintain personhood. He was also concerned with how a therapeutic milieu (what he called social psychology) could be maintained, and the role that measurement and quality standards had to play in this. Kitwood had developed Dementia Care Mapping (DCM) as a means of assessing the impact of the social and psychological environment for people living with dementia. DCM has been through a number of changes since 1997. The current version was launched in 2005 following a period of systematic international development and validation (Brooker and Surr 2006). The worldwide spread of DCM has been remarkable, with the tool and training mate-rials now translated into 10 different languages, with estimates of around 12,000 practitioners trained worldwide. Whether DCM has had a sustained impact on practice is difficult to assess, although a large-scale cluster randomized controlled trial is in progress (Surr et al. 2016). DCM provided the foundations for an observational tool designed specif-ically for inspection and regulation of health and social care (Brooker et al. 2007). The power of observation upon staff practice in the area of advanced dementia has been demon-strated by the AwareCare Programme (Clare et al. 2013) and in the development of PIECE-dem in researching the experience of those with advanced dementia (Brooker et al. 2013). The numbers of evaluation tools and measures within dementia care have continued to grow (Wilberforce et al. 2016). A major development in this area is also the recognition that many people living with dementia can provide direct feedback on the quality of their care without an overreliance on observation as the main form of evaluation (Innes and McCabe 2007). However, a combination of observations and interviews may offer the most comprehensive and inclusive approach. Approaches such as Talking Mats (Murphy et al. 2007), using pictures, artefacts and physical places to stimulate memories and opinions, are also developing.

At the time Kitwood was writing, the stereotype of someone living with dementia was very much conflated with care homes and institutional care. Kitwood, however, spent a good proportion of this chapter discussing the importance of good community care in maintaining personhood. Twenty years on, the need for effective community support is even more pressing, with many more people living with dementia and being diagnosed at earlier stages. Earlier diagnosis provides the opportunity for people and their families to make lifestyle changes and choices that will build resilience for the long term (Brooker et al. 2014). The evidence for the effectiveness of different types of post-diagnostic interventions is growing (British Psychological Society 2014; MODEM 2014). The problem is, however, that a means of delivering comprehensive post-diagnostic interventions is not widely available in local communities where they can be readily accessed. 'Dementia advisers' are now widely commissioned in the UK to provide signposting and some support, although formal evaluation suggests they need to be firmly embedded within local care pathways to work effectively (Clarke et al. 2013). Family carers provide the vast majority of care and support to people with dementia, yet the support they receive varies markedly. Isolation and loneliness are major issues both for those living with dementia and family carers (Alzheimer's Society 2014). Perhaps not surprisingly for someone who had trained in psychotherapy, Kitwood highlighted the value of counselling, particularly in the earlier stages of dementia. This area continues to grow in interest in terms of skills development (Lipinska 2009), although the work of counsellors and psychotherapists in this area is not widespread. Evidence reviews (Cheston and Ivanecka 2017) and some controlled trials (Logsdon et al. 2010) suggest limited evidence of benefit, but greater understanding is required to identify the change processes that lead to successful outcomes.

The Dutch psychologist, Dr Bère Miesen, founded the Alzheimer Café movement in the Netherlands in 1997 and these are now widespread in a number of countries across the world (Alzheimer's Disease International 2017). Alzheimer and Memory Cafés offer monthly meetings where people and families can come together in a relaxed atmosphere to learn about dementia and to build peer support. Some Dementia Friendly Communities initiatives have utilized social assets and social capital to address the provision of place-based support on a local level. The Dutch Meeting Centres Support Programme (Dröes et al. 2004) appears to have much to offer having shown clear improvements for people and family carers, and by successful replication in a number of different countries (Mangiaracina et al. 2017; Brooker et al. 2018). Kitwood also presented a case study of a person with dementia living in 'sheltered housing'. Extra Care housing and Assisted Living facilities are now much more widespread in many countries and, with structured interventions, appropriate design of the built environment and staff training, these can support a positive lifestyle for people living with dementia (Atkinson et al. 2014). Community programmes that engage people in outdoor activity, sports and nature are also emerging (e.g. Whear et al. 2014; van den Berg et al. 2015; Carone et al. 2016). The use of technology to support people in their day-to-day lives is now widespread, although practical and ethical challenges remain (Meiland et al. 2017).

Since Kitwood wrote this chapter, we now have more research evidence for the positive impact of person-centred care approaches for people living with dementia in care homes. Developing a robust evidence base for person-centred care that, by its definition, is tailored to individual need and contextual relationships, is a major challenge. Person-centred care is not a simple intervention like administering a new drug. The development of the VIPS framework (Brooker and Latham 2016), to help care providers understand and evaluate their care in the round, built directly on Kitwood's ideas. The challenge is to describe service-level interventions that enable practitioners and professionals to provide interventions in a person-centred manner that supports personhood rather than detracts from it. Despite this significant challenge, however, there are now a number of cluster randomized controlled trials that have evaluated a range of multi-level complex interventions (Fossey et al. 2006; Chenoweth et al. 2009; Mork Rokstadt et al. 2013; Ballard et al. 2018) where person-centred approaches have a more positive outcome than 'treatment as usual' or placebo controls. Studies have shown that by implementing multi-component programmes (staff training, specialist staff roles, activity programming, social interaction, active review of care plans), both quality of life and the experience of behavioural and psychological symptoms of dementia can be improved.

Kitwood reported on some early findings supporting the concept of 'rementia' – in other words, that people with dementia could improve their cognitive function. This was a radical idea at the time. Research into the study of individualized cognitive rehabilitation in dementia has continued to develop, structured around identifying and addressing personally meaningful goals (Clare 2008). Cognitive rehabilitation addresses the impact that cognitive changes can have on managing everyday life. The focus is on supporting day-to-day functioning rather than directly aiming to improve cognition. Emerging findings show that trained cognitive rehabilitation therapists are able to work with individuals with mild to moderate dementia to help them improve their day-to-day functioning (Clare et al. in press). In the case study of Brenda and Duncan Baker, Kitwood tells a story of deep despair that sadly still rings true today. This is a devoted couple who are overwhelmed by a young-onset dementia of an unusual subtype, with concomitant unstable physical health issues, being met with unhelpful and unskilled care and support. The couple become increasingly isolated and eventually Brenda dies in horrible circumstances at home with no palliation. Research that takes a longitudinal view of the journey with dementia, that can help us understand the complex interplay of personal resources, support and coping (Clare et al. 2014), is starting to emerge. Nowadays, we have more timely and skilled diagnosis from memory assessment services. We have skilled care from primary and hospital care practitioners who are adept at managing pain, delirium and multi-morbidities. We have input from dementia advisers and community support teams that could help Duncan care for his wife at home; and, in those final months, we have palliative care that could have enabled Brenda to die peacefully. Unfortunately, it is still the case that these things are not available as a matter of course. The term 'postcode lottery' is used frequently in the UK when describing the localized variation in services and support versus what should be people's rights to the best-quality care and support. Ensuring that good practice to support personhood becomes standard practice, rather than the exception, is still a major challenge.

The dialectics of dementia: a third look

Kitwood's contention that it is not solely the neurological impairment in dementia that leads to the disintegration of personhood, but that much could be done to ameliorate this through good care and support, has stood the test of time. There is more evidence now to show that much can be done across the trajectory to help people cope better, and indeed to enjoy a good quality of life. However, putting it into practice has been slow. Outside of the pockets of excellent practice (that certainly exist) most of us live with the uneasy reality that the experience portrayed in the case study of Brenda and Duncan is still the experience of many worldwide. I was particularly struck by Kitwood's observation in the opening section to this chapter about good practitioners trying to find their voice. There has not been the shift in everyday practice that suggests this has changed. Good person-centred care in some contexts almost feels mythological. Person-centred care is seen as the unreachable ideal. Lack of resources, low levels of staffing and skills in the face of increasing need and complexity seem insurmountable barriers. It is not the evidence that is lacking, but the wherewithal to make it a reality.

Reflection points

- How relevant to the present day are Kitwood's views on the maintenance of personhood?
- What are the main barriers to putting evidence-based person-centred care into practice?
- Is it possible for people with an earlier diagnosis of dementia to protect their own personhood?

5

The experience of dementia

Tom Kitwood

One of the most encouraging signs in recent years is that at last people with dementia are being recognized as having true subjectivity. In a very short time considerable progress has been made, and the knowledge that has already been gained has the potential to bring a great enrichment to care practice.

For the greater part of the period in which dementia has existed as a clinical category, the subjectivity of those who are affected has been almost totally disregarded. In Britain it was clearly put onto the agenda by Alison Froggatt (1988), but her pioneering venture was not widely followed. Also, as is clear from a recent review, such work as was then done in this field was mostly with those who had only mild cognitive impairments (Keady 1996). Even in several major textbooks of psychiatry and clinical psychology published since 1990, there is no mention of this topic at all. Why this lacuna should exist seems, at first sight, to be mysterious, especially considering that at least some attention has been given to the experience of other distressing conditions, such as schizophrenia or depression. Is it that people with dementia were considered to have no experiences? Is it that their needs were displaced by the needs of carers? Is it that their subjective world was assumed to be so disordered that it could not be discussed in a rational way? Is it that they were no longer deemed to be persons, and thus that their thoughts and feelings were not worthy of consideration? Whatever ground is given for this flight from intersubjective engagement, it bears the marks of a rationalization born of fear (see pp. 10–11).

In this chapter we will look at some of the relevant research, and I shall add a number of observations of my own. It is possible to draw up a rough guide to the darker areas of the subjective domain of dementia, and even to gain a few clues about its lighter side. The whole topic should be approached with great sensitivity to methodological issues. For it is essential to recognize that in every instance, whether or not there is an impairment of mental powers, there are limits in the extent to which one human being can understand another.

Intersubjectivity and its limits

In the course of everyday life we often have the impression that we can sense something of what another person is thinking and feeling, and there are grounds for believing that this experience is grounded in reality. All human beings have the same genetic make-up, except for very minor differences; since we all have the same components in the central nervous system, it is reasonable to assume that we process information from the external and internal environments in much the same way. Some degree of intersubjectivity is guaranteed by having a language that is shared. Even more significant is the language of the body: expression, gesture, posture, proximity, and so on. This conveys emotion and feeling with great authenticity, and here we are coming close to cross-cultural universals.

It is impossible, however, to enter fully into the experiential frame of another person, simply because each person is unique. In relation to dementia there are additional problems, which have been acknowledged rarely if ever – even in recent work. No one has returned from this particular journey of cognitive impairment in order to tell us what it is like. We are far more dependent on inference than in most ventures in intersubjectivity. Also, there is an essential contradiction. If we try to describe the experience of dementia in ordinary prose, we are using the calm, detached and highly ordered vehicle of language in order to convey impressions of a state of being that is often fragmented and turbulent. Furthermore, we are attempting to capture in concepts what it may be like to live in a subjective world where concepts are not holding up any more. The further we go into the domain of severe cognitive impairment, the more serious does this problem become.

Each person's experience is unique

Everything that we have considered already in relation to the uniqueness of persons (pp. 12–13) has relevance to the experience of dementia. Generalizations are only guides and signposts; if they are taken too literally, they will detract from the attempt to understand any particular person.

Some glimpses of the way in which the experience of dementia may differ from one person to another can be gained from studies of personality. Within psychiatry this topic has been considered only very rarely, although some helpful suggestions have been offered by Alan Jacques (1988). On the basis of clinical experience he identifies six main personality types. These are the *dependent*, who accept help readily, but are sometimes reluctant to stand on their own feet or take initiative; the *independent*, who may resist facing the truth about their disabilities, and who like to feel that they are 'in charge'; those with *paranoid* tendencies, who easily resort to suspicion and blame; the *obsessional*, who are beset by self-doubt, and very fearful of the loss of order and control; the *hysterical*, who may be very demanding and attention-seeking; and the *psychopathic* (a very small minority) who tend to be impulsive and lacking any signs of concern for others. Jacques also suggests that in each 'normal' personality there are tendencies towards one or more of these types.

Among the studies of personality based on psychometric testing, several have made use of the NEO Personality Inventory (Costa and McCrae 1985). This instrument attempts to measure five main traits: neuroticism or tendency to anxiety, extraversion, openness to experience, agreeableness, and conscientiousness. The NEO-PI is designed so that it can be completed through self-report or by a third party. In a descriptive study of 132 persons with dementia in residential care Sean Buckland (1995) identified six main personality clusters: anxious–passive (30 per cent), stable–amiable–routine–loving (28 per cent), emotional–social–active (26 per cent), emotional–withdrawn–passive (8 per cent), stable–outgoing–industrious (4 per cent) and emotional–outgoing–controlling (4 per cent).

The use of traits to provide a broad description of personality types provides at least a glimpse of how varied the experience of dementia may be. For example, people clearly differ in the extent to which they are able to cope with the failing of their cognitive abilities; those who are described as independent and obsessional by Jacques may have particularly strong defences against recognition and acceptance. Some people are much more able and willing to look to others around them for comfort and support. Those who are described as anxious–passive by Buckland (who roughly correspond to Jacques' dependent type) may be particularly susceptible to apathy and despair, which from a purely observational standpoint has often been characterized as vegetation.

An ethogenic approach, which views personality as resources for action (pp. 12–13) brings out other aspects of the experience and process of dementia. When resources are lost (whether the prime cause is neurological or social-psychological) grief reactions commonly occur. As with the grief that accompanies bereavement, several different patterns can be discerned (Tatelbaum 1984). 'Normal' grief often follows a sequence, in which the main stages are denial, anger, depression, acceptance and reconstruction, and there are parallels to this in dementia. Among the forms of so-called 'pathological grief' probably the most common in the case of dementia is that in which a person gets 'stuck' in depression, perhaps recapitulating on other griefs that were never resolved.

In relation to what I have called the 'experiential self', there seems to be a very wide interpersonal variation. At one extreme are men and women who move into dementia with very little insight. When things go wrong, they tend to blame other people, or develop delusions, perhaps of theft or mysterious interference. Eventually their dementia envelops them, like an impenetrable fog. In some instances powerful, raw emotions break through as psychological defences collapse. At the other extreme are those who have an intense and poignant awareness of what is happening to them, and who remain highly open to their experience, without evasion or blame. Only a very small minority of people, so it appears at present, are able to face the onset of dementia without high defences; and it is likely that for them the experience will be relatively benign. There is even a little evidence to suggest that those who are most open to experience may be less liable to develop dementia, whereas rigid and obsessional personality traits may be dementogenic (Oakley 1965; LeShan 1983: 24–31). In the last few years there has been a move towards providing counselling and psychotherapy for people who have dementia fairly soon after diagnosis (Sutton 1995; Cheston 1996). The issues of insight and acceptance seem to be ones where, for some people at least, a degree of therapeutic change is possible.

Seven access routes

There are many ways in which we can gain insight into the subjective world of dementia, and in this section I shall give a brief account of seven of them. My method will be rather like that of creating a collage: laying fragments side by side and gradually building up a general picture. In the section that follows I shall offer a summary, and return to the issue of the uniqueness of persons.

The first access route is through the accounts that have been written by people who have dementia during a period when their cognitive powers are relatively intact. Several books have been written along these lines. One of the most striking is *Living in the Labyrinth*, by Diana Friel McGowin, who received a diagnosis of dementia well before retirement age, following a minor stroke. Whether her condition was Alzheimer's disease in the strict sense, or a vascular condition, is not completely clear. Among the feelings she describes are 'paralysing fears', of which the most terrible relate to the possibility that she might be abandoned, or that her husband might die; a lack of sense of worth, together with feelings of guilt about her inability and dependency; intense frustration at what she can no longer do, and at the obtuseness of others; her heightened sexual desire; her development of obsessive behaviour in order to try to feel safe. Above all of these, what stands out from her account is her struggle to remain a person, despite her disabilities:

> If I am no longer a woman, why do I still feel one? If no longer worth holding, why do I crave it? If no longer sensual, why do I enjoy the soft texture of silk against my skin? If no longer sensitive, why do moving lyric songs strike a responsive chord in me? My every molecule seems to scream out that I do, indeed, exist, and that existence must be valued by someone! Without someone to walk this labyrinth by my side, without the touch of a fellow traveller who understands my need of self-worth, how can I endure the rest of this unchartered journey?
>
> (McGowin 1993: 123–4)

While accounts such as this can shed a great deal of light on the experience of dementia at a time when the cognitions are still relatively intact, they can but give a small part of the picture. We also should remember that only a person who was exceptionally articulate, open and assured would be able to write in this kind of way.

Second, insight into the experience of dementia can be obtained by careful listening to what people say in some kind of interview or group work. John Keady and Mike Nolan (1995) have made a detailed study of the ways that people cope with their cognitive impairments. Malcolm Goldsmith (1996) has also presented remarkable evidence that people with dementia can express themselves, and argues strongly that their voices be heard. Studies along these lines highlight such issues as the fear of being out of control, and the fear of being seen by others as out of control; the feeling of being lost, and of meaning slipping away; the concern not to be burdensome and the desire to be useful; anger with dementia itself, and resentment that life has been marred by its presence. Again, the picture is not wholly negative. Some people express acceptance of their disabilities, and some their gratitude for the good things in their past. A recurrent theme is that of reassurance through the company and support of other people. Structured listening might involve the use of images or objects onto which people can project aspects of their own experience. One small study has used the pictures of the TAT (Thematic Apperception Test). This brings out the sense of giving up, of deepening despair, and the urgent desire that some people feel for closeness and comfort (Balfour 1995).

The conduct of group work with people who have dementia has been vividly described by Rik Cheston (1996). He suggests that the stories people tell about events in their past are often rich in metaphor related to their present situation. One man, for example, described episodes from his war service in Malaya, where he flew missions in the jungle. The persistent advance of the vegetation and the constant battle to keep it back seem to serve as a way for him to talk about his own struggle with neurological impairment. A woman gave her account of being a nanny to two children during the war, and of the return of the father – thin, bewildered, and looking like someone who 'had really lost his way'. Cheston suggests that she may be talking about her own condition: her own sense of lostness, her need for loving contact, and her desire to be of use to others, as she once had been when a nanny. Interpretations of this kind are, of course, speculative, but they do give a convincing explanation of some of the ways people with dementia describe their past.

Third, it is possible to gain insight into the experience of dementia by attending carefully and imaginatively to what people say in the ordinary course of life. The mode of expression may be different from that of everyday speech; meaning may be conveyed in a concrete, metaphorical or allusive way.

On one of my home visits I spent some time with Peter, who had developed dementia in his 40s. He and his wife went to great lengths to be hospitable to me, and Peter talked, in a rather fragmented way, about his life. He could remember some parts of his distant past, but he had no memory at all for many of the more recent events. After some time Peter took me for a walk round the garden. He took me to some lattice-type fencing, and began to feel it with his fingers. He told me that the older fencing was very sound, but that some that had been put in more recently was already rotting; he showed me an example, and crumbled a fragment in his fingers. I cannot prove it, but I felt sure that he was using this as a way of telling me about himself and his memory losses; it was like a repetition, in tangible terms, of our earlier conversation.

Here is another example where a knowledge of the broader context gives meaning to a person's words.

> Janet has come into a residential home for two weeks' respite care. She often looks out of the window, and talks about the trains that are passing by. In fact there are no trains.

Her apparently strange remarks begin to make sense in light of the fact that she and her husband Roger often used to go by train to see their son and his family, who lived some 200 miles away. Roger still goes to visit them, and he does so when Janet is in respite care. Is it possible that she has some inkling of this? Perhaps she is yearning to see her son, and asking to be taken too.

Fourth, and along very similar lines, it is possible to learn from the behaviour of people who have dementia; or, putting it more accurately, their actions and attempts at action.

> Henry had had a career as an academic before retirement, and he used to be very skilled at word-processing. After the onset of his dementia he continued to use his computer as before, refusing to acknowledge that anything was different. Sometimes it took him several hours to write a paragraph, and even then it was full of errors. Later he began to blame the computer for malfunction, and gradually he gave up using it. Sometimes he was extremely irritable, and sometimes despondent and apathetic.

Perhaps here we see something of the struggle of a man who had rich resources of intellect, but whose 'experiential self' was only poorly developed. First he denied that anything had changed, then he projected, and later he got 'stuck' on the borderland of depression.

In the course of dementia a person will try to use whatever resources he or she still has available. If some of the more sophisticated means of action have dwindled away, it may be necessary to fall back on ways that are more basic, and more deeply learned; some of these were learned in early childhood.

> Arthur had been a highly respected member of the community, and a pillar of his local church. Now he is very confused and frail, and he is confined to a wheelchair. He often offends people with his foul language, and some care staff are afraid of him, because when they come close he often punches or bites them.

It is possible that this is Arthur's way of expressing his anguish at his loss of significance. Biting others may, almost literally, be his last way of 'making his mark'.

Some people who have very severe dementia show a range of repetitive bodily movements, such as rubbing parts of the body, pinching at the face or hands, rocking to and fro, or crumpling and twisting items of clothing. Tessa Perrin (1997), who has made a detailed study of these behaviours, suggests that they should be understood as forms of self-stimulation. When the external environment has largely failed to provide security and occupation some people retreat, so to speak, into a 'bubble' that occupies a little more than their own body space. Within it they create a place of minimal safety, and make their last desperate bid to remain psychologically alive.

Fifth, there is the possibility of consulting people who have undergone an illness with dementia-like features, and who are able to recall something of what they have experienced. Two particularly relevant examples are meningitis and depression. One of the people who have had meningitis whom I have interviewed, for example, describes her memories of behaving in odd and unfamiliar ways, and yet knowing (with the residues of an ordinary consciousness) that this is so. Among the experiences she recalls are being told that she had had a certain visitor earlier in the day, but yet, alarmingly, having no direct recollection of the fact; trying to say something, and then losing the sense of it, 'like a break in transmission'; playing cards, but needing to be reminded of the rules each time a new hand was dealt. Much of the experience she reports is suffused with a sense of strangeness, of weirdness, as if she both is, and is not, herself. She also tells of the huge effort that was required, even for the simplest of mental tasks.

Here, too, is a brief account written by a person in the depths of a severe depression.

> I'm frightened all day of the night to come because I know I'll get restless and tense up, won't be able to breathe, won't be able to swallow, will start feeling numb and petrified – all the time I drum into myself that I've got to snap out of it. There's far more going on in my head than what's on paper, I just feel all the time there is a way to unjumble it all please somebody to help me to find it.
>
> (Rowe 1983: 11–12)

The writer here is living on the edge of panic, with its terrifying bodily effects, and she is fearful about being in a state of panic. Her self-esteem is shattered, and she is caught up in self-accusations. She cries out desperately for someone to support her. An account such as this is particularly poignant when we remember that many people become deeply depressed during the course of dementia; for some, the experience may be very similar to what is described here.

The sixth route into the understanding of dementia is through the use of our own poetic imagination. There are some aspects of human experience for which the ordinary prosaic forms of speech are too thin, too linear, too precise; poetry provides a more condensed and powerful linguistic form. John Killick, for example, has spent many hours in the company of people with dementia, and written a series of poems expressing his attempt to respond to their hopes and fears, using their phrases and metaphors. Here are three short extracts from his work. The first expresses a sense of weirdness and alienation, the second that of futility; and the third the pain of abandonment.

I'm sure it isn't me
that's gone round the bend.
It seems as if

I'm like a buzzing toy –
it buzzes round and round
but it doesn't mean much.
You have hurt me,
You have hurt me deeply
Because you will go away.

(Killick 1994: 12–13)

Several years ago, after I had spent a good deal of time with people who had dementia in settings that epitomized the old culture of care, with its malignant social psychology and pervasive neglect, I attempted to express, imaginatively, something of what the experience of 'unattended dementia' might be like. This is part of what I wrote.

You are in a swirling fog, and in half-darkness. You are wandering around in a place that seems vaguely familiar; and yet you do not know where you are; you cannot make out whether it is summer or winter, day or night. At times the fog clears a little, and you can see a few objects really clearly; but as soon as you start to get your bearings, you are overpowered by a kind of dullness and stupidity; your knowledge slips away, and again you are utterly confused.

While you are stumbling in the fog, you have an impression of people rushing past you, chattering like baboons. They seem to be so energetic and purposeful, but their business is incomprehensible. Occasionally you pick up fragments of conversation, and have the impression that they are talking about you. Sometimes you catch sight of a familiar face; but as you move towards the face it vanishes, or turns into a demon. You feel desperately lost, alone, bewildered, frightened. In this dreadful state you find that you cannot control your bladder, or your bowels; you are completely losing your grip; you feel dirty, guilty, ashamed; it's so unlike how you used to be, that you don't even know yourself.

And then there are the interrogations. Official people ask you to perform strange tasks which you cannot fully understand: such as counting backwards from one hundred, or obeying the instruction 'If you are over 50, put your hands above your head'. You are never told the purpose or the results of these interrogations. You'd be willing to help, eager to co-operate, if only you knew what it was all about, and if someone took you seriously enough to guide you.

This is the present reality: everything is falling apart, nothing gets completed, nothing makes sense. But worst of all, you know it wasn't always like this. Behind the fog and the darkness there is a vague memory of good times, when you knew where and who you were, when you felt close to others, and when you were able to perform daily tasks with skill and grace; once the sun shone brightly and the landscape of life had richness and pattern. But now all that has been vandalised, ruined, and you are left in chaos, carrying the terrible sense of a loss that can never be made good. Once you were a person who counted; now you are a nothing, and good for nothing. A sense of oppression hangs over you, intensifying at times into naked terror; its meaning is that you might be abandoned for ever, left to rot and disintegrate into unbeing.

(Kitwood 1990e: 40–1)

Finally there is the possibility of using role play; that is actually taking on the part of some-one who has dementia, and living it out in a simulated care environment. If a person does this in a wooden and superficial way, relying mainly on an external imitation of behaviour, very little is likely to be learned. Those who take on their role with sincerity, flexibility and real commitment, however, tend to find that it is both disturbing and enlightening. For as we play such a role we begin to make contact with our own stock of dementia-like experiences, together with the accompanying feelings: intense anxiety, fear of abandonment, general-ized rage, the desire to create chaos, dreadful feelings of bewilderment, boredom, betrayal and isolation. (Such role-playing should of course be done under conditions where people are psychologically safe, and where there is plenty of opportunity for debriefing and a thorough shedding of the role.)

It might be claimed that this has very little to do with the experience of people who have dementia, and that it is much more to do with the hidden memories of the role-players. In a sense, this is true. Most counsellors and therapists believe, however, that it is impossible to enter fully into another person's frame of reference. In getting close to the experience of dementia, perhaps the best we can do is to draw on our own stock of emotional memories and create an inner narrative which has at least some resemblance to living with dementia. These ideas are close to the theory that underpins the method of acting developed by Stanislavsky, and his views about the way that a convincing part is created (Margashack 1961). Thus the role-playing of dementia may be one of the most powerful routes to under-standing. For here we are going far beyond a merely intellectual grasp, and coming closer to a genuine 'standing under': feeling the shape and weight of things, knowing them in action rather than in mere reflection (Kitwood 1994b).

The domain of experience in dementia

As the evidence from all the different sources is put together, a picture or map of the expe-rience of dementia begins to take shape. Some pioneering work on this topic has been done by Cheston and Bender (1996), and what follows is a development from their ideas. We know much more, thus far, about the difficult and painful aspects of the experience of dementia, and this will be the main topic for discussion here. This part of the map has three main areas, as shown in Figure 5.1.

The first area is occupied by *feelings*; that is, subjective states where emotions are clearly associated with specific meanings: for example, anger at the insensitivity of a neigh-bour, frustration at not being able to drive the car, or a sense of uselessness because of inability to do the housework. Feeling states such as these are available to people when cognitive impairment is relatively slight – when their capacity for precise meaning-giving is essentially intact. Not everyone, however, has access to them; some people have never developed a personal 'feeling language' through which to encompass the range of their experience (Hobson 1985).

The middle area is occupied by *global states*. Three of these are raw emotions associated with a high level of arousal of the sympathetic nervous system. Here meaning is diffuse – not attached to specific situations, persons or objects. The fourth state in this area is one of general confusion, and this may accompany high or low levels of arousal.

The third area contains '*burnt-out*' *states*, which typically ensue after the nervous system has been at a high level of arousal for a long period; there comes a stage when it can no longer sustain such intensity of discharge. The burnt-out condition is not one of positive

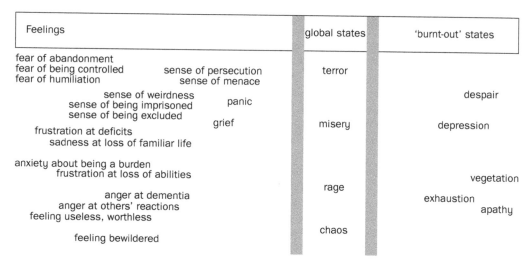

Feelings			global states	'burnt-out' states
fear of abandonment fear of being controlled fear of humiliation	sense of persecution sense of menace		terror	
	sense of weirdness sense of being imprisoned sense of being excluded	panic		despair
		grief	misery	depression
frustration at deficits sadness at loss of familiar life				
anxiety about being a burden frustration at loss of abilities				vegetation
	anger at dementia		rage	exhaustion
anger at others' reactions feeling useless, worthless				apathy
			chaos	
feeling bewildered				

Figure 5.1 Domain of 'negative' experience

peace, but of very severe depletion. The vegetative state that is claimed to be the end-point of the dementing process lies at the extreme; it seems likely that for some people who reach this, their personhood has been so depleted that there can be no return.

With the possible exception of those who have 'burnt out', people with dementia can travel across this domain many times, and in different directions, having access to a variety of emotions and feelings, and possibly experiencing more than one simultaneously (for example, extreme confusion and terror). The journey is, to some extent, independent of the ordinary sense of the linear course of time (Bell and McGregor 1991). An old grief or fear might erupt into the present, with all of its original freshness (as many people working in dementia care noted around the VE Day memorial events of 1995). Often a person with dementia seems to have no sense of his or her true age, relating to someone who is much younger as if they were a parent. The intensity and vividness of emotional experience often seems to be comparable to that of childhood. The 'splitting' of a person into two – a 'good' and a 'bad' object, as Kleinian therapists might say – is fairly common.

The older view was that there can only be a one-way journey, from left to right. Now, however, as a richer body of evidence becomes available (a sample of which was presented in Chapter 4), that view is no longer tenable. Some people undergo a degree of 'rementing', and reacquire capacities for meaning-giving that had, apparently, been lost. Also, as more is learned about how to give psychotherapeutic help to people with dementia, it is becoming clear that some can actually acquire new forms of 'feeling language', and it may be possible to work through some of the experiences of pain and 'relax into' cognitive impairment.

Individuals will vary greatly in what they experience, according to their personality and biography – and hence their coping style. Those who have never had access, in conscious awareness, to highly differentiated feelings are particularly vulnerable. It is likely that at some point, when cognitions are severely impaired, the defences will collapse and raw emotions will break through, with an agonizing intensity. A few (perhaps those with extremely phlegmatic temperaments) may be able to sustain their defences, and pass slowly through to the burnt-out area. The intensive use of tranquillizing medication, of course, promotes such a process, and bypasses subjectivity.

What do people with dementia need?

The dark picture of dementia that we have explored probably represents a state of affairs where psychological needs are, at best, only poorly met. If we combine the results of this exploration with the evidence from more objective studies, it is possible to make a tentative inference about the nature of those needs.

The topic of need is notorious both for its conceptual difficulties and for the empirical problems that it raises. The concept that I shall use here is a strong one, meaning 'that without the meeting of which a human being cannot function, even minimally, as a person'. In this sense it can be said that vines need soil containing lime, or cheetahs need wide open spaces. Our needs as a species are grounded in our evolutionary past, and related closely to the way the nervous system functions. Needs are experienced as desires, but some desires do not represent needs (Ollman 1971). Concepts of need are always expressed within a particular cultural framework, and thus impregnated with that culture's meanings and values; my account here is no exception.

In contrast to theorists who have postulated hierarchies, I suggest that we might consider a cluster of needs in dementia, very closely connected, and functioning like some kind of cooperative. It might be said that there is only one all-encompassing need – for love. This view has been eloquently expressed by Frena Gray-Davidson on the basis of her experience as a carer. She asserts that people with dementia often show an undisguised and almost childlike yearning for love. By this she means a generous, forgiving and unconditional acceptance, a wholehearted emotional giving, without any expectation of direct reward. The presence of dementia, she suggests, may provoke a psychospiritual crisis in family members: 'If we do not deal with our own issues of love, and grief around the failures of love, we cannot live with Alzheimer's disease' (Gray-Davidson 1993: 161).

For our purposes, however, we require a little more detail, and it may be helpful to think of five great needs which overlap, coming together in the central need for love, as shown in Figure 5.2: comfort, attachment, inclusion, occupation and identity. The fulfilment

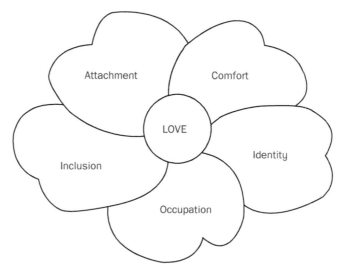

Figure 5.2 The main psychological needs of people with dementia

of one of these needs will, to some extent, involve the fulfilment of the others. The distinctions are arbitrary; the boundaries are blurred.

While these needs may be assumed to be present in all human beings, they are not in evidence for most people most of the time. Probably the needs are sufficiently well met to allow at least a minimal level of function, and the gaps and deficits are often concealed. It is when a person is under great pressure, or facing severe privation, or when some hidden wound from earlier life is painfully reopened, that the needs come into the open. Then they can be recognized by their voracious, obsessive quality, as if they are insisting that nothing else matters in the world. The needs are more obvious in people with dementia, who are far more vulnerable and usually less able to take the initiatives that would lead to their needs being met. The pattern of need will vary according to personality and life history, and often the intensity of manifest need increases with the advance of cognitive impairment.

Let us look now at the needs in a little more detail.

Comfort

This word, in its original sense, carries meanings of tenderness, closeness, the soothing of pain and sorrow, the calming of anxiety, the feeling of security which comes from being close to another. To comfort another person is to provide a kind of warmth and strength which might enable them to remain in one piece when they are in danger of falling apart. In dementia the need for comfort is likely to be especially great when a person is dealing with a sense of loss, whether that arises from bereavement, the failing of abilities, or the ending of a long-established way of life. It has urgent moments, for example in times of parting, and it is also a continuing theme. The heightened sexual desire that is felt by some people with dementia may be interpreted, in part at least, as a manifestation of this need.

Attachment

Ours is a highly social species, and this is clearly shown in the forming of specific bonds or attachments. The pioneer of research in this field, John Bowlby (1979) claimed that bonding is a cross-cultural universal, and instinct-like in its nature. He suggested that it creates a kind of safety net, particularly in the first years of life, when the world is full of uncertainty. Without the reassurance that attachments provide it is difficult for any person, of whatever age, to function well. The loss of a primary attachment undermines the sense of security, and if several bonds are broken within a short time the effect can be devastating. There is every reason to suppose that the need for attachment remains when a person has dementia; indeed it may be as strong as in early childhood. Life is overshadowed by new uncertainties and anxieties, and some of the good memories from past secure attachments may be lost. Bere Miesen (1992), who has studied this topic in some detail, suggests that people with dementia are continually finding themselves in situations that they experience as 'strange', and that this powerfully activates the attachment need.

Inclusion

The social nature of human life has another aspect, related to the fact that we evolved as a species designed for life within face-to-face groups. To be part of the group was essential for survival, and in some cultures temporary exclusion was a form of severe punishment.

The need for inclusion comes poignantly to the surface in dementia, perhaps in so-called attention-seeking behaviour, in tendencies to cling or hover, or in various forms of protest and disruption. In the ordinary settings of everyday life it is still very rare for people with mental impairments to be included with ease. Very often the social life of those who have dementia tends to dwindle away, as the dialectical interplay between neurological impairment and social psychology takes its course. In many old-style residential settings the need for inclusion was not addressed at all, as people were left together, but profoundly alone. Individualized care plans and packages, while a vast improvement, sometimes overlook this issue. If the need is not met a person is likely to decline and retreat, until life is lived almost entirely within the bubble of isolation that Tessa Perrin has described (p. 88). When, however, the need is met, a person may be able to 'expand' again, recognized as having a distinct place in the shared life of a group.

Occupation

To be occupied means to be involved in the process of life in a way that is personally significant, and which draws on a person's abilities and powers. The opposite is a state of boredom, apathy and futility. The roots of occupation lie in infancy, as a child acquires the sense of agency: the realization that it is possible to evoke a response from others, and make things happen in the world. A person might be occupied in the company of others, or in solitude, in obvious action, in reflection or in relaxation. Often occupation involves having some kind of project, whether in work or leisure; it might, however, simply consist of play. If people are deprived of occupation their abilities begin to atrophy, and self-esteem drains away. The need for occupation is still present in dementia; it is clearly manifested, for example, when people want to help, or eagerly take part in activities and outings. It requires a great deal of skill and imagination to meet the need without imposing false solutions, crude and ready-made. The more that is known about a person's past, and particularly their deepest sources of satisfaction, the more likely it is that solutions will be found.

Identity

To have an identity is to know who one is, in cognition and in feeling. It means having a sense of continuity with the past; and hence a 'narrative', a story to present to others. It also involves creating some kind of consistency across the different roles and contexts of present life. To some extent identity is conferred by others, as they convey to a person subtle messages about his or her performance. How each individual constructs his or her identity is unique. In the 'old culture' of dementia care many of a person's sources of identity were taken away, particularly through the extremes of institutionalization and the removal of all contact with the past. We are learning now that much can be done to maintain identity in the face of cognitive impairment. Two things seem to be essential (Kitwood 1997a). The first is knowing in some detail about each individual's life history; even if a person cannot hold on to his or her own narrative identity, due to loss of memory, it can still be held by others. The second is empathy, through which it is possible to respond to a person as Thou, in the uniqueness of his or her being. We have touched on this topic already, and in Chapter 8 there will be a great deal more to say.

The prime task of dementia care, as we have already defined it, is to maintain personhood in the face of failing of mental powers. Now it is possible to go further, and suggest that this will occur through the sensitive meeting of this cluster of needs. If one main need is met, this will have an effect on the other needs too. For example, a person who feels more secure in attachment is likely to be able to give more attention to an occupation, being less distracted by anxiety and less invaded by fear; as a result of having a higher level of occupation, the sense of identity will be replenished. Many kinds of 'virtuous circle' can be envisaged. As the whole cluster of needs is met, it is likely that there will be an enhancement of the global sense of self-worth, of being valuable and valued. At some point in the meeting of needs a person may be enabled to move out of fear, grief and anger, into the domain of positive experience that we have thus far left uncharted.

The experience of person-centred care

We now are going to move into new territory, inconceivable to most people working in dementia care even as recently as five years ago. What might the subjective world of dementia be like when the five needs we have identified are well met? Although what follows is highly speculative, it is derived from careful observation; and as with the description given on page 89, I am deliberately drawing on my own poetic fantasy. This imaginative account depicts the experience of a woman in her 80s who has severe cognitive impairments, and who is now in residential care.

You are in a garden, at the start of a summer's day. The air is warm and gentle, carrying the sweet scent of flowers, and a slight mist is floating around. You can't make out the shape of everything, but you are aware of some beautiful colours, blue, orange, pink and purple; the grass is green as emerald. You don't know where you are, but this doesn't matter. You somehow feel 'at home', and there is a sense of harmony and peace.

As you walk around, you become aware of other people. Several of them seem to know you; it is a joy to be greeted so warmly, and by name. There are one or two of them whom you feel sure you know well. And then there is that one special person. She seems so warm, so kind, so understanding. She must be your mother; how good it is to be back with her again. The flame of life now burns brightly and cheerfully within you. It hasn't always been like this. Somewhere, deep inside, there are dim memories of times of crushing loneliness and ice-cold fear. When that was, you do not know; perhaps it was in another life. Now there is company whenever you want it, and quietness when that is what you prefer. This is the place where you belong, with these wonderful people; they are like a kind of family.

The work that you do here is the best you have ever had. The hours are flexible, and the job is pleasant; being with people is what you have always enjoyed. You can do the work at exactly your own pace, without any rush or pressure, and you can rest whenever you need. For instance there is that kind man who often comes to see you – by a strange coincidence his name is the same as that of your husband. He seems to need you, and to enjoy being with you. You, for your part, are glad to give time to being with him, his presence, strangely, gives you comfort.

As you pass by a mirror you catch a glimpse of a person who looks quite old. Is it your grandmother, or that person who used to live next door? Anyway, it is good to see her too. Then you begin to feel tired; you find a chair and you sit down, alone. Soon you become aware of a chill around your heart, a sinking feeling in your stomach – the deadly fear is coming over you again. You are about to cry out, but then you see that kind mother-person, already there, sitting beside you. Her hand is held out towards you, waiting for you to grasp it. As you talk together, the fear evaporates like the morning mist, and you are again in the garden, relaxing in the golden warmth of the sun. You know it isn't heaven itself, but sometimes it feels as if it might be halfway there.

It is impossible to say, as yet, how many people might have this kind of experience if there were a serious and sustained attempt to meet their psychological needs. The project hasn't yet been tried on a large enough scale. Even at this time, however, we can be certain that many people will be more at ease with their limitations, more able to live without a historical sense of time or a geographical sense of place. They will feel far better supported, far less alone, in whatever suffering is unavoidable. They will have a new chapter in life, with its own special delights and pleasures. And finally, they will be more able to accept with tranquillity the coming of death.

The experience of dementia

Commentary by Keith Oliver and Reinhard Guss

We were invited to write this commentary together. This was because we have developed a professional friendship over recent years since Keith's diagnosis and we both have thought deeply about the experience of living with dementia. At the time Kitwood was writing, such a friendship, alongside the joint writing of a chapter like this, was unheard of, and the issue of professional and personal boundaries would have been raised, particularly in relation to psychological working. Helpful and necessary as boundaries are in the relationships between service users and professionals, they also carry risks to mutual understanding. Boundaries can imply barriers, be restrictive and act against a sense of common purpose, combined and collective thinking and action, resulting in being 'done to' rather than 'done with'. Some people feel safe and comfortable with boundaries and associated place and hierarchy, but it can leave the person living with dementia feeling excluded, manipulated and exploited – all features of Kitwood's malignant social psychology. For us, a successful professional friendship of this type has to be individual and person centred. There needs to be trust, caring, patience, respect and understanding between both parties, and good communication based upon the preferred method of the service user, who is often less able to adapt than the professional. Kitwood's understanding of an 'I–Thou' mode of a meeting of persons has informed and helped us build and negotiate all these over time. When we began our friendship there was no precedent for this way of working. We can now both cite numerous examples where the benefits to individuals and broader services are extraordinary. This suggests that culture change in the way that Kitwood described and envisaged has begun to happen in dementia care.

To enable this commentary to be genuinely co-produced, and completely consistent with both of our experiences and views, it was written during a series of face-to-face sessions at Keith's house, followed up with discussion and emails between the two of us.

We came upon *Dementia Reconsidered* in very different ways.

Keith's first encounter with *Dementia Reconsidered*

Having received a diagnosis, at the Canterbury Memory Clinic, of Alzheimer's Disease on New Year's Eve 2010, aged 55, my career as a primary school head teacher came to a close. Having spent three or four months with my wife, Rosemary, coming to terms with this, I felt a need and a desire to fill the vacuum with something useful. I was immensely fortunate that at this time I met Reinhard and, having begun to try to understand what dementia was doing to me, and was likely to do to me in the future, I determined to retain a balance of maintaining myself as a person.

Although I think the name of Kitwood may have been introduced to me sooner after my diagnosis, the first time I logged this was in August 2012 through Mycal Miller, an early collaborator and professional friend who at the time worked as a trainer for Dementia UK. It is Mycal I must thank for so much connected to Kitwood. It was he who showed me the Kitwood flower, explained it in context, and then, more importantly, consistently demonstrated through his actions and support what Kitwood would have wished all professionals working with people with dementia to demonstrate. I carry the Kitwood flower with me every day, glued into my diary, and if I had a tattoo that's what I would go for!

Reinhard's first encounter with *Dementia Reconsidered*

For many years, while growing up in Germany, dementia formed part of my family's experience, though at the time there were no diagnoses, no explanation and no services until the very late stages. During my studies of Psychology and Gerontology, dementia became a particular interest, and I remember how helpful it was to discover new ways of understanding the changes that it brought about in a much loved person.

Like many of my contemporaries in clinical psychology in the 1990s, I was also excited by the prospect of establishing psychology as a 'proper science' with gold standard experimental designs and evaluations of effectiveness. Cognitive Behaviour Therapy (CBT) was the new and better evidenced model of psychotherapeutic intervention informing my early research and practice with groups and individual support for carers. However, anything 'cognitive' somehow did not seem suitable for people with a dementia, who we felt were losing their ability to utilize their thinking abilities, struggling to understand models and formulations, and forgetting to complete homework assignments. On the remaining long-stay wards of the old institutions we used the more behavioural approaches when referrals arrived, which asked us to assist with 'attention-seeking behaviour', 'aggression' or 'wandering' of patients with a dementia, and in our neuropsychological practice we occasionally assessed people with failing intellectual skills to assist our colleagues in psychiatry with the finding of a diagnosis.

While I had read some of Tom Kitwood's earlier papers and attended a training course in Dementia Care Mapping that he led at Bradford University, it was not until *Dementia Reconsidered* that something clicked. I felt I had found a philosophical and conceptual underpinning that could be applied across all areas of psychological working in the dementia field. It brought together work with systems, with staff groups, in families and, perhaps most importantly, opening avenues for working directly with people experiencing dementia. No student, assistant or trainee has since escaped my lectures or supervision without this book on their reading list or discussions of how to apply what we learned from it in our clinical practice and in our thinking about services for people affected by dementia.

What we make of the chapter in the light of 2017

While so much of this chapter is clearly of relevance to our services and practice today, some of Kitwood's thinking can feel strangely grating in the context of relationship and our joint work on local and national advisory bodies. This is particularly the case when we contrast it with the Dementia Engagement and Empowerment Project (DEEP), with its dozens of politically engaged groups of people living with a dementia. To understand Kitwood's perspective writing in the 1990s, it becomes important to set it in the context of that time and the changes that have affected how the dementia care scene is today.

When Kitwood wrote his book, the predominant social and professional discourse around dementia was characterized by fear, stigma and lack of services. People tended to hide or dismiss symptoms for as long as possible, and professionals did not recognize early signs as a cause for concern. Consequently, people came to the attention of services in much later stages of dementia. Kitwood, therefore, mainly met and wrote about people who had already experienced many years of increasing cognitive disability. A year before the publication of *Dementia Reconsidered*, donepezil, the first of a group of drug treatments for Alzheimer's-type dementia, was approved in the USA. While not a curative treatment, the availability of a pharmacological intervention led to a surge in interest in diagnosis from the general public as well as in the medical profession. Policy makers and health economists began to calculate the benefits of delays in admission to care homes versus the cost of the medication. As these treatments are licensed for some forms of dementia but not others, accurate diagnosis of a sub-type of dementia became important, and due to the initially high cost, guidance was introduced as to where in the overall trajectory of a dementia prescribing was seen as most effective. 'Memory Clinics', which had previously been located mainly in research institutions, rapidly developed and became much more accessible across the National Health Service in the UK.

Earlier diagnosis has developed apace since, with technological developments in neuroimaging and the lowering cost of brain scans, and it is recommended that diagnosis should be available to all who want it. Early diagnosis is a cornerstone of national dementia strategies around the world. This has opened up increased opportunities for people affected by dementia to adapt, to adjust, to plan ahead and, most importantly, to make sense of their often disconcerting, worrying, detached, or downright frightening, distressing or depressing experiences. This development has also opened doors to support and interventions at an early time, when they can have an impact that might avoid the terrible states in which Kitwood often found people with dementia. There is greater awareness of psychological and psychosocial treatments of dementia and of their benefits, particularly in earlier stages, contributing to the availability of such support to many people in a way that was not envisaged in Kitwood's time. In recent years much has been said and written about 'living well with dementia', a concept that Kitwood could only aspire to. On good days, when our needs appear to be met, this is possible, but on foggy days, for many, it can be a cause of frustration, guilt and sense of failure. Many prefer the phrase 'living with dementia', which removes some of the pressure on individuals to perform to the expectation that they should be well. There is also an increasing recognition that the ageing population is a very diverse one. It becomes even more imperative that we take an understanding of the individual's perspective as a starting point.

Seven access routes revisited

The seven access routes to the experience of dementia now feel rather dated and we had to smile at some of the formulations. The first four access routes focus on what we can learn from people who are living with the condition, be it by reading their written contributions, listening to their communications in individual and group conversations, or making an effort to understand their behaviours. There are now many people in the public domain, who have spoken directly about what it is like to live with dementia and about the support they would want. Christine Bryden, Richard Taylor, the Kent Forget Me Nots, Kate Swaffer, Helga Rohra, Keith Oliver and Wendy Mitchell have all published books about their experiences (Bryden 2005; Taylor 2006; Jennings and Forget Me Nots 2014; Swaffer et al. 2016; Rohra et al. 2016; Oliver 2016; Mitchell and Wharton 2018). All have made TV and radio appearances too. Sir Terry Pratchett (Russell 2009, 2011, 2017) made a number of TV programmes about his experiences and about the issue of assisted dying in dementia. Chris Roberts (David 2016) and his family made an in-depth fly-on-the-wall documentary about living with dementia. It is taken as a matter of course that researchers and clinicians seeking to understand the experience of dementia will draw upon the rich and varied accounts available. Dementia Diaries, for example, is a lively and ongoing collection of voice reports from a wide variety of people living with dementia about their lives and concerns, which are telephoned through and collated to the central website (Dementia Diaries 2018). There are workshops with involvement groups through the Dementia Engagement and Empowerment Project (DEEP: Dementia Engagement and Empowerment Project 2015) and a growing number of first-hand blogs on the Internet (e.g. Fordyce 2018; Houston 2018; Mitchell 2018; My Dementia Story 2018; Potocny 2018; Shorthouse 2018; Swaffer 2018). Truthful Loving Kindness (Truthful Loving Kindness 2018) publishes monthly updates of collated blog posts. There are also many presentations and talks that people with dementia give at national and international conferences, which are available on the Internet.

We have reservations about the latter three access routes to dementia experience. There is today no need to extrapolate from people experiencing other forms of cognitive disability when such a rich body of first-hand evidence is readily available. One of the access routes Kitwood highlighted was the use of poetic imagination. In the chapter he cites John Killick as using *his* creative skills to access the experience of people with dementia through poetry. Killick's work has developed since to include co-creation with people with dementia to a much greater extent (Killick 2017). Importantly, people with dementia are publishing their own poetry about their experience – for example, Tracey Shorthouse (Shorthouse 2018) and Kate Swaffer (Swaffer 2016). *In Welcome to Our World* (Jennings et al. 2014), a group of people with dementia published their own collection of poetry and life writing and would take a dim view of further professional efforts to speak for them. The experience of a central character living with dementia has also been the topic of a number of box-office movies – *Iris* (Eyre 2001), *Still Alice* (Glatzer and Westmoreland 2014) and *Ashes* (Whitecross 2012) – and most soap operas have run storylines featuring a character living with dementia. Role-play certainly has a place in training that aims to develop staff empathy and understanding. Kitwood could not envisage including people with dementia in this, while we know today that people with dementia are quite capable of expressing roles within, and outside of, life with dementia.

How we now understand the experience of dementia

Tom Kitwood worked in a world where the stigma attached to dementia was considerably greater than it is today, where service structures to support timely, or early, diagnosis did not exist, and where the majority of people with an identified dementia had already reached later stages. We acknowledge that it is more difficult to access the experience of dementia in the very late stages. We applaud the efforts being made in involvement programmes to address this, and Kitwood's thoughts on accessing experience continue to be relevant here.

At the same time, the experience of people with dementia today also includes their roles as decision makers on committees, steering groups and boards, as active agents in the promotion of better services and campaigners for a better quality of life. People with dementia across the world are finding their voice through organizations such as Dementia Alliance International (DAI). By way of example, in the past few years, UK activists living with dementia have contributed in the following ways:

- On the National Board of the Dementia Action Alliance – Peter Ashley, Peter Dunlop, Tommy Dunne and Keith Oliver have shaped the working programme
- European Working Group of people with dementia – Chris Roberts spoke at the European Summit on Disability and Rights
- 3 Nations Dementia Working Group – bringing together people from across the UK, established by Hilary Doxford, Chris Roberts and Keith Oliver
- At the World Dementia Council – one of the leaders of this is Hilary Doxford
- Disability Rights at the UN Committee for the scrutiny of compliance with the UN Charter of Rights of Persons with a Disability – Keith Oliver represented the DEEP think-tank at the United Nations.

Twenty years ago, many of these people probably would not have been diagnosed with dementia until much later. Traces of the view that 'proper' dementia is characterized by loss of the ability to meaningfully communicate about one's condition can today be found in the ongoing debate over the diagnostic criteria for mild cognitive impairment (MCI), and what differentiates it from a dementia. Reading this chapter, sceptics as to the involvement of people with dementia would feel confirmed in their view that people like Chris Roberts, Wendy Mitchell or Keith do not really have dementia at all. The growing political engagement of people with dementia, and their involvement in advisory and policy-making groups was something beyond the imagination 20 years ago.

The Kitwood flower

Kitwood champions the approach to individual experience through stepping inside the person's world, and by understanding the diversity of life experiences and values. He underlines that all this shapes the experience of dementia. His work has continued to be utilized in the growth of narrative approaches to understanding the values and life stories of people living with dementia (e.g. Kaiser and Eley 2016), and in supporting adaptation to a diagnosis right through the trajectory of living with dementia. There is now a general recognition that, following an (early) diagnosis, the experience of dementia can be significantly improved by a personalized individual care plan (Department of Health 2009; Thompson et al. 2013; NHS England 2015). A poorly written or non-existent care plan is consistent with Kitwood's table (Figure 5.1 Domain of 'negative' experience). However, a more person-centred plan based on his well-known flower (Figure 5.2 The main psychological needs of people with dementia) is more likely to improve the person's experience. While, in the later stages, family and professionals will need to compile care plans based on individual needs, wishes and values, the majority of people with dementia today will be perfectly capable of co-producing care plans as active participants with a voice and views of their own. Such care and such plans in themselves, where in place, change the nature of the experience of dementia from one of incomprehensible and uncontrollable deterioration to a more integrated and participatory one of active agency.

So much is written and said about person-centred care, that often, alas, these are just words said by professionals wishing to be identified by the wisdom and theories of Kitwood. The term *person-centred care* has been so overused in the context of health services that its original Kitwood meaning at times appears to be all but lost. Sometimes resources or lack of integrated care are cited as obstructions to delivery of what the person with dementia needs and requires. While we understand and respect this, often they are created for the benefit of professionals, of care provider organizations, or the wider health and social care system. When delivering training or lecturing students, we make no apology for advocating Kitwood's work, often using the flower and emphasizing 'love' at its centre. We hope that Kitwood would approve.

Keith says:

Figures 5.1 and 5.2 do accurately portray what the experience of dementia is like for many of us with this wretched condition, and I know from my experience that both can feature in my life even in the same day. I try to express this by the use of the metaphor of the sun (the flower predominating) or the fog (the negative experiences). There is no doubt in my mind that professionals and service users alike find talking about these negative experiences difficult; far easier to consider someone who is 'living well with dementia', but for too many this is not always the reality. Kitwood cleverly constructed this model and then followed it with the flower, which can help lessen the negative impacts. I would much rather the six aspects of the flower be a preventative, coherent and consistently established model that benefits all.

Conclusions

Currently there is a sharp focus on the human rights of those affected by dementia. When reading this chapter, while one could suggest that it is there implicitly, there is no real sense of this back in 1997. The last 10 years have seen some significant gains and changes but they are still inconsistent and fragile, and in order for the results Kitwood hoped for within this chapter these rights do need to be addressed. In 2010, 41 organizations, which later went on to form the UK's national Dementia Action Alliance, asked people affected by dementia and other key organizations what type of care and support they would hope to receive in the future. Informed by these conversations, they created the National Dementia Declaration (Dementia Action Alliance 2010), a set of seven expectations or statements of what life should be like for people with dementia. These statements were a central thread of policy and practice up until 2017, when they were reviewed and rewritten with the rights of people affected by dementia at their core. The original statements became known widely as the 'I' statements, and the updated version replaces this with 'We', in acknowledgement of the impact dementia has on both the person with the diagnosis and those closest to us. This is also important in how the statements were written and how we seek to implement them.

It is only through the thinking outlined in this chapter that those of us being diagnosed in the past 10 years have been able to engage with professionals to produce significant work such as the Dementia Statements. Kitwood could not have imagined this happening and that these statements were co-produced and not the product of role-play, or imagining the needs of people with dementia and their loved ones albeit with the best of intentions from well-meaning, diligent professionals. The experience of dementia in 2017 for many is so different from that of those who were living with it in 1997, and for that we all owe a great deal of thanks not only to Kitwood but to all those living with dementia, and caring for us either in a paid or unpaid capacity. It is only by us all working together, as evidenced by some of the work we have undertaken in the past seven years, that the experience of dementia will change for the better.

Reflection points

- How would one go about accessing and understanding the experience of people with dementia today?
- In what ways do you feel the 'domain of negative experience' of dementia is as relevant today as it was in 1997?
- Given that the experience of dementia is unique for each individual, how can the model introduced by the Kitwood flower be applied in dementia care today?

Co-production

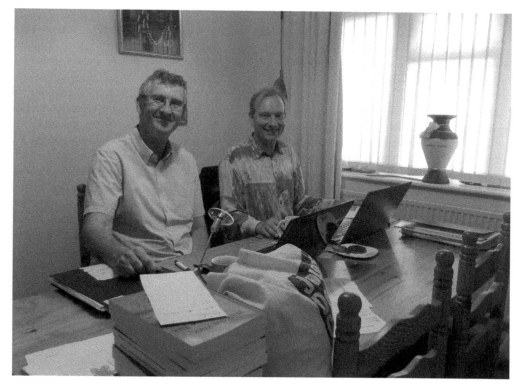

Keith and Reinhard working together, with a laptop each.
Copyright: Keith Oliver.

6

Improving care: The next step forward

Tom Kitwood

If we were to compare the standards and expectations of dementia care held 10 years ago with those that are held today, the change would seem almost revolutionary. We have better methods of assessment, positive care planning, a rich and varied range of activities, a commitment to the needs of people rather than of institutional regimes, purpose-built physical environments, and many other huge improvements. The leading edge of dementia care has been radically transformed in areas such as these, even if there is still a large mass lagging far behind.

The case for better care has become overwhelmingly strong. An ethic of respect for persons requires it. Empirical evidence confirms it; much more is known now about the capabilities of people whose cognitions are impaired, and how to maintain their well-being. Care practice can no longer be seen primarily as a matter of attending to physical needs, and no one can justify sentencing people with dementia to gross psychological neglect for three-quarters of every day. Even in this period of history, when cost-effectiveness has been made into a fetish, the warehouse model of residential care has become obscene.

In many of those settings where the quality of care is now very high, as judged by former standards, improvement seems to be reaching a ceiling. This is not primarily a result of structural inadequacies, or of poor staffing levels, but of the limited interactive capabilities of staff. In many small studies using Dementia Care Mapping (for example Fox and Kitwood 1994; Barnett 1995; Bredin et al. 1995; Perrin 1997) it has been observed that positive interactions tend to be very short-lived and relatively inefficacious. The majority of these (where physical care is not involved) last for less than two minutes, and a substantial proportion consist of very stereotyped exchanges along the lines of:

Hello Janet are you all right?

Yes, thank you.

Well, it will be lunchtime soon, and I'll see you then.

Even where malignant social psychology has been almost totally eliminated, it is rare to find that the space has been filled by a social psychology that is thoroughly empowering and sustaining. Psychological needs such as the five identified in the previous chapter are still only engaged with in a very superficial way.

It is sometimes argued that sustained interaction is not possible in settings where the staffing ratio is, say, one to seven, and where the levels of physical dependency are high. Of course this is true, although there is often the opportunity for a much higher quality of interaction while essential tasks are being carried out. The crucial test cases are those settings where the staffing ratio is highly favourable, say one to three or four. Here, where all the conditions are advantageous, it is still common to find that interactions are brief and superficial; when staff have done their essential duties they tend to chat with each other or find something 'practical' to do. The limits we encounter again and again are those of interpersonal awareness and skill.

So the principal item in the new agenda for care practice is improving the quality of interaction, and this is the central topic of this chapter. First we will look at interaction in general, and then I shall develop a theory of what, on page 75, was termed 'positive person work'. I shall also show why and how the very ambitious view of care that I am setting out can be justified. The chapter ends with a provocative suggestion, following the theoretical line developed in Chapters 3 and 4; that the whole project is not a matter of providing the very best of palliative care, but of actually reshaping the course of neuro-degenerative diseases.

The nature of interaction

To be a person is to live in a world where meanings are shared. In all but a few cases our instincts are of an 'open' kind – made complete and filled out with meaning in a cultural setting. Interaction is not a matter of simply responding to signals, but of grasping the meanings conveyed by others; it involves reflection, anticipation, expectation and creativity. These ideas are central to the body of theory known as symbolic interactionism, developed as a more accurate account of human social life than that which was offered by behaviourism (Burkitt 1993). In understanding dementia and dementia care it is essential to maintain this general view, even while recognizing that it will need to be modified so as to take cognitive impairment into account. As soon as people with dementia are seen as merely 'behaving' (in the sense of having meaningless body movements or verbalizations) an essential feature of their personhood is lost.

Everyday life proceeds remarkably smoothly, most of the time. People generally seem to know what to do and how to coordinate their actions together. Part of the explanation seems to lie in the idea of a 'definition of the situation'. Once it is clear to the participants what kind of situation they are in, certain overarching rules about appropriate conduct are called into play. Even acts of hooliganism, so it has been claimed, have their own internal order (Marsh et al. 1978).

At a more detailed level, each episode of social life may be considered as having a microstructure consisting of a series of triadic interactions, in which interpretation and reflection have a vital part (Kitwood 1994a). Let us consider two persons, P_1 and P_2, each with his or her own distinct personality: that is, a stock of resources for action, including an 'experiential self' that has developed to some degree. A single triadic unit would have the following form:

P_1 (a) an individual with a unique personality,

   (b) in a particular sentient state (mood, emotion, feeling, etc.),

   (c) defines the situation in a particular way and,

(d) with certain desires, expectations, intentions, etc.

    – makes an action.

P_2 (to whom considerations a–d also apply)

interprets P_1's action and

    – responds.

P_1 interprets P_2's response and

    – reflects

(for example checking whether P_2 understood correctly, and considering whether the action is likely to be successfully completed).

After a further reflective pause the next initiative might be taken by either P_1 or P_2, or of course, by some other person.

During the actual process of interaction most of what occurs is 'preconscious' – below the level of ordinary awareness, although accessible to it. Matters only come to the surface when there is some problem that needs special attention, such as a sudden interruption or a misunderstanding that causes the situation to break down. Any social act can be analysed as a succession of these minute triadic units. It might be as complex as a six-hour surgical operation, or as simple as a ticket inspection on a train.

Human existence, unfortunately, is far from idyllic. History reveals a continuing succession of organized acts of violence, cruelty, oppression and exploitation. Very few societies have found lasting ways of minimizing these abuses; the problems are particularly great where there is a gross imbalance of wealth and power. We have to face the fact that those finely developed capacities that human beings have for cooperation can be harnessed in highly destructive ways.

Much more prevalent and insidious, however, at least in 'civilized' society, are those subtle ways of demeaning and discounting the person that are incorporated into ordinary interaction: tiny remarks tinged with mockery or cruelty; exercises of social power; subtle manipulations; insinuations that the other is inadequate; avoidances of direct emotional contact. These often pass unnoticed at a conscious level, and are simply taken as 'normality'. A central part of the problem here is that very few people are able to give 'free attention' to one another for more than a few fleeting moments. New recruits to counselling courses often learn, with surprise and shock, how incompetent they are in active listening, and out of the whole population, these are the very people in whom this skill is likely to be relatively well developed.

> The scene is a beach, on a day in the height of summer. In the background there are sounds of play and laughter, but a little girl aged 3 or 4 is crying piteously. Her parents are sitting nearby in their deckchairs. 'Stop that crying, or I'll give you something to cry for'. The child continues to wail. She is slapped on the leg. She cries some more, then slowly stifles her sobs. She moves a little further away from her parents, and begins to dig in the sand, alone.

This tiny episode is paradigmatic. In many people's eyes it would be construed as part of ordinary parenting. At a level below consciousness, perhaps the child learned some important lessons: that her innocent desire to play with others will be frustrated, that she must submit to parental power, that she would do well to conceal her feelings of anger and dismay. Through acts such as this her exquisite sensitivities are cauterized; her personality becomes imbued with wariness and psychological defence.

Observations along these lines have been made by many psychologists involved in some way with counselling and psychotherapy, for example Rogers (1961), Miller (1987) and Bradshaw (1990). In Buber's terms, the problem is the repeated failure to meet a person as Thou, and the imposition of an I–It mode of relating. We have come to accept the diminution of persons as a norm in everyday life, and many people live in an interactional prison without ever recognizing the fact. The malignant social psychology which comes into the open so obviously in contexts such as dementia care is but an exaggerated and shameless form of the 'normal' social psychology of everyday life, whose malignant effect might be compared to that of low-level background radiation.

Positive person work

If we make a close observation of really good dementia care, at the level of the basic triadic units from which it is composed, it becomes clear that several different types of interaction are involved. Each one enhances personhood in a different way: strengthening a positive feeling, nurturing an ability, or helping to heal some psychic wound. The quality of interaction is warmer, more rich in feeling, than that of (British) everyday life. An episode that can be described in an ordinary way (reminiscing, going for a walk, having a meal, etc.) usually consists of a sequence of short-lived interactions of different types, like beads on a string. Sometimes the succession of interactions does not make up a social act of a recognizable kind; here it is as if the 'definition of the situation' changed on the way, and perhaps changed several times. Something very similar often happens in children's play.

The 12 different types of positive interaction that are outlined here form only a very provisional list. It is consistent with the ideas of workers who have developed and used the Quality of Interaction Schedule (Clarke and Bowling 1990; Dean et al. 1993). However, building on the observational method of Dementia Care Mapping, it provides a considerably higher level of detail. A full elaboration still awaits detailed research.

1 *Recognition* – Here a man or woman who has dementia is being acknowledged as a person, known by name, affirmed in his or her own uniqueness. Recognition may be achieved in a simple act of greeting, or in careful listening over a longer period – perhaps as a person describes an earlier part of his or her life. Recognition, though, is never purely verbal, and it need not involve words at all. One of the profoundest acts of recognition is simply the direct contact of the eyes.

2 *Negotiation* – The characteristic feature of this type of interaction is that people who have dementia are being consulted about their preferences, desires and needs, rather than being conformed to others' assumptions. Much negotiation takes place over simple everyday issues, such as whether a person feels ready to get up, or have a meal, or go outdoors. Skilled negotiation takes into account the anxieties and insecurities that often pervade the lives of people with dementia, and the slower rate at which they handle information. Negotiation gives even highly dependent people some degree of control over the care that they receive, and puts power back into their hands.

3 *Collaboration* – Here we gain a glimpse of two or more people aligned on a shared task, with a definite aim in view. The true meaning of collaboration is 'working together', and

this may be literally the case; as, for example, in doing the same household chores. Less obviously, it can occur in contexts of personal care such as getting dressed, having a bath or going to the toilet. The hallmark of collaboration is that care is not something that is 'done to' a person who is cast into a passive role; it is a process in which their own initiative and abilities are involved.

4   *Play* – Whereas work is directed towards a goal, play in its purest form has no goal that lies outside the activity itself. It is simply an exercise in spontaneity and self-expression, an experience that has value in itself. Because of the sheer pressures of survival, and the disciplines of work, many adults have only poorly developed abilities in this area. A good care environment is one which allows these abilities to grow.

5   *Timalation* – This term refers to forms of interaction in which the prime modality is sensuous or sensual, without the intervention of concepts and intellectual understanding; for example through aromatherapy and massage. The word itself is a neologism, derived from the Greek word *timao* (I honour, and hence I do not violate personal or moral boundaries) and stimulation (with its connotations of sensory arousal). The significance of this kind of interaction is that it can provide contact, reassurance and pleasure, while making very few demands. It is thus particularly valuable when cognitive impairment is severe.

6   *Celebration* – The ambience here is expansive and convivial. It is not simply a matter of special occasions, but of any moment at which life is experienced as intrinsically joyful. Many people who have dementia, despite their suffering, retain the capacity to celebrate; perhaps it is even enhanced as the burdens of responsibility disappear. Celebration is the form of interaction in which the division between caregiver and cared-for comes nearest to vanishing completely; all are taken up into a similar mood. The ordinary boundaries of ego have become diffuse, and selfhood has expanded. In some mystical traditions, this is the meaning of spirituality.

7   *Relaxation* – Of all the forms of interaction, this is the one that has the lowest level of intensity, and probably also the slowest pace. It is possible, of course, to relax in solitude, but many people with dementia, with their particularly strong social needs, are only able to relax when others are near them, or in actual bodily contact.

While each of the seven types of interaction that we have examined has a strongly positive content, three others are more distinctly psychotherapeutic.

8   *Validation* – This term has a long history in psychotherapeutic work, going back some time before Naomi Feil made it famous in dementia care (e.g. Laing 1967). The literal meaning is to make strong or robust; to validate the experience of another is to accept the reality and power of that experience, and hence its 'subjective truth'. The heart of the matter is acknowledging the reality of a person's emotions and feelings, and giving a response on the feeling level. Validation involves a high degree of empathy, attempting to understand a person's entire frame of reference, even if it is chaotic or paranoid, or filled with hallucinations. When our experience is validated we feel more alive, more connected, more real; there is every ground for supposing that this is true in dementia as well.

9   *Holding* – This, of course, is a metaphor, derived from the physical holding of a child who is in distress. To hold, in a psychological sense, means to provide a safe psychological space, a 'container'; here hidden trauma and conflict can be brought out; areas of extreme

vulnerability exposed. When the holding is secure a person can know, in experience, that devastating emotions such as abject terror or overwhelming grief will pass, and not cause the psyche to disintegrate. Even violent anger or destructive rage, directed for a while at the person who is doing the holding, will not drive that person away. As in the case of childcare, psychological holding in any context may involve physical holding too.

10 *Facilitation* – At its simplest this means enabling a person to do what otherwise he or she would not be able to do, by providing those parts of the action – and only those – that are missing. Facilitation of this kind merges into what I have called collaboration. The more truly psychotherapeutic interaction occurs when a person's sense of agency has been seriously depleted, or when action schemata have largely fallen apart. Perhaps all that is left is a hesitant move towards an action, or an elementary gesture. The task of facilitation now is to enable interaction to get started, to amplify it and to help the person gradually to fill it out with meaning. When this is done well there is a great sensitivity to the possible meanings in a person's movements, and interaction proceeds at a speed that is slow enough to allow meaning to develop.

Each of the types of interaction that we have considered thus far represents a form of 'care', in the sense that the person with dementia is primarily at the receiving end, or is being actively drawn into the social world. There are some interactions, however, in which the situation is reversed; the person with dementia takes the leading role, and the caregiver is offering an empathic response. As with the other types of interaction, these might continue for several minutes, or be as short-lived as a single triadic unit. This topic needs a much closer analysis, but two typical types of interaction are as follows.

[11] *Creation* – Here a person with dementia spontaneously offers something to the social setting, from his or her stock of ability and social skill. Two common examples are beginning to sing or to dance, with an invitation to others to join in.

[12] *Giving* – This is a form of interaction that approximates to the I–Thou mode. The person with dementia expresses concern, affection or gratitude; makes an offer of help, or presents a gift. There is sometimes a great sensitivity to the moods and feelings of caregivers, and a warmth and sincerity that puts the rather frigid culture of ordinary Britain to shame.

This view of interaction in dementia care can be illustrated by a small vignette, which contains three passages sufficiently detailed for a rough analysis to be made.[1]

Stuart is 65. Besides his dementia, he has considerable speech impairments. His wife Mary works at the local school. One Friday, only his fifth time at the day centre, he arrived rather flustered and unsettled. The minibus had come to collect him an hour late, with the result that Mary was delayed in getting into work.

Stuart was greeted and welcomed, and he seemed to settle over a cup of tea. He good-naturedly allowed a game of dominoes to take place around him.   REC
REL

At the end of the morning, he was invited to move to the dinner table. Instead, he first searched around, apparently for his jacket, and then went to the outside door.   NEG

He was offered company at the table by several helpers. He refused this with a wry smile, and an air of '*Of course* I'm not staying for dinner'.

Martin suggested that they sit at a separate table, and Stuart clearly said, 'No, I'm going, she'll be there'.

NEG

Martin then calmly said to Stuart: 'Mary was late for work this morning, wasn't she? Were you worried?'

Stuart looked around him, still wanting to go.

Martin said, 'Mary rang here this morning, she knows you're coming home at three o'clock. Will that be OK?'

VAL

Stuart was no nearer to settling down to his dinner. 'She . . . It's this . . .'

Martin said, 'Mary will be at work now, Stuart, and she knows you're here. You have managed well this morning, since you've been worried about Mary.

How about a walk before dinner?'

NEG

Stuart accepted this idea immediately. Martin and he walked briskly round the block, holding hands.

FAC

As they walked back inside, Martin said, 'That was a nice bit of fresh air, Stuart, wasn't it? I'm ready for my dinner now, would you like to join me?'

NEG

After dinner Stuart began to search in his pockets.

'You've paid for your dinner, Stuart, thank you.'

Stuart acknowledged this, 'Yes, good, but it's . . . this . . . no this . . . not. . . I'm looking for . . .'

VAL

'Stuart, you haven't brought a key, because Mary is expecting to be home before you. If you hang on until we can take you, Mary will be there.'

Martin offered to work with him on a collage he had started the previous week. Stuart concentrated on this for only a few minutes.

COL

He was offered a game of darts. 'I used to . . . go down with . . .' (his gesture signified drinking).

NEG

He was clearly a good darts player, and enjoyed the efforts of the people who played with him. He played for 40 minutes.

RCR

Then Stuart said, 'I . . . not long . . .'

Maureen showed him her watch, 'We will all be going at three o'clock, Stuart. I will be going with you.'

VAL

This example is sufficient to illustrate the general point. We can see here instances of at least six of the types of interaction: recognition (REC), negotiation (NEG), collaboration (COL), relaxation (REL), validation (VAL) and facilitation (FAC).

Good dementia care, then, has a kind of ecology, in which a variety of types of interaction merge into one another, and there is a continuing succession. We might imagine a natural forest of conifers, interspersed with patches of alpine meadow in which a hundred species are to be found in a few square yards. Poor care, in contrast, is dead and regimented; there are long periods of neglect, and small episodes of malignant social psychology fill a few of the spaces. We might think of a conifer plantation cultivated purely for the purposes of agribusiness, where the trees are in rows and almost nothing grows between them; there is virtually no sign of the grace and beauty of a natural system, and the atmosphere is dark and depressing.

Interactions between people with dementia

This aspect of the ecology of care has, until recently, been almost totally neglected in the literature. In some formal care environments such interaction hardly occurs at all. Or if it does, it is generally destructive: the contagion of unattended distress, perhaps, or persistent small acts of aggression. In other environments, however, where the participants carry roughly the same degree of cognitive impairment, there is a great deal of communication and contact of a positive kind. One person takes another to the toilet, and patiently waits for her to finish . . . a man and a woman form an unspoken bond, which takes on some of the appearances of a long-standing marriage . . . one person senses that another is still hungry, and brings him an extra plate of food . . . two women sit side by side, doing 'pseudo-knitting' – hardly speaking but with evident rapport . . . three people go out together, perfectly at ease, relaxing in the sun. Here we have glimpses of a special form of social life, which was invisible in former times.

At a purely verbal level, some of the interactions that occur are intelligible to an imaginative listener, and can be analysed using orthodox linguistic tools (Sabat 1994; Frank 1995). Other interactions seem to make very little sense in terms of accepted linguistic conventions. Here it is likely that the greater part of the message is being conveyed non-verbally; in some instances the words are more of an adornment or accompaniment than the main vehicle for communicating content. Languages have many forms, and there are some that depend far less on grammar and vocabulary than those of Europe, relying much more on tone, gesture and context. Conversations in these languages might make no sense at all if simply transcribed from a tape recorder in the conventional way. For these reasons it would be unwise to dismiss any interaction between people who have dementia as meaningless or nonsensical. We might, instead, applaud their ingenuity in creating special communicative forms that compensate for cognitive impairment.

It would be very worthwhile to enquire in detail into the question of why such rich interactions occur in some care settings, and not in others. The basic answer seems to be a simple one, although it has not yet been substantiated by research. It is that when a person-centred approach to care has been applied consistently, and over a long period, many psychological needs begin to be met. Experience is continuously validated; there is a security of holding and a continuity of facilitation. Personal resources are no longer dwindling away, and the spectre of vegetation has vanished. Hope is restored, and the people involved have the confidence to live their lives as social beings.

Good care, it must be said, does not aim at creating the fool's paradise of consumerist society, a place of selfishness and instant gratification. This is not what a mature adult way of being consists of, and it is not a model for the life of those who have cognitive impairments. Where the whole environment is safe and sound, the participants are able to deal with a degree of conflict, challenge, change, frustration, loss and disappointment. They can appreciate to some extent the needs of others, and move beyond their own concerns. There is an endemic danger then, of underestimating what people with dementia can do, when there is a serious and sustained attempt to meet their main psychological needs. The illusion of incapacity has been created because life was so often set up for them on impossible terms.

Sustaining interaction

If the first psychological task in dementia care is helping to generate interactions of a really positive kind, the second is that of enabling the interactions to continue. In the ordinary course of everyday life the latter is not usually a problem; most people are well-practised, and the necessary abilities are intact. Here, however, interaction is much more liable to break down. On the part of those with dementia, psychological defences that formerly kept anxiety at bay may have been weakened, and in some cases collapsed completely; some are highly vulnerable to invasion by rage, grief or fear. If cognitive impairment is severe the capacity for defining situations, or for holding definitions in place, may have been affected. Intentions, once formed, may be forgotten on the way. The ability to fit the components of a practical task into a sequence may have been lost. Not surprisingly, then, the actions of people with dementia tend to become blurred, or get aborted. Caregivers, for their part, bring their own lack of interactive competence, and many other problematic features that we shall consider at a later point in this book.

Suppose the person who has dementia is called D. If interaction is to go forward, the caregiver's part will involve at least the following:

1   to recognize when D is attempting an action, and to respond;
2   to use empathy and gain some sense of what D may be experiencing;
3   to understand D's definition, or proto-definition, of the situation;
4   to help fill that definition with meaning; not 'correcting' it in order to make it more easy to deal with, or to fit it in with institutional arrangements;
5   to appreciate and respond to the desire or need that D may be expressing; to help, if necessary, to convert it into an intention;
6   to enable D to sustain his or her action; to keep it from falling into the void because of failure of memory;
7   to respond sensitively to any signs that D's definition of the situation is changing, and to move with any changes that occur;
8   to provide enough 'containment' to enable D to pass through whatever emotional experience the interaction may entail;
9   to be ready either to initiate or respond when one triadic unit of interaction has been completed; neither rushing in too quickly, nor holding back for too long;
10 to help carry the whole process through, so that the sequence of small units becomes a completed action in the social world.

There are many ways in which a caregiver who lacks the necessary skill and insight might unwittingly prevent interaction from going through to completion. The following are particularly common:

1   failing to recognize D's first attempt at action; or writing it off as agitation, perseveration, 'naughtiness', etc.;

2   operating in an overcognitive way, and not being sensitive enough at the levels of feeling and diffuse awareness;

3   imposing his or her framework, or that of the institution, on D;

4   being overcommitted to a single and definite course, once interaction is in progress;

5   rushing the interaction, rather than letting it go at its natural pace;

6   withdrawing from interaction before the social act is completed;

7   responding to an inner sense of threat or insecurity rather than to D's need; perhaps blocking D's communicative efforts, or using tactics for distancing or discounting.

It is clear, then, that sustaining positive interaction requires a great deal from the caregiver. Much of the malignant social psychology that we examined in Chapter 3 might be viewed as a well-meaning but misguided attempt to fill the interactive void. Some of the qualities and skills for positive person work are similar to those that are needed in a counsellor or psychotherapist, and some are specific to dementia care. The more severe the dementia, the greater the need for special interactive competencies will be.

Dementia care and psychotherapy

I have portrayed good dementia care as consisting, essentially, of a series of high quality interactions, taking place in a context of stability and secure relationship. Some of these interactions are, clearly, of a therapeutic kind. So is care, taken as a whole, at all like psychotherapy, and if so, in what way? Can we expect any genuinely therapeutic outcomes? Our topic here is not the counselling of those who have recently received a diagnosis of dementia, although that is undoubtedly one of the growing points of present practice. We are considering, rather, the possibility of a form of psychotherapy for those who are deep into a dementing condition, who might score virtually zero on any cognitive test.

It all depends, of course, on what we mean. In an earlier exploration of this topic I offered a general (and rather optimistic) definition of psychotherapy – one on which practitioners from many different schools might agree.

> It is a process through which a person is enabled to change his or her way of being in the world, and especially of relating to others; a process in which old wounds are healed, hidden conflicts resolved and unfulfilled potential brought out. As a result, life becomes more satisfying, secure and productive.

(Kitwood 1990c: 43)

The reasons for scepticism are obvious. If people with dementia have such problems in sustaining attention, how could they possibly become truly engaged in a therapeutic process? If their memory, especially of the short-term kind, is so seriously impaired, how could new insights be maintained? If they are so limited in the ability to make plans and carry them through, how could they create and then consolidate a new pattern of life? And if their personality is slowly being dismantled, isn't it ridiculous to expect the kind of profound inner reorganization that psychotherapy aims to bring about? From the traditional standpoint on dementia – that there is an autonomous process of neurodegeneration – the whole project seems hopeless and futile. But it does not do so from the position that I have taken in this book, and the experience of many practitioners is beginning to suggest that the traditional view is incorrect.

Although people who have dementia are greatly disadvantaged, there are some respects in which they may be more open than others to therapeutic change. For example, they are often extremely sincere and open in expressing what they are feeling and needing, whereas many people who are cognitively intact hide behind conventional masks and pretences. People who have dementia are markedly sociable, and there are many who are positively relationship-seeking, whereas our culture often engenders withdrawal or self-isolation. Psychotherapy generally aims to help a person lower their psychological defences, and in a sense become more vulnerable; many people who have dementia are in that state already, even though it was not of their choosing. If severe dementia were compared to severe depression, it might be considered a more hopeful arena for psychotherapeutic work.

There are several different theories about how therapeutic change occurs. One highly respected view attaches relatively little weight to cognition, and regards the whole process as fundamentally relational (Symington 1988: 25–38). During the course of therapy a special kind of relationship is formed, one which is far more tolerant, accepting and stable than is common in ordinary life; for some people it is the first time ever that they have been acknowledged truly as a person. The good relationship is slowly internalized in emotional memory, helping to make up for deficiencies in early parenting. Through 'holding' a person may be able to work through unresolved conflicts and painful emotions. Through validation a person develops the capacity to experience his or her life in a richer way, with less need to use defence to blank out subjectivity. Through facilitation new action schemata are formed, particularly of a relational kind, and these are then transferred to relational contexts elsewhere. There is a gradual reorganization of the inner world, with greater resilience and a reservoir of positive feelings.

Any view of the therapeutic process is, of course, somewhat speculative, and I have given a highly idealized account of this one. However, there is good reason to suppose that much of this is available, at least to some people with dementia. If we observe interaction closely, it is possible actually to see the therapeutic process occurring.[2]

Bridget attended the day centre twice a week. She was often anxious, and expressed her emotions readily. During this particular incident Bridget was wandering around in the large room, crying, asking everyone she met, 'Have you seen my mother?' She was approached by a care worker who walked with her. The conversation went as follows:

'Are you looking for your mother?'

'Yes, have you seen her? I want to go home. I want my mother.'　　　REC

'What does she look like?'

'She looks . . . ummm . . . normal looking'

'Was she a big woman or small?'

'She's normal. Where is she? I want my mother'　　　VAL

'Do you miss her?'

'Yes', Bridget cried, 'Take me home. I want my mother. Where's my mother?'

'I'm sorry Bridget,' the care worker said softly, 'she's not here.'　　　HOL

Bridget cried as the care worker gave Bridget a hug.

'If your mother was here what would she do?'　　　REC

'Nice things'

'Would she give you a nice cuddle? Would you like me to give you a nice cuddle?'

'Yes'

⎤ REC

They cuddled and the care worker led Bridget over to a sofa where they sat. ⊐ HOL

The care worker held Bridget and smoothed down her hair. ⊐ TIM

'I'm sure your mother loved you very much, and you were a very good daughter to her.' ⎤ VAL

'Yes, and I love her very much. And I love you.' ⊐ GIV

'Well, I'm right here with you, Bridget.' ⊐ HOL

They sat together for a while, then Bridget was able to enjoy a cup of tea and a cigarette. Later she rejoined the rest of the group. ⎤ REL

In the microstructure of this episode we can discern at least seven of the types of interaction described earlier in this chapter: recognition (REC), validation (VAL), holding (HOL), negotiation (NEG), timalation (TIM), relaxation (REL) and giving by the person with dementia (GIV). Holding and validation here have a particularly strong therapeutic quality.

There is, however, a crucial difference between ordinary psychotherapy and the best dementia care. In the former case a point is reached where sufficient change has occurred, and begun to be consolidated, for therapy to come to an end. The learning that has taken place can then be implemented in everyday life without the continuing support of the therapist. With dementia this does not occur. Therapeutic change can endure, but there is no point at which the therapeutic work is done. Personhood must be continually replenished; if it is not, relational confidence and good feelings will drain away, leaving a person with a subjective world that is again in chaos and ruin. Therapeutic interactions such as holding, validation and facilitation will need to be sustained, and actually increased if cognitive impairment advances. Ordinary psychotherapy seeks to attain a point of stable equilibrium. The psychotherapy of dementia can only achieve a meta-stable state, and this is easily destroyed – for example by sudden change or the repeated failure to meet an urgent need. Interdependence is a basic fact of human existence, and in maturity this is balanced with autonomy. With dementia autonomy is necessarily diminished to some degree, and interdependence comes clearly into the open.

Even if fragments of the therapeutic process can be directly observed, the most significant test is that of therapeutic outcomes. Relatively little research has been carried out on this topic as yet in relation to dementia, although many experienced care practitioners have anecdotal evidence. My own small study, reported on pages 71–72, clearly shows the reality of therapeutic change, and as the quality of care improves we may reasonably expect to find this occurring in a much higher proportion of cases.

Two kinds of justification

A sceptic might object that my portrayal of dementia care is absurdly idealistic; that I have underestimated the damage caused by neurodegenerative disease and suggested an impossible agenda for care, especially at a time when resources are so limited. I have continually made reference to what people with dementia can do, rather than to their obvious impairments, and 'problem behaviour' doesn't even get a mention as such. The sceptic can be answered in two ways.

The first argument is an ethical one. If it can be shown that a form of practice is logically consistent with an ethic to which one has become committed, that practice can be said to be morally valid. The ethic outlined in Chapter 1 contained three central ideas: *respect for persons, moral solidarity* and *I–Thou relating*. It may be claimed that the view of dementia care that has been put forward throughout this book is consistent with this ethic; whereas strict behaviour modification, crude reality orientation, or the intensive use of sedatives are not. Moral validity is not an empirical matter. It is simply a question of whether a form of care practice is logically consistent with an ethical stand that has already been taken.

This, however, is only a partial answer. It would not satisfy those with a practical turn of mind, or anyone who wants care practice to be based where possible upon research. The central point is that many forms of action might be ethically justifiable, and it is still necessary to adopt some rather than others. The obvious basis for choice is manifest efficacy. If a particular practice that was perfectly justified on ethical grounds had no observable good consequences, it would be advisable to think again. So the second answer to the sceptic is that the view of dementia care that I have advanced must be brought before the court of empirical inquiry. It should be tested by research.

The wrong approach is to use research designs that attempt to mimic those of drug trials. Here there is a rigorous attempt to separate the effects of the different variables; the person is treated as an isolated individual; and the effects that are looked for are relatively short-term. This type of research has often been attempted with dementia care interventions, and the results have been relatively disappointing – even when ordinary observation has suggested a different conclusion (Holden and Woods 1995: 39–62).

A better research strategy, I suggest, involves assessing the consequences of a pattern of care practice taken as a whole, without attempting to subdivide it minutely into separate variables. This kind of approach is realistic in accepting that any particular care intervention, under its formal label (group reminiscence work, music therapy, etc.) in fact involves many different types of interaction, such as those described earlier in this chapter. It also recognizes that it is impossible to separate an intervention in itself from the personal and moral qualities of those who deliver it. A so-called programme of behaviour modification might in fact be an exemplary instance of person-centred care; a fashionable piece of validation therapy might turn out, in practice, to be a ghastly exercise in malignant social psychology. With a more holistic (or ecological) approach, sound designs are still possible. However, they do not closely resemble those of 'pure' research. They are more like those of R & D (research and development) where the aim is to attain to a product with specified performance characteristics, and it is often accepted that the whole system is too complex and interactive for it to be separated into discrete variables (Kitwood and Woods 1996).

Furthermore, our real aim in providing care is to maintain personhood through the entire process of dementia, and to enable a peaceful and person-centred death. Research with a long-term view has been sadly neglected, perhaps on the assumption that it is too difficult or too expensive. It is possible, however, to do such research with sufficient rigour to ascertain what is really important, and it is less expensive than might appear to those whose mind-set is formed by the drug-trial model. Long-term inquiry will be the crucial empirical test of the validity of the concept of person-centred care.

Beyond palliation

If we accept the dialectical view of dementia that has been set out in this book, and if we recognize the full implication of the fact of embodiment, one conclusion seems inevitable.

It is that the nature of care has physiological concomitants and consequences, via the psycho–neuro–endocrine systemic relation. Good care increases vitality and lowers stress; it provides the very kind of internal environment that is conducive to general health and tissue repair (Ornstein and Sohel 1989; Siegel 1991; Benson 1996). We have hints from several studies of 'rementing' that good care promotes better nerve function; it is possible that it also creates the conditions that allow some degree of neuroregeneration. Bad care devalues the person, and so puts the entire organism at risk. It enhances anxiety, rage and grief, and these bring all manner of pathology in their train. So we are actually involved in changing the course of Alzheimer's and other neurodegenerative diseases.

The quality of care can be assessed empirically, as we have already seen in Chapter 4. As care improves the long-term patterns of dementia may prove to be very different from those described in the older literature, and epitomized in the standard stage theories. We may reasonably expect to find far less vegetation – possibly none at all. There should be a much higher level of sustained well-being, and in a proportion of cases the kind of long-term therapeutic changes that I have described. Dementia will then be a different set of clinical conditions from those we have inherited, and which are described in the standard textbooks of today.

All of this is open to thorough investigation, by the accepted methods of social science. Popper suggested that a good scientist should be willing to make risky and falsifiable statements, ahead of actual testing. So here is mine. If it is found that better care, as operationally defined, is accompanied by no change in the overall long-term pattern, the account of dementia that I have given will have been falsified. If, however, the kind of changes that I have reported from one small study, and those others that I have predicted, are indeed found, we can no longer regard the disease processes that accompany dementia as autonomous, the 'standard paradigm' will have been falsified. The door would then be open for a radical reconstruction of the whole field, giving dementia care an immensely more important place. As the epidemic of dementia advances, year by year, this is one of the most crucial of all topics for research.

Notes

1 This vignette was supplied by Lisa Heller, Darnall Dementia Group, Sheffield.

Types of interaction in dementia care

Recognition	REC
Negotiation	NEG
Collaboration	COL
Play	PLA
Timalation	TIM
Celebration	CEL
Relaxation	REL
Validation	VAL
Holding	HOL
Facilitation	FAC
Creation (by the person with dementia)	CRE
Giving (by the person with dementia)	GIV

2 This vignette was supplied by Deborah Smith, Respite Care Organizer, Alzheimer's Disease Society, Hammersmith and Fulham Branch, London.

Dementia care as interaction

The 'positive person work' in dementia care is essentially that of interaction, according to each individual's needs, personality and abilities. This work requires a high level of 'free attention' on the part of caregivers.

Pat and Michal collaborating in a shared moment, touching a wood carving of great beauty in a library in Worcester, UK.
Copyright: Cathy Greenblat.

Bhanumati frequently performs a finger ritual to ward off evil spirits, and also to show that she is caring and loving to all the aides at the Nightingale day programme in Bangalore, India.
Copyright: Cathy Greenblat.

Improving care: The next step forward

Commentary by Richard Cheston

In this chapter, Kitwood begins to alter the emphasis of *Dementia Reconsidered*, away from a concern with the lived experience of dementia towards his vision of what 21st century care should look like. In doing so, he reminds his reader of the almost revolutionary manner in which the leading edge of dementia care had been transformed over the previous decade, even if there was still a 'large mass lagging far behind' (p. 104). If we fast-forward twenty years to the present day, then the pace of change at the forefront of dementia care is still just as startling as it was in 1997. Driven partly by the way in which dementia has entered public consciousness and political discourse, so almost every week brings new reports of advances and breakthroughs. Models of service delivery have evolved, while digital technology has provided new opportunities for radical reimagining of care. At the same time, however, for the majority of people living with dementia and their families the reality of daily life is still one that Kitwood would be all too familiar with. Indeed the 'fetish' of cost-effectiveness (p. 104) that he described has only strengthened its grip within a UK context at least, so that it is now enshrined within a model of commissioning and delivery.

This chapter, however, is neither an exercise in self-congratulatory smoke blowing nor an idealized fantasy of what the future of care might be. Instead, it sketches out how the phenomenological understanding of dementia that Kitwood has set out in the preceding chapters can be realized within relationships that are truly person centred. In doing so, Kitwood reminds us not only that his paradigm has its origins within a framework of counselling, but that his early years as a psychologist focused on how patterns of familial interaction shaped the moral development of children (e.g. Kitwood 1983). The chapter resonates with the core components of person-centred counselling: congruence, unconditional positive regard, and empathy. However, the focus is not on the *doing* of therapy as, for instance, might be the case within a therapy group immediately after a diagnosis; rather it is on the *being* of therapy – on how incorporating these therapeutic elements into relationships may mean that people living with dementia experience a sense of being understood, valued and emotionally contained. From this perspective, counselling principles are woven into the tapestry of care such that it helps the person who is living with dementia to manage their feelings of insecurity and stress. This is still the stuff of revolution: to imagine that almost every interaction with a person with even severe levels of cognitive impairment could be based on empathy for that person's frame of reference; that care workers can enact unconditional feelings of respect for the personhood of the individual; and that all of this is built on a foundation of genuineness. This truly would be person-centred dementia care.

As a way of embodying how this might work in practice, Kitwood provides a series of examples of positive, person-centred interactions, three of which (validation, holding and facilitation) have a distinct psychotherapeutic flavour. He also draws on a vignette and a transcript of an interaction to provide a more closely worked argument for how these therapeutic patterns of interaction might take place. These ways of relating, he argues, are important for at least two reasons: first, as a method of counteracting the insidious, subtle ways of 'demeaning and discounting' the person that are often incorporated into ordinary interactions; and, second, because for people who are living with dementia 'psychological defences that formerly kept anxiety at bay may have been weakened, and in some cases collapsed completely; some are highly vulnerable to invasion by rage, grief or fear' (p. 112).

I was especially struck by this passage, which seems to me to provide a powerful, contemporary description of the emotional challenge that dementia presents. Anyone who has walked through a hospital ward or care home and witnessed the distress that is symptomatic of unattended dementia will be able to locate in that experience the collapse of defences and the 'invasion of rage, grief and fear'. All too often dementia is framed as a process of cognitive loss without recognizing the existential challenges that confront people who are living with dementia, and by extension those who witness this struggle (Cheston et al. 2015).

In the 20 years since *Dementia Reconsidered* was published, dementia research and practice has built on some of these insights, while others have been neglected. One, clear, gain has been in our understanding of challenging behaviour, and how this reflects the communication of unmet needs, including those for emotional security (Moniz Cook et al. 2012; James and Jackman 2017). A Dutch contemporary of Kitwood, Bère Miesen, was perhaps the first researcher to make a convincing, evidence-based argument that the behaviour of some people who are living with more severe cognitive impairment could productively be understood as attempts to increase their emotional security (Miesen 1992, 1993; Miesen and Jones 1997). Using the framework of attachment theory, Miesen has argued that the emotional impact of the cognitive deterioration that causes dementia could be understood as creating a permanent 'strange situation' (Miesen 1999). Consequently, depending on the level of impairment, and the strategies that they had built up over the course of a lifetime, the person with dementia would respond to this insecurity by initiating attachment-seeking behaviour – in other words, attempting to find a greater sense of emotional safety.

Miesen described one of the security-seeking behaviours that he identified as parent-fixation (Miesen 1993). By this he was referring to a person with dementia acting as if they believed one of their parents was still alive (when they were in fact dead) – for instance, by calling out or actively searching for them. In the years since Miesen formulated his concepts research evidence has begun to emerge that is broadly supportive of his claims that this behaviour reflects a way of establishing security (e.g. Browne and Schlosberg 2005). Thus Osborne et al. (2010) found that parent fixation was more common in individuals living within residential care than for those who continued to live at home with their spouse or another member of their family. This is what Miesen's theory would suggest – that when an attachment figure is more likely to be present, then the person has less need to fall back on a symbolic figure.

There is also some evidence to support another of Miesen's suggestions – that the behavioural strategies that people have learned to use over the course of their lifetime as ways of reducing distress, may be linked to the different behaviours that they fall back on when they have dementia (e.g. Osborne et al. 2010). Thus people who behave in a way that psychologists would describe as an avoidant attachment style (i.e. people who before they had dementia would have emphasized the importance of self-reliance and not needing close relationships) are more likely to become paranoid when they develop dementia and to be more stressful for carers to look after (Magai et al. 1996; Magai and Cohen 1998). If we understand, therefore, that some forms of challenging behaviour are actually attempts to create emotional security, then the clear implication is that care providers need to find ways of creating greater emotional security. If this is to occur, then it is therefore crucial that carers are able to use the person-centred and therapeutic skills that Kitwood identified in this chapter. Only in this way can care staff create the secure and valuing relationships that for most people are the basis of greater emotional security.

Attachment theory, however, also suggests that people find other ways to create security – and these have increasingly been used in dementia care. Thus, the use of dolls in dementia care (James et al. 2006) is grounded in the knowledge that people use transitional objects as a way of bridging an emotional gap in their lives. More generally, the way in which people living with dementia in residential care use a variety of objects to create emotional security has been recognized (e.g. Stephens et al. 2013). Similarly, Simulated Presence Therapy, or playing the voice of a husband, wife or child as a means of providing emotional reassurance, is now increasingly being explored (Evans et al. 2015).

A final application of attachment theory within dementia care has stemmed from the realization that the interaction between family carers and the person with dementia will influence the latter's behavioural response (Crispi et al. 1997; Cooper et al. 2008; Nelis et al. 2012). Thus Perren et al. (2007) studied 116 married couples where one spouse had dementia and was being cared for by their partner. Where caregivers had an avoidant attachment style, and at the same time the person with dementia was prone to be emotionally insecure and to need more reassurance, then this was associated with increased levels of challenging behaviour and lower levels of caregivers' well-being. The authors account for these findings by suggesting that it may be that as the distress associated with dementia increases, so some people who are living with the illness may respond by looking for more reassurance from their spouse. For those partners who found this need for emotional security especially difficult to provide, then the alternative is to retreat away from the person with dementia in an emotional sense. This in turn creates an increased need for reassurance, and a vicious circle develops. More generally, Edwards et al. (2017) reviewed the literature and found some evidence (albeit weak) to support the contention that the quality of the couples' relationship at the time of diagnosis was related to the degree of challenging behaviour later on. This body of research, therefore, suggests that the capacity of couples to nurture each other and to sustain as close an emotional relationship as possible during the illness plays an important role in determining outcomes. Indeed, attachment style has also been identified as being associated with burn-out among ward staff working with people with dementia (Kokkonen et al. 2014).

These two decades of research into attachment theory within dementia care support Kitwood's contention, then, that good dementia care consists, in essence, 'of a series of high quality interactions, taking place in a context of stability and secure relationship' (p. 113). For Kitwood, this claim embodied his belief that the potential for psychotherapeutic growth and change was not dependent on cognitive capacity alone, but also spoke to the person's lifetime of experiences, their personality and, crucially, the quality of the social-psychological world around them. Good dementia care, therefore, involves relationships in which there is a combination of validation, holding and facilitation. When this occurs it can facilitate a radical reorganization of the person's inner world, with greater resilience and a reservoir of positive feelings. To this list of emerging core conditions, then, we would add that good dementia care also recognizes that people who are living with dementia, like all of us, have an enduring need for emotional security, and that this need can be expressed in many different ways. The challenge of working with people with dementia, then, continues to be one in which we find ways of meeting all of the needs of the person living with dementia.

Reflection points

- Kitwood argued that emotional support should be at the centre of dementia care, and that, when the relationships around the person with dementia recognized their personhood, then they were capable of growth regardless of their cognitive capacity.

- There are many obstacles to implementing person-centred counselling within person-centred care. These operate at the systemic or institutional level, as well as the social and personal.

- Recognizing the emotional needs of people with dementia and finding practical ways to support the needs of a person with dementia for emotional security, may provide important and sustainable methods of developing care.

7

The caring organization

Tom Kitwood

Whenever people join together to perform a complex task, a number of questions inevitably arise. How is the task to be divided up? Is there any way of ensuring that people do their jobs correctly? Who is accountable, to whom, and for what? How much scope is to be given for individual creativity and initiative in each role? Who holds authority, and over what domains? Questions such as these apply to all types of context (production, communication, human services, etc.) and to all types of organization, from the small and informal (such as a family) to the large and bureaucratic (such as an international bank or the entire civil service). Many of the older theorists of management held the view that there was one best way for all organizations to function. Now, however, it is generally accepted that there is a valid place for many organizational forms, and that it is necessary to find the form that is best fitted to the task.

Dementia care brings its own special organizational issues, although these generally have not been addressed with the depth and thoroughness that they deserve. The crux of the matter is this. Caring, at its best, springs from the spontaneous actions of people who are very resourceful and aware, able to trust each other and work easily as a team. However, employees vary greatly in their experience and skill, and in their motives for being involved in this kind of work. Thus the organization has to find a way to set each person free to do his or her best work, while also safeguarding against slovenliness and inconsistency; there are standards to be maintained. An optimum solution has to be found, and in a general economic context of limited resources.

In any organization that delivers a human service, there will be a close parallel between the way employees are treated by their seniors, and the way the clients themselves are treated. If employees are abandoned and abused, probably the clients will be too. If employees are supported and encouraged, they will take their own sense of well-being into their day-to-day work. Thus if an organization is genuinely committed to providing excellent care for its clients – if it is committed to their personhood – it must necessarily be committed to the personhood of all staff, and at all levels. Every one of the issues that we have explored thus far in relation to the needs of people with dementia applies also to those who are employed in their care.

In this chapter we will be looking principally at the characteristics of a single unit involved in dementia care: a residential home, a nursing home, a hospital ward, a day centre. These units usually function as part of a larger organization and they are constrained in many ways by policies, procedures, and financial plans over which they have little or no control. If, however, we can discern some of the factors that enable a single unit to function well, this may say something about how the larger organization might operate in a more relevant and effective way.

Organizational style and structure

Those who have made a detailed study of organizations often suggest that there are several different common types of style and structure, each suited to a different purpose. One type, for example, centres on personal power and influence, and operates with very few formal procedures; another has very strict role definitions, and relies heavily on bureaucratic practices; another functions by bringing expertise to bear on a particular problem, and maintains very high flexibility; and so on (Handy 1976, 1988). Most organizations have elements of more than one ideal type, and some very large organizations have different forms in their various levels or sectors.

Remarkably, the style and structure that is well-suited for a unit involved in dementia care has hardly been researched at all, although a number of other related issues have been examined in some detail: small or large units, dementia-specific or 'mixed', the design of equipment and the physical environment. Perhaps this neglect of the question of good management is a reflection of the Cinderella status of dementia care in general. We will look at some of the general issues by contrasting two different types of unit involved in dementia care, which will be termed type A and type B. Let us suppose that in each case there are three main grades: manager, senior care team and direct care staff. There is no systematic research base for this analysis; what follows here is derived in part from my own unstructured observations, and in part from consultation with several people who have had extensive experience in this field. I am also drawing on data gathered during training courses, where the participants share their experiences of good and bad organizational practices. My general method is that of creating slightly abstract ideal types, and I am suggesting that type B is highly suited to dementia care, whereas type A is not.

In type A settings the manager tends to take a position of superiority, simply on the basis of the role. A hierarchy is constructed, in which orders flow downwards and information flows upwards, rather as in the armed forces and the old-style factory. Constructive suggestions from 'below' are very rarely heard. The manager is involved in administration and external relations, and hardly ever in the direct delivery of care. He or she is seen by staff as remote, unapproachable, preoccupied, out of touch with day-to-day details concerning the clients and their care. In type B settings the authority of the manager rests on a different basis, involving respect and trust. The manager's role is thus much more one of enabling and facilitating than of controlling, and this involves giving a great deal of feedback to staff.

In type A settings several forms of 'us–them' barrier are maintained. There is a divide between manager and senior care team, and another between senior care team and the care assistants. These divisions engender a barrier between the staff and the clients, who are easily made into aliens or non-persons. Type B settings, in contrast, minimize all us–them divisions, and do not divide tasks rigidly according to formal definitions. The whole staff group thrives on cooperation and sharing. The differences of status that do exist are underpinned by mutual respect and trust. Staff members can take pleasure in each others' skills. As a counterpart to this general openness and egalitarianism, people who have dementia belong to a community.

The type A organizational form often makes a fetish of procedures and paperwork, but is strangely inept at dealing with personal and interpersonal matters. The communication pathways simply don't exist. Members of staff may discover that their responsibilities or working hours have been changed without any prior consultation. Important information concerning the well-being of a client (for example that their spouse has just died) is not passed on. A specific request made by an employee is ignored and no reason given. Corresponding to this lack of care over detail, the clients tend to be stereotyped and isolated. The type B organization is highly skilled in interpersonal matters, and has well-developed communication channels. Vital information is stored and made available, and there is also a rich body of knowledge that is held within the living culture. In this kind of setting each member of staff can be in touch with the experience of others who are present, staff and clients alike; it is possible to be flexible, efficient and highly responsive. Each person who has dementia can be known in his or her uniqueness, through a skilled combination of empathy and personal knowledge.

This brings us to a more directly psychological point. Type A settings are insensitive to what members of staff are experiencing, and especially to what they are feeling. It is not a norm of the organization to operate on the feeling level. Care practice, correspondingly, is out of touch with the clients' feelings, and there is a strong tendency to resort to the control of 'problem behaviour' through drugs. Staff have no option but to maintain a professional front in the workplace; feelings have to be sorted out elsewhere, or they are simply repressed at great personal cost. In type B settings staff are more able to be themselves; whatever their role or status, feelings are on the agenda. If anyone feels fragile or vulnerable, they do not have to hide the fact. They can bring matters into the open, knowing that they will not be criticized, but given the acceptance and support that they need. The parallel to this is the clear and open way in which feelings are dealt with in the practice of care.

In many respects, then, the difference between the two types of setting is a matter of power. In dementia care, perhaps more than any other context, there can be great disparities, and hence huge potential for corruption and abuse. In type A settings power and status matter. Staff who are at the lowest level often feel powerless, and their self-esteem in the workplace is low. The clients are at the bottom of the pile, and their true disabilities are compounded with their disadvantages in the organizational setting. The low self-esteem of direct care staff is communicated to them. In type B settings, however, there is a strong commitment to minimizing the differential of power, and each person is appreciated as they are, regardless of their role. The emphasis is on a different and much more constructive type of power: resilience, creativity, generosity, the capacity to enable good things to happen. The clients have more confidence in their own abilities; they are affected by the climate of empowerment.

These are the kind of issues that experienced workers in dementia care bring forward when they are asked to reflect on the way care settings function. It is significant that when asked to make a contrast between 'bad' and 'good' organizations, they can usually describe the former in more vivid and concrete terms. For some, good organizations are merely a hypothesis. Here is the summary of a portrait of a type A residential home which one group produced. Ironically, they named it 'Cosinook'. It had 50 residents, 30 with dementia and 14 others with some form of physical disability. The (male) manager was remote and authoritarian, and hardly ever seen in the care environment. The staff (largely female) consisted of the manager, six 'seniors' and 30 care assistants, 28 of whom were part-time. A typical day shift would be staffed by a total of five persons. Problem behaviours were routinely

Table 7.1 Two types of care settings

	Type A	Type B
Manager's role	Authoritarian, remote	Exemplary, accessible
Status divisions among staff	Large, rigid	Small, flexible
Status of clients	Lowest of all	Equal to staff
Communication	One way, impersonal	Two way, interpersonal
Feelings and vulnerabilities	Concealed, not dealt with	In the open, dealt with
Power differential	High	Low

controlled by tranquillizers such as Melloril. Even the physical layout was unhelpful, with no ways of distinguishing one floor or corridor from another; the toilets were a long way from the communal areas. The life of the residents was drab in the extreme, with endless hours of sitting with nothing to do. There was a continuing undercurrent of hostility and distress. For the staff it was largely a matter of survival, doing the bare minimum and watching the clock for their shift to end. The description of 'Cosinook' arose from their direct experience; it was only just a caricature. The differences between the two types of setting are summarized in Table 7.1.

Stress, strain and burn-out

The condition we have come to know as burn-out was first described as a loss of energy, enjoyment, vision and commitment, and as a general sense that it is impossible to do a job as it should be done (e.g. Freudenberger 1974; Maslach 1982). Burn-out is clearly different from simple exhaustion, which is remedied by rest and recreation. In some instances the onset of burn-out is dramatic; a person may feel, quite suddenly, that they cannot face going to work. It is more common, however, for the process to be gradual, happening over a period of months or even years. Factors of a personal kind are, of course, involved in burn-out. A considerable body of research on this topic, however, comes strongly to the conclusion that the main causes lie in the way organizations function, particularly inadequacies in the design of jobs, the lack of support structures, and in the workload itself.

Burn-out is particularly likely in occupations that have a strong vocational quality, and a close study has been made of it in the caring professions (e.g. Chernis 1980). It has not been subjected to close research, however, in the field of dementia care, although there is good reason for believing that it is a serious problem here. Burn-out is more likely when there is a very needy client group (Maslach 1978).

Three main stages have been identified in the development of burn-out, the first of which is stress, as shown in Figure 7.1. Here there is a serious attempt to do the job, giving close attention to all its aspects. An employee has vision, energy and determination, and for a short time it seems to be possible to do the job well. The output of good work is high. The demands, however, are too great for this effort to be maintained. A state develops in which the body is in a more or less permanent state of overarousal. Health may begin to be affected, with a lowered resistance to viral infections, or such symptoms as headaches or lower back pain. There may be an experience of recurrent anxiety; patterns of sleep may be disturbed. Stress arising from the workplace tends also to have secondary effects; for example a deterioration in close relationships, or a loss of interest in leisure pursuits. A sensitive person may be inclined to internalize the problem, and frame the state of stress

Figure 7.1

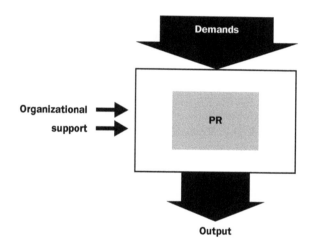

Figure 7.2

as a consequence of personal inadequacy. This, unfortunately, is a view with which some organizations very readily collude.

The second stage is often described as one of strain, as shown in Figure 7.2. Now the output of good work declines, as the recognition grows that the job as originally envisaged is impossible. As with stress, strain has its counterpart in changed body chemistry, particularly in enduring adverse changes in hormone balance. It is as if the body has been constantly on the alert, but never identified what it has to fight against or run away from. Prolonged strain seems to be associated with a greater susceptibility to serious illness such as cancer, ulceration of the gut and heart disease (e.g. Cooper 1984). The chronic fatigue syndromes, which are still only very poorly understood, may also have some connection with continued strain.

Figure 7.3

The third stage is one of more steady low-level functioning, as shown in Figure 7.3. Now there is no longer an attempt to do all that the job really requires. A new equilibrium is established between personal resources and organizational demands. Many tasks are performed in a minimal way, and in care work there is a tendency to withdraw once the basic tasks are done. The idea of attempting to meet the full range of clients' needs is abandoned, and there is a kind of psychological disengagement.

Burn-out is expressed in different ways. The obvious initial signs are lateness, absenteeism, carelessness, disowning of responsibility, and high rates of sickness. Often there is a cynical or resentful attitude, with criticism directed at anyone who does more than the accepted basic minimum. Much of this resembles the state of 'learned helplessness' (Mukulineer 1995); a person has discovered that efforts at bringing change are futile, and that the outcomes are out of his or her control. The third stage, then, is a kind of stalemate, which has evolved as a form of self-protection by employees. Perhaps it is the only way they have of coping while the organization sets up their work in such an unrealistic way.

This account of burn-out in the caring professions may shed light on what has been happening in dementia care. In the tradition of practice that we have inherited, where staff were given very little support or help in their work, it is possible that the majority of those who survived had moved into a chronic state of low-level burn-out. The situation was all too easily accepted, and transformed into the idea that a basic minimum of physical care was all that people with dementia needed. It is essential, then, as we seek to improve dementia care, that organizations take on the full range of psychological and moral responsibilities, and create conditions where their employees can flourish.

Taking care of staff

Thus far the improvements that have been made in dementia care have been far more concerned with the quality of life of the clients than with that of staff. The well-being of care assistants, especially, has been sadly neglected. Sooner or later, however, it becomes clear that there is a close connection between the personhood of clients and that of the staff; it is only a short-term expedient to ignore the latter issue. There are many ways in which an organization can take care of staff, and we will look briefly at eight of these. What follows is based on a document written by Robert Woods and myself for a charity wanting to improve its dementia care; it draws in part on our own experience, and in part on consultation with several very experienced practitioners (Kitwood and Woods 1996).

Pay and conditions of service

The central point is simple and obvious. Staff should be properly rewarded for their work. A good organization makes provision for sickness and holidays, and gives the opportunity for those who wish it to contribute to a pension scheme. Where these arrangements are not made, the organization is expressing to staff that they are little more than casual labour; it is not surprising if they, on their part, show casual attitudes and low commitment. A sound framework of pay and conditions, on the other hand, creates security and conveys to staff that they are valued.

Induction

Experience in the first few weeks after starting work deserves very careful attention. It is easy to underestimate the apprehension and lack of confidence that many new employees feel. A well-designed induction process might take place over, say, two months, giving time for the newcomer to assimilate all necessary information and learn all the basic tasks. One possibility is to have two induction packs. The first contains details of conditions of service, pay and pensions, health and safety, fire precautions, disciplinary procedures, etc. The other is more related to the job itself, with a clear statement of what is expected in a particular role, and information on care planning, supervision and quality standards. It might also have some material on the nature of dementia and dementia care. During the induction period an employee will need a higher level of supervision, and should have ready informal access to an experienced person who can give guidance and support.

Creation of a team

Care is much more than a matter of individuals attending to individuals. Ideally it is the work of a team of people whose values are aligned, and whose talents are liberated in achieving a shared objective. It is unlikely that this will happen just by chance; if teambuilding is neglected it is probable that staff will form their own small cliques, and begin to collude in avoiding the less obvious parts of care. Some developmental group work may be necessary, in order to facilitate self-disclosure and to lower interpersonal barriers. The formation of a close-knit senior care team is especially important, with a consensus about the nature of good practice, and a common framework for their supervisory work. As new employees arrive, they should be properly integrated into the team.

Supervision

In an area so fraught with uncertainty as dementia care it is vital that staff should be given regular feedback about their work, and have the opportunity to discuss issues from it with someone who has greater experience. In the best care settings all employees, including the manager, receive regular supervision. A good arrangement is for there to be an hour of supervision per month, and for new members of staff to have an hour per fortnight during their first few weeks in employment. Effective supervision involves forming a kind of 'learning alliance', with a clear understanding of the purpose and the format (Hawkins and Shohet 1989). A rough boundary should be drawn between issues that are genuinely work-related, and those of a more personal kind (which might need to be dealt with through counselling outside the workplace). However, it is appropriate for supervision to provide some kind of 'containment' for painful feelings arising directly from work. Supervision might lead to agreements about what action is to be taken, for example if it has become clear that a particular skill is missing. In some settings supervisees are given the opportunity to give feedback to their supervisors; it is almost a supervision in reverse. There is also a place for some small group supervision, perhaps in order to learn from a critical incident of a positive or negative kind.

In-service training

In care work at all levels, the proper aim is to promote the formation of a 'reflective practitioner' (Schon 1983) – one whose work is flexible, assured and full of understanding. A mechanized approach, which merely deals with acquiring 'competences', does not go nearly far enough. The training of staff, if well designed, will set up a process of experiential learning, involving a cycle of action, reflection, and consolidation of better practice (Kolb 1992).

Much of the in-service training can be carried out by the manager and senior care team if the organization has enabled them to learn how to do this work. Training is better done with teams than individuals, because members develop shared goals, and can support each other in the improvement of their practice. Single 'shots' of training are relatively ineffective, because the learning cycle is unlikely to be completed. A structured programme of, say, six two-hour sessions over six months, is far more likely to bring about creative change. The content of training should never be merely theoretical as has often happened with dementia. It should stimulate staff to subject their practice to continuing reflection.

Individual staff development

Over and above the more obvious training issues, there is the question of how to enable each member of staff to flourish in his or her own unique way. In any care team there is likely be a rich array of abilities and interests, which could be drawn into the work. When staff are simply made use of, or when care is defined in too narrow a way, these remain largely hidden. A caring organization will make it possible for staff to take courses, offer more flexible hours so that a special interest can be pursued, encourage innovations in the activities arranged for clients, and allow jobs to be redesigned so as to take new interests into account.

Accreditation and promotion

An organization that is concerned for its staff will make it possible for those who are highly committed to gain some form of accreditation, and will have a route for promotion out of the care assistant grade. Several programmes are available for enabling people to gain nationally recognized accreditation in dementia care, through to university level qualifications. If individual accreditation is to become an established practice, it will probably involve one or two members of the senior care team themselves becoming qualified as assessors, tutors or mentors, in addition to their ordinary role in supervision. Indirectly, the heightened level of activity will improve the quality of care. Also, as more opportunities are provided for staff members to gain qualifications specifically related to dementia care, the general status of this work is likely to rise.

Effective quality assurance

Generally quality assurance is viewed as a way of protecting the needs and interests of clients, and of satisfying inspectors and senior managers that basic standards of care are being met. The whole process also has another function; it is a way of giving systematic feedback to staff, and hence, if handled rightly, of giving them assurance in their work. In all assessment of care practice, then, great attention should be paid to the 'developmental loop'; that is, data collected should be made available to staff as a basis for discussion, in order that a plan can be drawn up for the improvement of care. Ideally each quality assurance round will generate such a plan, and the next round will provide information on whether the plan has actually been effectively implemented. There is an insincere way of going about quality assurance, which consists essentially of 'being seen to be doing the right thing'. It is more challenging by far to confront the realities, and in particular to assess what is actually occurring to the clients in the process of care. When this is done it will be necessary to face up to some issues that had been avoided, but there is the possibility of setting a virtuous circle into motion, with huge increases in job satisfaction.

Employing the right people

If an organization is to function well, it is of course essential that it has a sound process for selecting its employees. This is not simply a matter of paper qualifications and experience; it is also a question of their potential for developing in the course of their work. A care setting may have all of the right structural features, including the eight points we have just examined, but if the employees are unsuited for their jobs, limits will very soon be reached. Fortunately, during this time when expectations of dementia care are rising, many more people who are well-suited to this field of work are making it their chosen speciality.

Drawing the right people into dementia care entails designing the jobs in such a way as to make them both challenging and attractive, along the lines of the previous section. For example, well-motivated people are encouraged to become care assistants if there is a route for promotion and opportunities for personal development. The job as described must be in touch with reality. Some residential homes are still denying the presence of dementia, and so not preparing staff accordingly. In sheltered housing, some providers still describe the job of the warden as if all the tenants were psychologically independent, whereas in reality this is now very rarely the case.

Great discernment is needed in the selection process. In many respects attitudes are the key. It is relatively easy to help a person to gain in knowledge and skill, but attitudes are often difficult to change. Ageism, rigidity, and that arrogance which bespeaks a lack of openness to new learning are particular drawbacks. These are the very kind of dispositions that tend to be held in place by strong psychological defences. Attitudes conducive to dementia care may have developed through such experiences as parenting, fostering, or looking after an older person in the family. Some people have developed counselling-type orientations through working for organizations such as the Samaritans or Cruse. Those who have worked in the field of learning disability are often well prepared for dementia care.

At this point in history, when so little has been done to provide training that is specific to working with dementia, paper qualifications of the conventional kind mean very little. Very few nurses, for example, have received any psychological preparation for working in this field. Even nurses who have been trained for mental health work may have been given little more than a simplistic induction into the medical model, which offers very little help with the practice of care. Similar points apply in social work training, where dementia has only had a very small place in the curriculum leading to qualification. Ironically, with some well-qualified professionals there is actually a task of 'unlearning' to be undertaken, because they have absorbed the pathologizing and distancing attitudes that accompany the older views. On the other hand, many people who show a remarkable aptitude to dementia care come to it without the standard professional qualifications. It is vital to establish routes for them to become qualified in formal terms, and so develop into the true specialists that this field so urgently needs.

In the process of selection it is often possible to discover a person's attitudes by asking them to describe examples of good and bad practice. Some employers invite applicants to come and spend a few hours in the care environment, and to be in direct contact with the clients. From observation of their mode of interaction it is often possible to discover who has a real aptitude for this kind of work. People with dementia generally have a clear sense of who has real concern for them, and so have their own selection procedures.

A crucial factor in satisfactory employment is the 'psychological contract' (Handy 1976). The contract is sound if there is a match between what the employee is wanting and expecting, the employer's requirements, and the real situation in the workplace. If there is a mismatch, problems are likely to occur. Suppose, for example, that an organization has generally low expectations of dementia care, and has designed its practices accordingly; a talented new employee who comes with high aspirations is soon going to be frustrated or disillusioned – a very likely subject for burn-out. Many excellent people have left dementia care because what they were required to do was incompatible with their values. Suppose, on the other hand, that an organization has set very high standards. There will be serious difficulties in getting good work from an employee who is mainly looking for a way of bringing in some money. Understandably, there are many people for whom this is the case; care work may be the only avenue of employment that is open to them. Problems of this kind can be accentuated if there is a large part-time workforce, who generally show a lower level of commitment (as in 'Cosinook', described on p. 125). The most creative solution is to provide an opportunity for real development in the job, so that the psychological contract can be renegotiated.

Organizational defences and dementia care

As we have noted at several points in this book, the human psyche appears to have devised various ways of warding off anxiety – the 'ego defence mechanisms'. We have also touched on the idea that there are defence processes which occur during the course of interaction; we will return to this in Chapter 8. Another hypothesis of depth psychology is that when people come together in some kind of collective, their defence processes can become aligned.

In many organizations it is as if the members have made agreements together, at an unconscious level, about what must remain hidden from awareness, and what it is safe to deal with at a conscious level through the ordinary processes of symbolic interaction (de Board 1978). When people are bound together in this kind of way, part of their individual psyche has, so to speak, been lost – 'made over' to the organization. So long as the organizational structure remains intact, the defences hold; if however it is dismantled, or if it breaks in crisis, the anxieties that were held at bay are mobilized, taking some people to the verge of paranoia.

It has been suggested that defence processes often operate in care settings. A famous study of nursing practice by Isabel Menzies (1972) brought this into the open. Her argument was that nurses are continually faced with situations that might be expected to provoke extreme anxiety, for which they are usually given no emotional support. They have to help people who are highly vulnerable, sometimes in pain, often anxious and alone; the powers of life and death are in their hands. It is likely that a range of powerful and sometimes contradictory emotions will be aroused: compassion, pity, fear, disgust, envy, sexual desire. Yet the nurses Menzies observed were generally very composed, and the norms of their profession endorsed an almost inhuman self-control. Menzies explained this contradiction by using the psychodynamic hypothesis of defence processes, and identified some of the 'irrational' procedures that seemed to serve a defensive function.

Dementia care presents a situation similar in some respects to nursing. The anxieties, as I have suggested, centre on two main issues: ageing and frailty, and madness and loss of self – with the additional threat that 'this might be me someday'. The actual task of caring, in addition, may provoke disgust at times, and feelings of powerlessness and guilt. In many old-style care settings defence processes similar to those Menzies describes seem to be at work. For example, there is often an unnecessary and 'irrational' form of regimentation. Care workers tend to give themselves readily to practical tasks, while neglecting the more subtle tasks of psychological care. There are various tactics for putting people with dementia at a distance, including the use of dehumanizing labels, and simple physical withdrawal. Often real relationships with the clients do not develop, and attachment needs are very poorly met.

Practices such as these can be very easily rationalized by making use of a simplistic medical model of dementia. The idea of advancing neuropathology can by a deft sleight of hand be made to imply that people who have dementia experience no suffering, and that they need little more than basic physical care. The most extreme form of neuropathic ideology that I have encountered was in a nursing home owned by a large private company. It had four units, one corresponding to each purported stage of dementia. The residents in the fourth unit, so a senior manager alleged to me, were 'virtually brain-dead'. They were given almost no human contact other than during the course of physical care. Presumably the ideology was what the majority of staff believed at a conscious level, and it relieved them both of anxiety and responsibility.

When defence processes are entrenched it is likely that an organization will be severely impaired in its ability to provide good care. The discourses of everyday life will be too trivial; too much feeling will go unexpressed; members of staff will have lost too much of themselves in the collective defences. Of the two styles and structures that we considered earlier in this chapter, type A is far more likely to operate in a highly defensive way; the exercise of power and defensiveness go together. However, while the existence of a more collaborative structure resembling type B provides a necessary condition for the lowering of defences, it does not guarantee it. The anxieties surrounding dementia are very great, and the unconscious is highly ingenious in creating new forms of avoidance. A caring organization would do well to take deliberate steps to enable the lowering of defences to be maintained.

Making change happen

It is never simple or easy to introduce new practices within an organization. Once a particular structure is in place, and a set way of doing things has been established, these tend to persist; changes that are introduced with a particular purpose may be diverted or subverted along the way; any threat to the status quo may meet with unconscious resistance. These considerations apply to virtually all forms of organizational change. When the central issue is that of moving to more person-centred practices in a human service, the problems are very great indeed. In recent years a great deal of attention has been given to the general topic of organizational change, and at last some of the knowledge that has been gained is being applied to dementia care. An article by Lynne Phair and Valerie Good (1995), for example, gives clear advice to anyone wishing to promote improvements in dementia care.

Let us suppose, as is highly likely in the case of dementia care, that the initiative is coming from one or more people in an intermediate position, and that the organization's overall structure is a form of hierarchy. Perhaps the change agents are persons around the level of the manager of a day centre, a hospital ward or a residential setting. One problem is how to get the organization, in the larger sense, to accept that the proposed change is a good idea and then positively to back it. Another is that of securing the commitment of staff. The success of the whole venture will require clear strategic thinking, a kind of Machiavellian awareness of where power and interests lie, and then a close attention to tactics. Many good ideas are lost because of a failure of practical (and in a sense political) intelligence.

It is necessary, for example, to be very clear about what it is that is to be done and to select a time at which it is realistic to attempt to do it. The proposals will need to be presented to those who have the power to approve and back them, and in a way that clearly aligns with some of the organization's overarching goals. A detailed plan should be drawn up, clearly showing how the change can be introduced, in what stages, and over what time scale. The plan should include ways of monitoring whether the changes have in fact been carried out, of assessing their efficacy, and of ensuring that they are consolidated. The costings must be realistic and justifiable.

Although person-centred care is out of step with many of the trends of the time, and certainly at odds with all moves towards routinization, standardization and cost-cutting, it now has a moral force that should not be underestimated. Most organizations involved with dementia wish to be seen as giving excellent care; it is certainly what their 'customers' desire. The challenge is to get organizations actually to do it, rather than simply maintain a façade.

The care setting and the community

Every organization is a part of society, enmeshed within it by historic, economic and personal ties. Every care setting has its local context, and its relationship to that context is crucial to its well-being. Many of the old-style mental hospitals were deliberately situated some way from the communities which they served – and usually in the country; perhaps there was an assumption that the patients needed fresh air and a complete change of scene. Often these places conveyed an aura of foreboding; innocent names like Fulborn, Cherry Knowle, High Royds or Craig Duneen became symbols of dread. Now, however, in dementia care as in most fields of mental health, the emphasis is on having smaller and more homely units, right in the heart of the community. In principle this is surely a positive move. It is still possible, however, for these places to be as isolated, in real terms, as any of the old asylums, and, just because they are so close to the community, they can be a source of even greater resentment and fear.

Huge benefits are to be gained when the doors of formal care settings are opened, giving access in both directions. The clients can maintain their links with the community, and more readily maintain a sense of their own history: doing some shopping, going to the pub, to the theatre, to church, taking a walk in the local park. People from the community – not merely relatives and close friends – can become regular visitors. In some instances a local school has established a strong contact with a day centre or residential home. Some organizations are making provision for people to become fully-fledged volunteer helpers, providing the necessary preparation and training (Kramer 1995; Heller 1996). When volunteers are fully drawn into dementia care there is even the possibility of having 'staff' to client ratios of 1:1.

Becoming more truly part of the community entails removing the barriers of mutual suspicion that often exist between family members and paid caregivers. Many people who have been deeply committed to looking after a person with dementia wish to continue to have an active part, even after that person has gone into residential care; the idea that they should now be mere bystanders doesn't make sense. If their wish is to be granted, paid staff will need to face up to the fact of being observed closely, and overcome their fear of being criticized. Family members, for their part, will need to shed their prejudices against paid staff, and appreciate how difficult their job really is; their attitude must be one of support, not disapproval. When the barriers are broken down there is the potential for huge improvements, as Jean Tobin (1995) has shown in her discussion of 'sharing the care'. Better channels of communication develop; family members feel more able to express their wishes. They are enabled to give the care that they truly want to give, without the crushing burden of having to do it alone. The care setting, has, in effect, added to its staffing, and at virtually no additional cost.

> Ruth had looked after John, her husband, with great devotion. He had had dementia for about five years, and now they were both over 80. John was a large, heavily-built man, and Ruth's strength and health were failing. Although she was receiving some additional help, Ruth realized, with great reluctance, that John would have to go into residential care. She found an excellent home not far from where they lived. At first John attended for days only, and she accompanied him. Later, when he became a resident, Ruth was present for the greater part of most days. Besides being with John, she got to know many of the other residents well. Her contribution was highly valued, and she for her part remained true to her commitment to her husband. This situation continued right up to the day of John's death.[1]

This is a strikingly successful instance of 'sharing the care'. Although in many cases matters are not so straightforward, it is at least a model to which practice can aspire. The more that the barriers between formal care settings and the community are broken down, the more the fears surrounding dementia will be dispersed. At the same time, professional practice will become more ordinary, more homely, more human – and carers of all kinds can take heart.

Note

1 The material for this vignette comes from the Bradford Dementia Group Carers' Support work.

The caring organization

Commentary by Bob Woods

Returning to this chapter after 20 years, it is Tom's voice I hear in my head – his careful and elegant choice of words and phrasing, his desire to explain and convince rather than to produce an academic text top heavy with references. Tom makes an explicit link between the section of the chapter on 'Taking care of staff' and some work we undertook together in developing a training and development strategy for dementia care in residential settings (Kitwood and Woods 1996), and indeed we discussed at length many of the ideas Tom elaborates on here. Our joint work also provides a context highlighting some of the issues that arise when implementation of these concepts is attempted.

The essence of the chapter is simple, and one I have cited repeatedly over the years: achieving person-centred care for people with dementia requires attention to the personhood of those employed to provide the care. Just like people with dementia, staff need to be respected, valued as individuals and work within a social environment that is supportive and provides positive feedback and encouragement. If staff are devalued, diminished and discouraged, the personhood of the people with dementia with whom they work will similarly be under threat.

Kitwood attempts to distinguish different types of care environment, adopting his familiar style of setting up a contrast between two opposite poles, here depicted as 'type A' and 'type B' care environments. In 'type A' there is a clear hierarchy of power (with the residents at the bottom and the care staff just above), and an authoritarian and remote management, perhaps with a 'fetish of procedures and paperwork' (p. 125). In 'type B' environments, in contrast, co-operation and sharing are evident, with an atmosphere marked by openness and a sense of community of all – staff and residents. Here there is equality among staff and residents, good communication, and an openness to feelings and vulnerabilities absent in 'type A' settings.

The negative consequences for people with dementia of diminished personhood are mirrored in the risk of strain and burn-out in staff. Without support from the organization, the daily demands and stress of providing care produce strain, impairing the staff member's ability to attend to the whole range of needs of the person with dementia – psychological, social and physical. Over time, in the absence of support, this strain becomes chronic and, in order to cope, the staff member becomes 'burnt out', withdrawing mentally and emotionally from the care-giving role and performing the role only at the most basic level.

The bigger picture: the status of care work

The strategies within the chapter for making a difference to the organization and its culture are explicitly focused on the individual care home or dementia care unit, rather than at a broader level – say of a care home chain, a broader system within the health care provider or society at large. The hope is that, in identifying what makes a difference for the individual unit, lessons can be drawn for the wider organizational context. There is one area where this approach, which might be said to be typical of a psychological, pragmatic perspective, appears least likely to be useful. This is the first approach listed in the section on 'Taking care of staff', relating to pay and conditions of service. Clearly, this is a major influence on the extent to which staff feel valued, but the external influences on these matters are close to overwhelming. In the UK, minimum and living wage policies from government have helped increase pay levels, but caps on public support for care home fees and for support at home impose significant constraints. A sociologist might argue that the low pay levels reflect the dual jeopardy of ageism and the stigma associated with dementia. As a society, we simply do not value those who support people with dementia; it is not seen as a profession, a job requiring skill and expertise. The fact that the great majority of care workers continue to be female adds the jeopardy of gender inequality, associated with lower pay and worse conditions of service. This is not to say that individual dementia facilities cannot operate good employment practices, and that these may make a difference to the staff involved, but rather that the external constraints are large and complex. The growth in numbers of people living into their ninth decade and beyond, with the concomitant increase in people living with dementia, leads to projections of greatly increased need for social care. Apart from the increased costs for government, taxpayers, families and individuals, there are real concerns that this would require an unprecedented growth in the social care workforce. Without a dramatic change in levels of pay and improved conditions of service, it is questionable whether this is achievable, and there are already reports of care agencies not being able to meet the demands placed upon them to provide care workers in the home environment, and of care homes being closed.

Putting the chapter into practice: action research project

Kitwood's description of 'Taking care of staff' is drawn from a training and development strategy that we developed initially for a leading care charity opening a new dementia care facility. We were then offered the opportunity to be involved in the initial implementation and evaluation of the strategy. The project is described fully by Lintern, Woods and Phair (2000a, 2000b) and by Lintern (2001). The main focus of the evaluation was on two of the aspects highlighted in the chapter: in-service training and effective quality assurance. The former took the form of two days of training from Tom, himself; the latter consisted of regular six-monthly cycles of Dementia Care Mapping (DCM), undertaken by independent mappers, with the results fed back leading to agreed action plans for quality improvement.

Although it had been hoped to influence the development of the culture of the home from the beginning, in the event, due to a number of delays, including difficulties in recruiting qualified mental health nurses, the training phase of the project began around a year after the first residents had been admitted to the home, when a culture of care had already developed. This was captured in the first round of DCM, as well as in interviews with care staff, from which several features of a 'type A' culture were apparent. The organization was hierarchical, and communication between qualified staff and care staff was lacking. Communication between staff and residents focused on physical care, and there were few activities, apart from those organized by external visitors. Staff did not appear to be confident in responding to residents' expressions of distress or anxiety, and routines appeared to have developed for the convenience of staff while denying residents opportunities for control and choice.

The training commenced with two days with the senior staff of the home, working together on how best to implement the various elements of the training and development strategy, such as induction and in-house training, supervision, care planning and involvement of families. Two-day courses were then provided for the care staff (split into two halves, so the home could continue to operate during the training). These were interactive sessions, with plenty of opportunity for reflection and discussion. There were exercises and demonstrations on personhood, communication, the importance of life history and on DCM, to assist care staff to consider and identify aspects of malignant social psychology and indicators of potential well-being.

Following this initial phase of training, there were a number of improvements evident. Care staff engaged in activities and interacted more with residents; they were more aware of residents' psychological needs and more likely to adopt problem-solving approaches when responding to residents. Attitudes were more positive, with staff showing increases in both person-centred and hopeful attitudes. However, disappointingly, a second wave of DCM did not indicate an overall improvement in residents' well-being. It appeared that training alone may have begun to lead to changes in staff attitudes, skills and approach, but had yet to make a difference to the culture of the home.

For various practical reasons, the feedback from the second wave of DCM was delayed for several months, but an action plan was drawn up with the staff team, to address issues identified in the mapping. This included changes in care practice, such as staff engaging in more activities with residents, and attention to residents who slept a great deal. Organizational changes included the introduction of supervision sessions for senior staff and provision of more 'hands on' leadership by example from an experienced practitioner working alongside direct care staff. A key change in creating greater continuity was to phase out a rota system whereby staff worked alternate months on the dementia section of the home and on a section for residents with primarily physical health needs. Despite the delay in drawing up the action plan, the third wave of evaluation identified further improvements in staff attitudes, especially hopefulness and in time staff spent engaging in activities with residents. DCM now began to show some change, with a greater proportion of positive care values, although individual resident well-being had not improved significantly.

On this occasion, a timely action plan was then drawn up with staff, immediately after this third wave of DCM. Among the aims of the plan was an increase in the range of activities in order to provide greater mental, sensory and physical stimulation, and to encourage greater independence among residents. Induction training was to be prioritized for new staff and a system put in place to ensure that temporary staff were inducted into the home's philosophy. A key organizational change was to set up rotas so that morning and afternoon shifts had a period of overlap, so that all staff (including direct care staff) could be included in handovers, thus enhancing communication between staff at all levels. The overlap period also enabled group supervision to be scheduled. Finally, the rather clinical uniforms worn by staff were to be replaced with a more casual dress code. After these changes had been in place for a further six-month period, the fourth wave of DCM identified a significant improvement in the average well-being of individual residents as well as in the proportion of positive care values. In fact, there was a 60 per cent increase in the proportion of the two highest levels of well-being (+3 and +5) compared with the first mapping before the interventions began. The improvements in attitudes and skills were maintained, but did not improve further at this point.

This project exemplifies clearly many of the messages of this chapter. A 'type A' organizational culture can develop very quickly, even when the intention is to be person centred. Training sessions – even when delivered by Tom Kitwood himself – were not sufficient to change care practice, although staff attitudes and behaviour did show clear improvement. Without the appropriate organizational support and context the efforts of individual staff will not produce a culture of person-centred care. By the end of the project, a number of the aspects considered in the section 'Taking care of staff' had been addressed, including induction and supervision, and there were some indications of a movement towards a 'type B' organization, with greater openness of communication between staff of all levels, less of a hierarchy and a more valued position for residents.

Quality assurance

In this example, DCM as a quality assurance tool was invaluable in leading to action plans that could address organizational obstacles and barriers, especially when the feedback was timely, so that it could be recognized and owned by the staff concerned. DCM has continued, of course, to be used as a driver of change, using DCM evaluations to change care practice, and the effects evaluated in several studies (see Brooker 2005; Surr et al. 2018). A large-scale randomized controlled trial of DCM as a tool for improving outcomes in care homes for people with dementia is now nearing completion (Surr et al. 2016).

The importance of staff attitudes

One of the unexpected outcomes from the action research project was an insight into staff attitudes and their relationship to the quality of care. Kitwood discusses staff attitudes primarily in relation to selecting the right people to employ in the care setting, suggesting that attitudes are more difficult to influence than knowledge and skills (p. 131). Negative attitudes to older people, rigidity, and a lack of openness to new ideas and learning were seen as a poor fit with a person-centred approach. Paradoxically, the training delivered by Tom could be characterized as focusing more on attitudes than on skills or knowledge, seeking to develop empathy with the person with dementia. For the purposes of the project, a new scale was developed: the Approaches to Dementia Questionnaire (ADQ) (Lintern 2001). Statistical analysis of responses suggested there were two dimensions represented here: recognition of the personhood of the person with dementia; and hopefulness, a sense that it was possible to make a difference to the lives of people living with dementia, that this was not a futile exercise. The results of the project suggested that attitudes could be influenced through training, and become more positive, and that the hopefulness dimension was especially important in predicting the quality of care provided by care staff. To be person-centred was not sufficient. Avoiding feelings of hopelessness when working with people with dementia was also important.

The ADQ has gone on to be used in numerous studies globally, and shown to be a useful indicator of attitude change following training of various types (e.g. Brooker et al. 2016; Surr et al. 2016). It might be expected that staff experiencing burn-out would report more negative attitudes, but in one of the few studies to examine the relationship between scores on the ADQ and those on the most widely used burn-out measure (the Burnout Inventory, MBI), a more complex relationship emerged (Kokkonen et al. 2014). As expected, there was a positive relationship between the hope factor from the ADQ and the Personal Accomplishment scale from the MBI, reflecting how staff felt about what they could achieve in their role, but there was also a positive association between hope and a second sub-scale from the MBI, Emotional Exhaustion. This may be interpreted as suggesting that staff with a positive sense of hope regarding dementia feel a sense of achievement in making a difference to the lives of people with dementia, but find this more tiring than colleagues who perhaps have fewer expectations of any response or outcome from the care they provide. It should be noted that burn-out levels in this study were mild to moderate, so that, presumably, staff with higher levels of burn-out had not reached a situation where they had effectively 'shut down' – they were more likely to be at the intermediate stage Kitwood envisaged, where the lack of organizational support, and the (partly self-imposed) demands of the role begin to take their toll. Kitwood comments (p. 132) on the many excellent people who have left dementia care, and it is perhaps those who have a vision of what can be achieved, but are frustrated by the organizational constraints and barriers, who are most at risk of being lost.

Staff training

Despite the clear message that staff training alone is insufficient to lead to quality dementia care, failings in dementia care have continued to be attributed to a lack of staff training. There have been numerous initiatives to develop training programmes and frameworks (Health Education England 2015), and there have been some attempts to evaluate their effects. Surr et al. (2017) reviewed the available evidence on the factors that contribute to an effective training programme in dementia care. 'Effectiveness' was analysed at four levels: reaction to and satisfaction with the training reported by the learners; learning, including changes in knowledge, skills and attitudes related to the training; changes in staff behaviour following the training; and changes in outcomes for the people with dementia receiving care. The 152 papers included in the review were of variable quality, with a third rated as high quality. Almost 40 per cent of studies evaluated behaviour change in staff, and 25 per cent reported on outcomes for people with dementia – mainly relating to agitation and aggression rather than to quality of life. Common features of those programmes that appeared to be more effective (across the four levels) were identified. Among these were the importance of an experienced facilitator, providing training directly relevant to the participants' roles, building on previous experience, and involving active face-to-face participation. The duration of the training was important – at least eight hours being needed – but participants also required support to put learning into practice. Clear guidelines or a structured tool to inform and guide delivery of care were also helpful. It is interesting to note that the training delivered by Kitwood in the action research project did indeed meet many, if not all, of these criteria.

Making change happen

In many respects, for all the developments over the past 20 years, how to go about achieving high-quality dementia care remains mysterious and elusive. While there are successes, sustaining quality can be difficult, and barriers can be difficult to circumvent. We know many of the ingredients, but the perfect recipe still seems to rely on trial and error. Worst of all, abuses still occur across all sectors of care, with shocking reports of personhood being denied continuing to emerge. How best to manage the 'organizational defences' that Kitwood refers to is challenging. It is widely accepted that leadership in dementia care is of comparable importance to staff training, but pinning down the precise leadership qualities and attributes required has yet to be achieved. Approaches such as 'appreciative inquiry' (Page et al. 2016) may help to build on the positive resources of those providing and receiving care, and reflect an openness to learning and a need for mutual respect. Involving families can certainly lead to improved well-being for people with dementia in care settings, once what Kitwood refers to as the 'barriers of mutual suspicion' between residents' relatives and paid care staff are overcome through open communication and engagement (Woods et al. 2007). Families have an important role in monitoring care as well as in assisting the person with dementia, if they so wish.

Some insights are provided by the CHOICE study (Killett et al. 2016). Extensive observations and interviews were carried out in 11 care homes in the UK, and analysed using an in-depth comparative case study design. The authors conclude that 'importing a set of organisational values or the "right" leader or staff' is insufficient; rather the key appeared to be finding ways of meeting the demands of day-to-day care practice that are consistent with the organization's values. Seven important, interrelated cultural elements were identified, which resonate strongly with the 'type B' environments Kitwood described. There is a sense of a shared purpose, a management style that protects staff from many of the external pressures, and empowers staff to take responsibility for the well-being of residents. There is an openness to change among staff and managers. These elements then underpin a sense of community of all those involved (including relatives), and a home characterized by person-centred activity and engagement, with attention paid to the care home environment, making changes and improvements for the benefit of residents.

There is a welcome growth in the application of implementation science in dementia care, which may help understanding of the factors that assist or hinder the take-up of promising new developments. For example, Brooker et al. (2016) carried out an implementation project scaling up a person-centred training programme to 106 care homes. While the results were good where the training was taken up, over a third of the homes did not complete the training in full. Competing time pressures and high staff turnover within homes were among the barriers identified. Successful implementation required a supportive management and organizational structure, stability within staff teams and staff being given protected time to put into practice what had been learned. Achieving this in times when health and social care for people with dementia is under immense pressure is a real challenge; if society (and politicians and policy makers) valued care and those who provide it more highly this would certainly help, but care facilities that really value and support their staff can already go some way to raising standards.

Reflection points

- What are the main reasons for the difficulty in recruiting and retaining sufficient staff capable of delivering high-quality care to people with dementia living in care homes?
- Why does abuse and neglect continue to occur in dementia care settings?
- What elements do you consider contribute to a care home offering people with dementia a good quality of life?

8

Requirements of a caregiver

Tom Kitwood

One of the consequences of depathologizing dementia is that there is no supreme medical authority to whom one might look for definitive answers, and there are no technical solutions, ready-made, on which to rely. If the treatable problems surrounding the failing of a person's mental powers lie principally in the interpersonal field, then the corresponding answers must be sought there too. In one sense this is a cause for relief; there is no need to continue that vigil in the temple of biomedical science that we have had to endure for so long. In another sense, however, it presents an enormous challenge, because it means a full acceptance of responsibility; we must find all the main resources for caring within ourselves.

It is not surprising that so often in the past there was no serious attempt to engage with the psychological agenda of dementia care, or that the requirements of a caregiver were trivialized into a matter of general kindness and common sense. If we look realistically at the task, it will appear daunting enough even in settings that provide exemplary conditions of work. These, however, are extremely rare, and it is much more common for staff to be poorly supported, undervalued, and given only little opportunity to develop their potential. Family carers, for their part, do much of their work alone; they have taken on a task that it is virtually impossible to do well under existing conditions, and it is not one that a human being was 'designed' to do.

In this chapter, then, we will examine in some detail what dementia care requires on the part of a caregiver, and the kind of personal development that may be involved. First, building on some of the ideas set out in Chapter 6, we explore the caregiver's part in creating person-enhancing interaction. Then we will move on to a less obvious topic – that of hidden motives that often draw people into care work. I shall suggest that when these motives are 'owned', understood and integrated, they can become a powerful resource. This leads on to the topic of empathy, important in all interpersonal contexts, but doubly so in this field, where the recipients of care are so easily depersonalized. Finally, we will look briefly at the depth psychology of care work, and I shall make a contrast between the psychodynamic processes that impede, and those that facilitate, effective care.

The caregiver's part in interaction

The first requirement is deceptively simple, though profound in its implications. It is that the caregiver is actually present, in the sense of being psychologically available. In counselling and psychotherapy this is sometimes known as giving 'free attention'; being present with and for another person without distraction from outside or disturbance from within; perceiving the other with far less of the distortions, projections and judgemental reactions that so often get in the way of real meeting. Giving free attention is difficult enough in any context, yet it is widely agreed that this is essential for doing psychological work that really helps and heals. Some people fail to give free attention because they are caught up in the self-importance that is attached to their professional role. Those who have a lot of power, such as medical consultants or senior managers, are particularly liable to fall into this trap. Sometimes the problem centres on sheer overload; the immediate demands on the psyche are too great for it to bear. More generally, however, people fail because they are strongly driven by their vulnerability, anxiety or pain. If, as I have suggested, dementia activates certain universal fears, there is a specially important issue here. In colloquial terms people don't give free attention because there is too much of their own emotional baggage getting in the way. Being present cannot be learned as mere technique; the baggage must be faced and dealt with.

Having the ability to 'be present' is a gift to other people, and it is a kind of liberation for oneself. It means being less troubled about the past, less fearful about the future, and thus more centred on what is immediately at hand. 'Being present' entails letting go of that obsession with *doing* which often damages care work, and having a greater capacity simply for *being*. It does not, of course, set a person free from pain, either physical or mental, although it may lead to better ways of dealing with pain. It is an absolute prerequisite of good caring. For presentness is the quality that underlies all true relationships, and every I–Thou meeting.

While the first requirement is a way of being, each of the types of interaction that we examined in Chapter 6 (pp. 107–109) does imply a specific way of doing. Here we gain a further glimpse of that special resourcefulness that dementia care requires.

- *Recognition* – The caregiver brings an open and unprejudiced attitude, free from tendencies to stereotype or pathologize, and meets the person with dementia in his or her uniqueness.

- *Negotiation* – The caregiver sets aside all ready-made assumptions about what is to be done, and dares to ask, consult and listen.

- *Collaboration* – There is a deliberate abstinence from the use of power, and hence from all forms of imposition and coercion; 'space' is created for the person with dementia to contribute as fully as possible to the action.

- *Play* – The caregiver is able to access a free, childlike, creative way of being.

- *Timalation* – The person with dementia receives pleasure through the direct avenue of the senses; and this means that the caregiver is at ease with his or her own sensuality – untroubled by guilt or anxious inhibition.

- *Celebration* – Beyond the burdens and immediate demands of work, the caregiver is open to joy, and thankful for the gift of life.

- *Relaxation* – The caregiver is free to stop active work, for a while, and even to stop planning. He or she positively identifies with the need that many people with dementia have: to slow down, and allow both body and mind a respite.

- *Validation* – The caregiver goes beyond his or her own frame of reference, with its many concerns and preoccupations, in order to have an empathic understanding of the other; cognitions are tuned down, and sensitivity to feeling and emotion is heightened.

- *Holding* – Whatever distress the person with dementia is undergoing, the caregiver remains fully present; steady, assured and responsive, able to tolerate the resonances of all disturbing emotions within his or her own being.

- *Facilitation* – Here a subtle and gentle imagination is called into play. There is a readiness to respond to the gesture which a person with dementia makes; not forcing meaning upon it, but sharing in the creation of meaning, and enabling action to occur.

- *Creation* (by the person with dementia) – The creative action initiated by the person with dementia is seen and acknowledged as such. The caregiver responds, without taking control.

- *Giving* (on the part of the person with dementia) – The caregiver is humble enough to accept whatever gift of kindness or support a person with dementia bestows, and honest enough to recognize his or her own need. Ideas of being a benefactor, or an old-time dispenser of charity, have no place.

Even this brief sketch is sufficient to show that good care requires a very highly developed person: one who is open, flexible, creative, compassionate, responsive, inwardly at ease. It is helpful also to look at the issue from the standpoint of Transactional Analysis (TA), with its conception of three main ego states: parent (controlling-critical or nurturing), child (adapted or free) and adult (Stewart and Joines 1987). The old style of dementia care, including a great deal of the malignant social psychology that accompanied it, proceeded from the caregiver as controlling-critical parent to the person with dementia as adapted child. Care as I have portrayed it here involves at least the transaction types shown in Table 8.1. This table should be taken as suggestive rather than definitive, since the nature of the interaction, from a TA standpoint, will depend very much on what ego states the persons involved actually have available. The key point is to recognize the resourcefulness of the caregiver and the richness of the ecology of care.

Direct involvement even with one person who has dementia, then, entails exceptional skill and awareness on the part of a caregiver; but of course that is only part of the story. In formal settings each member of a care team is usually required to attend to several persons, and so has to find a way of dealing with competing demands. There are severe constraints on giving undivided attention one to one. Many situations arise where no ideal solution is possible, leaving a caregiver with feelings of inadequacy or guilt. For example, a member of staff may have to face up to the anger or disappointment of a family member, and this is especially difficult if that person is projecting their own sense of failure in caregiving. A member of a care team who is highly competent may have to work with colleagues

Table 8.1 Ego states and dementia care

Caregiver	Person with dementia	Type of interaction
Adult	Adult	Recognition, negotiation, collaboration
Nurturing parent	Child	Timalation, validation, holding, facilitation
Child	Nurturing parent	Giving (by the person with dementia)
Child	Child	Play, celebration, relaxation, creation (by the person with dementia)

who are less well developed, at times having to sort out the chaos caused by their ineptitude. A care setting that is functioning well may have to bear the consequences of blunders in other parts of the system; it is, unfortunately, very common at present for a person to return from a stay in hospital very distressed and confused, and sometimes the personal deterioration cannot be reversed.

Within the British cultural tradition the standard reaction to such complexities is to retreat to a highly cognitive, 'managerial' way of coping. If this is effective, it is so in only a very limited sense. It avoids many of the more difficult issues, and cuts off some of the most relevant information, conveyed through the feelings. The solutions that are found in this kind of way also add unnecessarily to the psychological burdens of the people who have dementia. In organizations where there is a big power differential, unresolved problems tend to be displaced downwards, to those who are at the bottom of the pile. Ideally, then, the members of a good care team will be open to complexity and not rush to simple short-term expedients; this requires an exceptional degree of psychological resilience.

Scripts and care work

People enter a field such as dementia care for a variety of reasons. At a time when jobs are scarce, becoming a care assistant is one of the easiest ways of finding employment. Whatever draws a person into this kind of work in the first instance, it is likely that many of those who stay in it do so because it has some special appeal. Today there are many women, and a small but increasing number of men, who have made a positive choice to work with those who have dementia, whereas 10 years or so [ago] this was very rare indeed.

It has often been suggested that there are hidden (and generally unacknowledged) motives that attract people to care work, and I want to make some very positive suggestions on this topic. One of the most illuminating ways of exploring the issues is through the idea of a 'script', particularly as developed within transactional analysis. The concept itself is a metaphor derived from the theatre. It implies that a person might be living in a way that resembles that of an actor who is performing a part; the lines were written by someone else, and the action takes place under stage directions. When 'in script' a person's choices are made from a limited range; there are hidden constraints on action, and there are patterns that are not consciously recognized.

It has been suggested by the TA theorists that the beginnings of a script lie in infancy. The script develops in early childhood, and is generally consolidated into a distinct way of being by the age of about 7 or 8 years old. In a sense this is simply an alternative vocabulary for describing how a person begins to acquire the set of resources for action that constitute personality, as in the ethogenic approach. Script theory, however, emphasizes the hidden constraints on action, and the existence of recurrent patterns.

A child has very little power, and a way of thinking that is often magical where causes are not well understood. He or she has to find a way of receiving attention and recognition, of minimizing hurt and harm, of being an autonomous person with some sense of identity. One child finds that it is possible to be a social star, always in the limelight; another that attention comes through being ultra-good and helpful; another that pain is best avoided by retreating into a private world. The solution that is found must, of course, fit in with the expectations of powerful others who are close at hand (and hence, probably, with their unmet and unacknowledged needs). So the child learns that the script works, and by late childhood it feels completely natural, as if there could be no other way of being. The script continues to be consolidated in adolescence and adulthood, affecting lifestyle, partner choice, occupation and destiny (Robins 1995). Among those for whom the script is highly maladaptive, some seek out counselling or psychotherapy.

Scripts, when formed, are extremely resistant to change, because they have been practised again and again. Presumably they are actually incorporated into nerve architecture (see pp. 13–15). If a person were suddenly to step out of the scripted way it would feel 'unnatural', and almost certainly it would cause extreme anxiety. Also, of course, living outside the script is likely to cause upset to other people, because their expectations would be violated.

Alison, who is very committed to caring for others, is going through a period of feeling very insecure and troubled. Often she begins to cry for no apparent reason. One day she is visiting her 80-year-old mother, and she tries to speak about her distress.

'I'm so shaky and weepy, Mother. I don't know what's happening to me. Perhaps I'm suffering from depression.'

'Don't be so silly. You're not depressed. I can't be doing with you suffering from depression.'

Even in this tiny vignette we can catch a glimpse of Alison's script and its origins – and possibly also of the underlying cause of her current malaise.

The theory of scripts cannot be tested in a rigorous way, but it has proved very valuable in counselling and psychotherapy, and it can be used to explore some of the hidden motives for becoming involved in care work. Perhaps the commonest caring script is that of the rescuer who tends to attract very dependent and needy people, and who is drawn repeatedly into involvement with those who have the corresponding script of victim. There is the guide, the kind of person who has an almost uncanny ability to know what others are thinking and feeling. There is the martyr, who is extraordinarily self-sacrificing, whose normal way of life seems to involve an almost superhuman workload meeting the needs of others. And there is the hero, one who stands out strongly for a noble cause, esteemed from afar, but sometimes lonely and unsupported in personal life.

There seems to be a common core of issues in scripts such as these, as has been recognized in the case of nurses (e.g. Herrick 1992), psychotherapists (Miller 1987) and social workers (Lawton 1982). Particular attention was given to this topic by the psychoanalyst David Malan (Barnes 1980). My own experience in doing depth psychological work with about 50 people deeply committed to dementia care certainly confirms this view, and I make no exception of myself. Essentially this kind of script emerges from the failure to meet some of a child's psychological needs. Perhaps the child was not given a consistent message that he or she was loved deeply and unchangeably; it was thus necessary to find some way of gaining attention and approval, or of earning a lesser kind of love. Often, with a care-related script, the child was in the presence of others with great need: illness, physical frailty, alcoholism, depression. In some instances the child was in danger, and so needed to develop a supersensitivity so as to know when abuse or violence was in the air, or when another episode of abandonment was about to occur. In these and other ways development into personhood was overwhelmed. The child was not given the freedom to be playful, to grow in genuine concern for others, to discover the full range of his or her abilities, or to come to terms with desire.

Adults who have such scripts tend to have a chronically low level of self-esteem behind their everyday façade. They may have difficulty with psychological boundaries, tending to confuse their own desires and needs with those of others. Here, almost certainly, are the roots of co-dependency, where a person becomes compulsively involved with others who are very needy (Mellody 1993). Some people with strong scripts of this sort, when they are in care work, have to endure a continual tension between their own privation and the needs of those who are in their care. If the underlying issues are not resolved there is serious danger of burn-out. A person may even turn, in deep resentment, against the very cause to which they had been so strongly committed, when at last the truth dawns that it will not meet their hidden need.

Scripts such as these do, however, have a very positive aspect. There is no place for a shallow cynicism, suggesting that all people who become caregivers are inadequate, or enter this kind of work for selfish motives. In each case the script meant developing resources of personality that are all too rare in a culture that is fixated on greed and egoism. Each script represents a creative choice, made in the face of difficulty. The child did not decide to become destructive, vindictive or utterly self-centred; the child did not decide to withdraw from social contact. Instead, the script entailed a resolve to help make the world into a better place. It was a first step towards morality in the true sense; it was a vote for humanity, and for life itself. As Robin Skynner has pointed out, the inference is not that people with such scripts are unsuitable for care professions. It is, rather, that it is important to 'feed the goose that lays the golden eggs' (Schlapobersky 1991: 155–69).

Recovery from script

People with deeply entrenched scripts of the kind we have examined can be a danger both to themselves and others. The script usually involves a lack of awareness, and even self-deception, and thus it puts a person out of touch with reality. In order to recover from a script some sensitive developmental work may be needed, eventually leading to a more full and honest awareness, a more secure and balanced way of life. I would suggest, both from my own direct experience and from the work I have done with others, that at least four things are involved.

The first is a kind of 'coming to consciousness'. If a person was not well loved as a child, or manipulated into overadaptation, or abused in some way – physically, emotionally, sexually, commercially, spiritually – it is necessary to own it, to face the sad and difficult truth. This means letting go of idealized images of parents, and Utopian stories of the past. A kind of mourning may be involved, with feelings of sorrow, anger, dismay and loneliness, such as accompany bereavement. Some people who go through this process find that depressive tendencies that have haunted them for years begin to disappear, and that they acquire a new sense of confidence, ease and peace.

The second thing is developing a more tolerant and generous attitude towards the self. Where the child lacked love from others, an inner love can make good some of the deficit. Where the child has been neglected, stifled or abused, there will be a special need for kindness and tenderness. Where there is a harsh and critical superego, forever insinuating 'not enough', 'not good enough', its voice is to be recognized and gently but firmly rejected. This inner kindness is not self-indulgence, nor is it self-pity. It is simply a matter of cultivating that true self-love which brings a greater resilience and flexibility, and from which springs a more genuine concern for others. Ideally, of course, self-love is the natural legacy of unconditional parental love. But where this has been seriously lacking, a deep process of healing needs to be set in train.

Third, a person can learn how to find new ways for some personal needs to be met. Along with the script there may be an almost superstitious belief that deep needs will be met through self-sacrifice or supreme dedication; this is a residue from the magical thinking of childhood. It is a big step forward, then, when a person begins to set up life in a way that is more realistic. Although some of the most deep-seated deficits may never be made good, major changes of lifestyle will almost certainly be possible. In the course of work a person may find that they can now state openly when they are feeling vulnerable and request support, or that they can ask for help in a direct and honest way. The care environment is not, of course, a place for engaging with the personal agenda of staff members; but it can often be a far more supportive place when people are able to acknowledge who they are and what they bring.

Fourth, there is a need for realism. Each of the scripts we have examined tend to draw a person into taking on too much. The origins of this may lie in a period when the child could not recognize the true powers and abilities of other people, and felt an unrealistic sense of responsibility. As awareness grows, a person begins to notice when he or she is undertaking too many projects, crowding out the day with too many engagements, and other workaholic tendencies. This is not easy in any area of work where there is very great need. Also, at the present time, many employers can easily cash in on scripted behaviour in the name of productivity. The task is that of creating a balanced existence, with a proper place for recreation, social life and personal renewal. Often the turning point comes when a person recognizes that he or she is not indispensable after all.

Scripted behaviour tends to be blind, compulsive; in some deep sense it lacks direction, other than that it is patterned by anxiety and driven by unmet need. As recovery occurs a person comes to see more clearly what he or she is up to, and learns to interrupt familiar scripted scenes. Choices become more realistic and objective, taking a greater range of factors into account. If, in the light of new awareness, a person decides to continue in work as difficult and demanding as dementia care, it will be on the basis of clear and heartfelt choice, and not an unacknowledged compulsion. A script, thus transformed, can become a true vocation.

Anne is the manager of a day centre. She is highly committed to her job, and she is very good at it. She has a strong tendency to overwork, and twice she has had to take time off due to stress and depression. Through the help of a counsellor she came to recognize her script. She was the eldest daughter of eight children, five boys and three girls. In all her earliest recollections she was her mother's helper, and she had very few memories of play. Her father seemed to have featured scarcely at all in her childhood, except when he came home drunk. Gradually Anne came to realize that she may have received little real love as a child; but at the same time she felt great tenderness towards her mother, and valued the many caring and helping skills that she had learned. As her insight grew, she took steps to become more relaxed and playful. She began to learn pottery, and she joined a women's walking group. She negotiated a half day off per week, and stopped doing many hours of unpaid overtime. She began to feel much better about herself, and she believes that the quality of her work has greatly improved and deepened.

Points of pain and vulnerability

There is another kind of issue, also related to a person's past, but arising more directly from what happens in the care setting. It may be a matter of the way the organization itself functions. A manager, perhaps, is perceived in phantasy as if he or she were a powerful parent. Two or more members of staff might find themselves in competition for attention or reward – unconsciously recreating a situation of sibling rivalry. There may be problems over the actual roles: one care worker might be secretly resentful about being expected to do so much, or another might feel that he or she is not being given enough responsibility. Some members of staff might be very insecure in their role, and need a good deal of reassurance.

> Morgan took a job as a care assistant at a time when he was unemployed; it was at least something to do. To his surprise, he enjoyed the work, and he began to feel committed to it. He even went, voluntarily, on two courses. However, he was never given feedback about his performance, and at times he felt that he was regarded as an intruder into a women's domain. As time went on he 'dwindled and dwindled', until his confidence ebbed away completely. Eventually he left care work, but with great regret.

Prejudices of many kinds may get in the way of good care practice – ethnicity, age, social class or sexual orientation, or as in the example above, simply gender. When there are inter-personal difficulties in areas such as these, it is likely that jobs will be done less effectively. Situations will be perceived with less realism because they will be distorted by projections; truthful communication will be impaired. Far too much of the work of the organization will be given over to meeting the unacknowledged needs of members of staff.

Difficult and unexpected feelings are sometimes aroused by episodes that occur in direct contact with the clients. This can happen in any kind of care work, but it is particu-larly likely in dementia care, where people are sometimes stretched towards their limits. Also, those who are the most willing to be deeply involved are most likely to be affected. A strong reaction might be evoked, for example, by a person's death. Someone on the care team might find that, over and above the grief that actually belongs to this event, he or she is caught up in overwhelming feelings of sorrow and loss. Perhaps other griefs, not fully worked through, have been activated. Or a person with dementia might make very pointed and personal remarks, causing a care worker to feel terribly hurt and fragile. It may be that a relationship with a client arouses emotional memories of some other relationship, perhaps with an older member of the care worker's own family. If there has been a case of dementia in the family of a staff member, there may be issues surrounding this which are not resolved. Another possibility is that a person may be feeling vulnerable because of problems in pri-vate life, and may feel overwhelmed by all the need and vulnerability in the workplace.

One function of the organizational defences that were discussed on pages 132–134 is to prevent matters such as these from coming to the surface, by blocking the feelings of staff members. The old idea of professional detachment, of not becoming 'too involved', clearly served this purpose. A highly defensive structure, however, means that real contact with the people who have dementia is impossible, and many of the deeper tasks of caring are never carried out. The alternative is to create a care setting in which feelings are experi-enced and expressed, and where people have 'permission' to ask for support when they feel they need it.

Psychological defences	Very high		Very low
Personal state	'blocked'	'in touch'	overwhelmed

Figure 8.1 The spectrum of defence in care work

> One afternoon Kate was sitting close to Michael, reading a magazine with him. Under-
> neath the magazine, Michael put his hand on Kate's thigh. She jumped up and left the
> room, and was later found, very frightened and angry, in the linen store. The following
> day, in talking the incident through with her supervisor, Kate acknowledged that her
> reaction had been 'over the top', and she was able to own that she had been sexually
> abused by her uncle. Kate's supervisor had herself found ways of warding off Michael's
> sexual advances, while at the same time meeting his need for closeness and contact.

Whether or not there is a maladaptive script, everyone brings issues of a personal kind into
their work; these are liable to be activated in an especially poignant way in a field such as
dementia care. The implication is that the most truly effective workers will be those who
have a well-developed 'experiential self', who are familiar with the world of feelings, accepting of their own vulnerabilities, and able to live with a low level of psychological defence.
We might envisage a spectrum as shown in Figure 8.1.

To be blocked is to be out of vital contact with the psychological realities; to be overwhelmed is to be ineffective in any practical sense. Between the two extremes, but towards
the low end, there is the range of greatest efficacy. Here a person is able to put his or her
feelings and intuitions to good use.

The psychodynamics of dementia care

The central idea of all depth psychology is that we have motives, conflicts, imaginings, of
which we are usually unaware. We can call these 'unconscious mental processes', although
it would be more accurate to speak of neurological activity that is not being registered in
consciousness and which, at that point of a person's development, cannot be; possibly the
necessary brain 'circuits' are not available for use or haven't been fully formed as yet. Most
of depth psychology has focused on what might be happening within the individual psyche,
and rather less attention has been given to interpersonal processes. In this section I want to
do both; first looking at the basis of empathy, and then at the nature of dementia care. Much
of this is speculative. The most that can be said is that it is compatible with what can be
observed, and that it seems to help some people have a better understanding of who they
are and what they are doing.

The nature of empathy

We have touched on this topic several times already in this book. The term itself, as I have
used it, means having some understanding of what another person may be experiencing,
getting some glimpse of what life might be like from within their frame of reference. Empathy

does not mean feeling what another person is feeling. It is unlikely that this is ever possible, because we are all so different.

When we develop empathy with someone who has all their mental powers intact, we attend both to their words and to their non-verbal signals. Sometimes we notice discrepancies between the two kinds of message. A person might, for example, claim to be feeling 'perfectly OK', while showing clear signs of anxiety or inner turmoil. Gradually, keeping all the information in a kind of 'soft focus', we gain a sense of what they might be experiencing. A person who has highly developed empathic skill is able to retain his or her own feeling states, while also being aware of the feeling state of the other. In developing empathy with a person who has dementia the issues are similar, but not exactly the same. As we have seen, words and sentences may not make ordinary sense, but yet have poetic meaning through metaphor and allusion. Non-verbal signals may be particularly clear. The full reconstruction of another's frame of reference, then, involves more than attempting to make sense piecemeal of the verbal and non-verbal signals that a person is conveying. It also involves drawing on feelings that are genuinely our own (see also pp. 84–85).

If this is the true foundation of empathy, it suggests that even the most difficult and painful memories can be turned to positive use. Most people will find, if they dare to look, that they have had experiences that might resemble, to some small degree, what a person with dementia is going through: times of abandonment, of betrayal, of acute loneliness, of feeling powerless or terrifyingly incompetent, or being outpaced or outclassed. Everyone has had to endure a share of the malignant social psychology that is present in everyday life, and been made to feel more like an object than a person. As the 'experiential self' grows, these emotional memories become available. Even those privations, deprivations and injuries that underlie scripts such as those we have examined, can be transmuted into resources for care work.

Projective and empathic identification

Let us return now to the one-to-one care situation. Metaphorically we may say that every person, regardless of whether or not there is cognitive impairment, has a 'child' within; and at times this child can be needy, helpless or demanding. This is illustrated in Figure 8.2.

Figure 8.2

Figure 8.3

Suppose now that the caregiver remains in a state of denial and self-deception, unable or unwilling to recognize areas of damage and deficit, and steadfastly holding up a professional front. It is likely that such a person will be caught up in the defensive process of 'projective identification' first described by Melanie Klein (Segal 1992): that is, the caregiver will 'see' aspects of his or her own self in the person who has dementia, and may even induce that person to act some of these aspects out; making them become more angry, more helpless, more confused, etc. as shown in Figure 8.3.

This radical disowning, this 'splitting off', is only possible, of course, if there is a person with obvious deficits who can be made into the carrier of the projections. The one who is cared for is induced into bearing a double burden: all that genuinely belongs, together with what has been projected. He or she may appear to be more impaired than is truly the case. The caregiver can maintain a state of self-deception, and at the same time misperceives the one who is being cared for. The needy child of the caregiver is looked after magically in the person who is cared for; the two are locked together in a way that hinders them both. This is illustrated in Figure 8.4.

These ideas have an obvious application in relation to formal care, and it is possible that projective processes of this kind operate in many medical settings, where there is a very great differential of power. When care is being given by family members or friends the psychodynamics of long-term relationships, which often involve projective identification, are likely to continue, and in some cases in an exaggerated and noxious form (see, for example, Sayers 1994).

In contrast to this, let us imagine now that the caregiver has gone some way to developing his or her experiential resources; the script is being dealt with, and the child within is being recognized and cherished. The psychodynamics of this situation are shown in Figure 8.5. Now the caregiver and the one who is being cared for are both on the same human level, and far more able to appreciate what they have in common. Both carry a needy child within, and both are dependent on the support and comfort that is supplied by others. The caregiving relationship, however, is not cemented by projection. The dementia-like experiences of the caregiver have become available for the development of empathy. The person with dementia is perceived more accurately; there is no dynamic to exaggerate his or her disabilities, and needs can be more truly recognized. The child

Figure 8.4

Figure 8.5

within the caregiver is being looked after in a more open and honest way, mostly outside the care setting. The process of caring is true, sincere, accurate, egalitarian, and the communication is congruent. The whole relationship might be described as one of empathic identification.

Two paths of personal development

When dementia care is seen in the kind of way that I have portrayed, it is indisputable that this work requires a very high level of personal and moral development on the part of those who undertake it. There can be no question of bolting on a body of knowledge, or of imparting a set of skills in a semi-automated fashion. We are looking for very intelligent and flexible action from a 'reflective practitioner'. The essence of what is required might be described as freedom from ego, so narrow, imperious, conformist, greedy, grasping and demanding. It is under the sway of ego that most people live their ordinary lives. No one is to be blamed for this; it is often a matter of survival, and to some extent it is what being a member of our kind of society involves. Paradoxically, as ego begins to be transcended the main thing that is given up is psychological limitation; it is a matter of becoming *more*, and not less, fully oneself.

Two main paths of personal development are available to us at present. The first has been opened up by psychotherapy, and the second by meditation. They are not rivals, as several experts have shown (e.g. Watts 1973; LeShan 1983). An individual can be involved in both together, and it is also possible to combine them in some form of group process.[1]

Psychotherapy attempts to deal with the issues that trouble a person, primarily by unravelling the content of those issues, and often by an exploration of their origins. If all goes well, and a relationship of trust develops, hidden feelings come out into the open, understanding increases, and there is a growth in self-esteem. We have touched on this process in our exploration of the relationship between psychotherapy and dementia care. Here, in contrast to the situation with dementia, we may reasonably expect that therapeutic outcomes will be consolidated, that new ways of being will be enhanced through practice, and that what is learned in the therapeutic relationship will be held in memory and autonomously transferred elsewhere.

In meditation, however, the approach is more indirect. A person undertakes exercises that are designed to strengthen the structure of the psyche, primarily through the cultivation of a still, serene centre that is not committed to inner talk. As this development occurs there is a gain in poise, awareness and flexibility. A person is more able to 'be present', and more able to act spontaneously and wholeheartedly. Wary and defensive postures that may formerly have served as a protection can gradually be laid aside. In meditation the aim, in a sense, is to learn how to 'not think'. The content of particular issues is generally not addressed, but left to reorganize itself. There is still a great deal of prejudice against meditation. In part this is because it has sometimes been parodied as weird or unworldly, and in part because of the obvious association with various religious traditions, which make it unfashionable in a secular age. The truth is that while some meditative practices are 'religious', there are several others that can be undertaken by a person who has no theistic assumptions, no religious convictions of the ordinary kind.

Whatever route of personal growth is taken, the difficulty of the task should not be underestimated. We need to remember that, as with care work, the task is not 'purely psychological', but neurological too. To change long-standing habits and attitudes may actually involve the dismantling of existing nerve pathways, and the gradual formation of new ones. And these, we might reasonably hope, have more connections than the old, enabling a person to be more aware, more in touch with what he or she is undergoing, and with the processes of life.

Note

1 This kind of work is done during the four day residential course The Depth Psychology of Dementia Care, run by Bradford Dementia Group.

Requirements of a caregiver

Commentary by John Keady and Ruth Elvish

When Tom Kitwood approached the writing of this chapter he did so mainly – but not exclusively – from the perspective of paid care staff, building on the constructions of malignant social psychology that existed in residential care environments for people living with dementia and where the threat to personhood and person-centred care was seen to be at its highest. The chapter is full of wonderful insights and challenges – for example, the importance of care staff in meeting the person living with dementia 'where they are' and the significance of care staff simply 'being present' in the same physical space, time and place as the person living with dementia. This relational connection between 'being present' and care staff interactions with the person living with dementia was seen to be a prerequisite for 'good caring' to take place and that the act of care is, in itself, located from within the value system, beliefs and empathetic abilities of the person prepared to give care. Put another way, in order for care staff to care for, or about, a person living with dementia, it is necessary for care staff to know who they are and to consider the motivations and life events/experiences that have led them, as a paid carer, to offer their support to a person living with dementia.

If the reader stands back and reflects for a moment on the meaning of this last statement, it is both confrontational and ground-breaking. What Tom Kitwood is saying here is that the responsibility for successful communication and interaction with people living with dementia is to be found from within the care staff and organizational culture/environment where care takes place, and not from within the person living with dementia. Any failure of care staff to address this need for their own self-awareness and 'healing' of past harmful events, for example, will result in the care provision for people living with dementia not being person-centred and/or of good quality. This emphasis on self-awareness and the preparedness of care staff to take on a caring role is why the chapter spends many of its pages focusing on transactional analysis and the need to identify life scripts from within the reservoir of human experience. For instance, it was seen as especially important to consider if care staff self-identified with a life script of 'rescuer' – and how this may have emerged – and why care staff may then attribute the life script of a person living with dementia to one of 'victim' . . . who, as the logical sequencing would go, is in need of rescuing. Changing the narrative turn of the attributed and assigned life scripts, especially those projected onto the person living with dementia, e.g. from 'victim' to 'person with agency' who no longer needs 'rescuing', is a complex set of psychological adjustment processes. However, as Tom Kitwood would suggest, they are ultimately necessary ones if genuine person-centred care is to emerge as a result. Indeed, negotiating and working through such feelings is as important to do today as when the words in Chapter 8 were first committed to print.

That said, in the 20 years since the publication of the chapter, there are areas in the text that would benefit from additional elaboration or inclusion. In this commentary we have chosen three such areas:

1   To extend the focus on the requirements of a caregiver to family carers of people living with dementia; this was mentioned in the chapter, but only briefly;

2   To consider advancements in the health and well-being at work literature, and how this adds to the self-reflection and resilience of care staff, building on the observations originally contained in the chapter; and

3   To highlight the role of the community as caring spaces and places; this focus on people with dementia living an active life outside of their own front door was not mentioned in the chapter, but it has grown in importance since the publication of *Dementia Reconsidered*; accordingly, we will draw attention to the development of dementia-friendly communities as a worldwide movement as testimony to this positive shift in societal and public attitudes.

These three areas are all major topics in their own right and, of necessity, what follows is an overview of key themes rather than an in-depth analysis.

Family carers

As can be seen in the writing for Chapter 8, Tom Kitwood identified that family carers 'do much of their work alone' and are undertaking work that 'a human being was not "designed" to do' (p. 143). These observations have been replayed countless times since and expressed in various ways. For instance, it is worth reminding ourselves that family carers of people living with dementia are estimated to provide between five and 20 hours of care each day (Marziali and Donahue 2006), and that such carers are:

- Exposed to the greatest degree of stress and burden across caregiving groups of any diagnostic condition (Alzheimer's Disease International 2009)
- Identified as the most important resource available for people living with dementia (Department of Health 2009)
- Mainly women – caring is a gendered experience that has attracted relatively little attention in the literature, especially in the domestic home setting (Erol et al. 2016)
- Found primarily within a dyadic relationship, but care also ripples out within and between families and generations, for which there has been limited study (Koo and Pusey 2017)
- Seen to exist throughout the world in different cultural groups, with different cultural 'norms' and expectations of what constitutes 'good care' (Hillman and Latimer 2017)
- The mainstay of the person with dementia's experience of well-being and quality of life, especially as the majority of people with dementia live at home rather than in supported living environments, such as in a care home (Alzheimer's Society 2014).

Against such a backdrop, numerous types of intervention aimed at supporting family carers of people living with dementia have been developed, such as individual counselling and education to enhance personal coping and resilience. Within these different types of intervention, there are variations in mode of delivery – for example, group, telephone, 1:1 and computer/video assisted. The sheer range of interventions available has made it challenging to evaluate the evidence base for these approaches, a challenge further exacerbated by factors such as the heterogeneous nature of caregivers as a group (Zarit and Femia 2008) and some low-quality studies (Maayan et al. 2014). However, given these challenges, just what have we learned over the past 20 years? A meta-analysis at the beginning of this century suggested that psychosocial interventions had no significant effects on carer burden (Acton and Kang 2001). However, the findings of two subsequent meta-analyses suggested small to moderate effects upon psychological morbidity and caregiver knowledge (Brodaty et al. 2003), and burden, depression, knowledge and subjective well-being (Pinquart and Sörensen 2006). By the turn of the current decade, evidence was beginning to be seen as moderately positive (Vernooij-Dassen et al. 2011), and this trend has continued. For example, a review of psychological interventions for carers of people living with dementia, by Elvish et al. (2012), found that multicomponent interventions were among the most effective, and interventions underpinned by cognitive/cognitive-behavioural models were suggested to produce meaningful change. This echoed the findings of a Cochrane Review that highlighted the importance of cognitive reframing in reducing psychological morbidity and subjective stress (Vernooij- Dassen et al. 2011). The other most effective group of interventions identified by Elvish et al. (2012) were those that combined individual and group sessions using either computer-assisted screen telephones or ordinary telephones. This finding is substantiated by a more recent Cochrane Review (Lins et al. 2014), which found that telephone counselling could reduce depressive symptoms for family caregivers. Moving forward, the role of technology in helping to support information needs and caring actions, such as through an app delivered via a tablet device at home, would seem important initiatives to develop and ones that simply were not available at the time of the original chapter production.

Well-being at work

Stress and ill-being are linked with a number of issues in the workplace, including motivation, staff turnover, absenteeism and staff relationships (Government Office for Science 2008), and has been a growing topic since 1997. This sharper focus on well-being at work can be demonstrated through a number of commissioned pieces of work, including: the Foresight Mental Capital and Wellbeing Report (Government Office for Science 2008), Wellbeing at Work (New Economics Foundation 2014) and Thriving at Work (Department for Work and Pensions and Department of Health 2017). Tom Kitwood makes implicit and explicit references to the topic of staff well-being in Chapter 8, arguing about the importance of psychotherapy, meditation and work–life balance. This insight has begun to be recognized within frameworks such as the 'mental health core standards' (Department for Work and Pensions and Department of Health 2017). These standards highlight the need for employers to monitor the mental health of employees, encourage conversations with staff about their mental health, provide emotional support to employees when needed, and encourage a healthy work–life balance. 'Enhanced' standards are also outlined for employers who can be seen to be leading the way, and include demonstrating accountability and providing in-house mental health support.

Over the past 20 years the nature of dementia care work has also developed. Thus, when talking of staff well-being in dementia care, we are making reference to a range of roles, including direct care work, assessment and treatment in memory services, and research/academic work. While discussion of the specific needs of different staff groups is beyond the scope of this commentary, issues such as long working hours, heavy workload and lack of support are common across direct care, clinical and academic environments (see for example, Kinman and Jones 2003; Lewis et al. 2010; Lim et al. 2010). Though these stressors may have long been known, we are only now putting them on a firm platform of recognition, with calls for change being made. While the number of studies exploring staff well-being in dementia care remains limited (Baker et al. 2015), Tom Kitwood's vision of the importance of techniques such as psychotherapy and meditation in the workplace is, perhaps, finally being realized in various forms of intervention. For example, Baker et al. (2015) highlight the potential benefit of mindfulness-based therapies for care home staff, and Blagg and Petty (2015) discuss the importance of reflective practice and positive management feedback as factors contributing to NHS staff well-being in in-patient mental health settings for people living with dementia. Our own example is the Staff Well-Being Service for the Neighbourhoods and Dementia Study in which we both play a leading role (Department of Health 2012; see also www.neighbourhoodsanddementia.org). To the best of our knowledge, the Staff Well-Being Service is the first to be specifically attached to a multi-site research programme. The service has been well received: more than 25 per cent of study staff (from a total staff population of 46) have made self-referrals for 1:1 sessions to date (March 2018). This indicates the need that exists and that we are just beginning to understand.

Dementia-friendly communities

Linked directly to the previous example, one of the most innovative developments since the publication of the *Dementia Reconsidered* book is that caring for a person living with dementia has become a responsibility for the whole of society, not simply a sole responsibility for family carers or paid care staff. This whole-scale shift in responsibilities and public perception about dementia has been made manifest through the dementia-friendly community movement at a local, national and international level (see, for example, Alzheimer's Society 2013; Alzheimer's Disease International 2015). The notion of what may constitute a dementia-friendly community can be open to interpretation (Lin 2017). Crampton, Dean and Eley (2012) have identified four key dimensions – people, places, networks and resources – with people living with dementia positioned at the centre of each dimension. While people living with dementia may, at times, be a little uncomfortable with the language of a dementia-friendly community, believing it is too self-identifying and exposing (Swaffer 2014), what is not in contention is that understanding people living with dementia is now a social responsibility that is attributed to all members of society. This responsibility extends from next-door neighbours to the streets where people with dementia live, and on to shops and civic/leisure amenities that are accessed in everyday life. As such, the steps that lead to 'being in the presence' of a person living with dementia, as Tom Kitwood so eloquently put it, is now everyone's responsibility. Indeed, being seen as caring and accommodating to people with dementia's cognitive and physical needs is now a measure of what it is to work for a well-informed and compassionate employer, for example, or, quite simply, to be neighbourly and a good citizen.

Arguably, this reconstruction about the meaning of care moves it away from its unidirectional 'carer to person living with dementia' formal context that is found in Chapter 8.

Instead, the act of care is now seen as a product of our individual and collective social consciousness and social actions. This dynamic shift in responsibility is the very manifestation of the suffix attached to the *Dementia Reconsidered* book title, namely: 'the person comes first'. It is, perhaps, a future that Tom Kitwood had glimpsed when writing the book but had yet to fully conceptualize. That said, there remains much to be done in the dementia-friendly community movement, and new ways to think about measurement of community, neighbourhood, civic and relational/caring actions. It is one of the most pressing and significant agendas ahead of the field.

Final thoughts

Tom Kitwood produced innovation and inventiveness on every page of *Dementia Reconsidered*. However, we would like to conclude our commentary on Chapter 8 by saying that carers and care staff bring innovation and inventiveness into everyday caring acts. An example of this from our own work recently was a family carer deciding to modify their home, placing LED strip lights leading from the bedroom to the toilet, to help the person living with dementia way-find more successfully at night. Such creative solutions to everyday problems are not taught but are, instead, thoughtfully planned and considered, individually tailored and work on a family-by-family basis. Not every act of care, or problem-solving activity, will be evidence based in the scientific meaning of that terminology. Human beings are instinctively innovative and inventive and, as Richards (2007) has noted, everyday creativity is not trivial, and 'represents a pervasive and dynamic way of being and knowing, and of encountering the world' (p. 48). Perhaps one way forward is for the dementia studies field to move away from the 'big idea' in carer interventions and, instead, embrace and accommodate creative acts by carers (of all types) and by people living with dementia, in everyday life. Embracing this 'little-c' approach to creativity (Kaufman and Beghetto 2009) would result in new ways of thinking about care, its meanings, embodiment and measurement. We just need to keep our horizons flexible and open to change and challenge, much as Tom Kitwood did in all his interpersonal and published work.

Reflection points

• How would you suggest that we start to improve the ways in which we support staff in the workplace?

• What makes a dementia-friendly community . . . friendly?

• How do people living with dementia demonstrate creativity in their everyday lives?

9

The task of cultural transformation

Tom Kitwood

In the radical reconsideration of dementia, we have travelled a very long way. As I have tried to show in this book, almost every cherished assumption has now been called into question. Even the category of 'organic mental disorder', which has underpinned a century and more of psychiatric practice, has not stood up well to the test of time.

Among all the changes that have occurred, one fact stands out above all others. It is that men and women who have dementia have emerged from the places where they were hidden away; they have walked onto the stage of history, and begun to be regarded as persons in the full sense. Dementia, as a concept, is losing its terrifying associations with the raving lunatic in the old-time asylum. It is being perceived as an understandable and human condition, and those who are affected by it have begun to be recognized, welcomed, embraced and heard. The achievements of biomedical science, although so much vaunted in the media, are insignificant in comparison to this quiet revolution.

While there is so much cause for encouragement here, the truth is that this process of humanization – or, more accurately, personalization – is occurring only very slowly. There are many obstacles in the way, and the forces of reaction are strong. It is conceivable that most of the advances that have been made in recent years might be obliterated, and that the state of affairs in 2010 might be as bad as it was in 1970, except that it would be varnished by eloquent mission statements, and masked by fine buildings and glossy brochures.

It is vital, then, to see the situation in its true light. The reconstruction of dementia goes far beyond piecemeal improvements in care practice, better staff development, the more efficient running of organizations and the like. It requires much more than a paradigmatic change of understanding. The strategic task is one of cultural transformation, at a time when many of the circumstances are not propitious.

Cultures of care and their broader context

A culture, in the sense that I am using the term here, might be taken to mean a settled, patterned way for providing meaning for human existence, and for giving structure to action within it (see, for example, Williams 1976). Each culture represents a form of adaptation to the environment, and becomes stabilized through a kind of evolutionary process. In the industrial (and post-industrial) societies of today there tends to be one overarching culture in a position of hegemony, providing the overall framework for economic and political life. Many smaller cultures are embedded within it, in varying degrees of compliance or resistance.

Three aspects of a culture are particularly important for our analysis here. First, there are organizations, which carry relationships of power in an enduring way. Organizations generate bodies of knowledge, reflecting dominant interests, and often subtly justifying the status quo. Each major institution has its 'regime of truth' (Foucault 1967). Second, there are norms, meaning standards and patterns of acceptable behaviour, particularly for the performance of the more visible roles. Third, there are beliefs, both about what is real and true, and about what ought to be. One of the most astonishing facts about human life is the great variety of cultures, each of which carries immense conviction to those who are immersed within it.

Once a dominant culture is established, it is extremely resistant to change. Institutions embody vested interests, and produce knowledge that justifies those interests. Norms are followed almost automatically, and become internalized as part of what Freud termed the superego. Beliefs, when backed up by accepted authority, acquire a kind of self-evident quality, and are transmuted into the unassailable verities of common sense. It has been suggested, furthermore, that each culture has its own way of concealing or occluding aspects of the painful truth about the pattern of life that it legitimates, and in this sense has a generalized ego-defensive function (Becker 1972). Some cultures are more defensive than others; where there is great social injustice (as, for example, under conditions of colonialism or apartheid), there is more to occlude. To change a culture is never easy. It not only involves a challenge to privilege and power, but also the dismantling of deep psychological resistance.

The old culture of geriatric care, which had evolved through several different phases, fitted in well with the larger cultural pattern that the western societies had created. Here the intellect reigned supreme, and the sensuous qualities of human life were relegated to the margins. Here people could be exploited *en masse* in the cause of industrial production, or sentenced to death *en masse* in the conduct of futile wars. Here the plundering of distant lands, and the subjugation of their entire populations, was accepted as a natural right. The warehousing of those who were old, frail or confused was entirely consistent with this callous disregard for human dignity and integrity. A person-centred approach to dementia care, as I have characterized it in this book and elsewhere, does not match this cultural tradition. Nor does it resonate with the spirit of post-industrialism, with its mania for 'information', its extreme emphasis on the autonomous and self-creating individual, its replacement of moral integrity by external control, and its almost religious veneration of the market.

The old culture and the new

Throughout this book I have been contrasting two different paradigms, or conceptual frameworks for understanding the nature of dementia. Each paradigm implies a 'culture of care'. In an earlier discussion of this topic (Kitwood 1995d) I set out 10 points of comparison. Seven of these are shown (with very slight revisions) in Table 9.1.

The 'old culture', as I have portrayed it here, is not a parody. If the set of propositions that convey its essence are simply listed, without any points of contrast, they still appear to be the truth to many people – even those who have a considerable experience in dementia work. The shift from the old culture to the new is not a matter of adding on a few items that

Table 9.1 Two cultures of dementia care

Old culture	New culture

General view of dementia

The primary degenerative dementias are devastating diseases of the central nervous system, in which personality and identity are progressively destroyed.	Dementing illnesses should be seen, primarily, as forms of disability. How a person is affected depends crucially on the quality of care.

Ultimate source of knowledge

In relation to dementia, the people who possess the most reliable, valid and relevant knowledge are the doctors and the brain scientists. We should defer to them.	In relation to dementia, the people who possess the most reliable, valid and relevant knowledge are skilled and insightful practitioners of care.

Emphasis for research

There is not much that we can do positively for a person with dementia, until the medical breakthroughs come. Hence much more biomedical research is urgently needed.	There is a great deal that we can do now, through the amplification of human insight and skill. This is the most urgent matter for research.

What caring entails

Care is concerned primarily with such matters as providing a safe environment, meeting basic needs (foods, clothing, toileting, warmth, cleanliness, adequate sleep, etc.), and giving physical care in a competent way.	Care is concerned primarily with the maintenance and enhancement of personhood. Providing a safe environment, meeting basic needs and giving physical care are all essential, but only part of the care of the whole person.

Priorities for understanding

It is important to have a clear and accurate understanding of a person's impairments, especially those of cognition. The course of a dementing illness can be charted in terms of stages of decline.	It is important to have a clear and accurate understanding of a person's abilities, tastes, interests, values, forms of spirituality. There are as many manifestations of dementia as there are persons with dementia.

Problem behaviours

When a person shows problem behaviours, these must be managed skilfully and efficiently.	All so-called problem behaviours should be viewed, primarily, as attempts at communication, related to need. It is necessary to seek to understand the message, and so to engage with the need that is not being met.

Carers' feelings

In the process of care the key thing is to set aside our own concerns, feelings, vulnerabilities, etc., and get on with the job in a sensible, effective way.	In the process of care the key thing is to be in touch with our concerns, feelings, vulnerabilities, etc., and transform these into positive resources for our work.

were missing, but of seeing almost every feature in a different way. I wish to highlight this contrast now, deliberately idealizing the new culture, in order to summarize the central theses of this book.

The new culture does not pathologize people who have dementia, viewing them as the bearers of a ghastly disease. Nor does it reduce them to the simplistic categories of some ready-made structural scheme, such as a stage theory of mental decline. The new culture brings into focus the uniqueness of each person, respectful of what they have accomplished and compassionate to what they have endured. It reinstates the emotions as the well-spring of human life, and enjoys the fact that we are embodied beings. It emphasizes the fact that our existence is essentially social.

The two cultures see dementia care in fundamentally different ways. The old culture generally denied the existence of psychological need in people with dementia, or blanked it out with tranquillizing medication. The old culture involved only minimal interaction, and then largely around basic physical tasks. The new culture, however, is committed to engaging with psychological need. The surprising and delightful discovery is that in many cases needs can be sufficiently well met to bring a new phase of relative peace and relaxation. The new culture has a highly positive view of interaction, viewing it as the truly healing component of care.

The new culture brings people of very different kinds together onto common ground, and seeks to minimize all those us–them barriers that prevent real meeting. The most obvious of these is that between people who have dementia and everybody else. But there are also the barriers between carers who are family members or friends, and those who are paid; between 'trained' and 'untrained' staff, and between those who do 'hands on' work and their more senior managers. On the broader front there are the barriers between the community and the places where formal care is provided. In the long run, so I have argued, all us–them divisions are artificial and unhelpful; their psychological substrate consists of suspicion, envy, resentment and fear.

The two cultures differ greatly in their conceptions of valid knowledge and true expertise. Twenty years ago, research into dementia signified three main kinds of activity. The first consisted of natural–scientific explorations of brain structure, function and pathology; the second consisted of experimental investigations, the majority with animals; the third was an individualistic study of the deficits associated with dementia, mainly in cognition. In all of this there was virtually no concern about the real life and experience of dementia, and no place for the kind of knowledge that comes from personal involvement. The new culture gives the traditional forms of research a relatively lower place. The highest priority by far is the day to day existence of people with dementia, and here the central topic is how to maintain personal well-being. Much of the most significant knowledge is held by those who are actually involved in dementia care. The investigative skills that are required are not those of the dispassionate researcher, but those that are engendered by commitment and engagement. Reflection on practice, done in a coherent and disciplined way, is the most valid of all forms of research.

The essence of the difference between the two cultures is this. The old culture was, in many respects, one of alienation and estrangement. Dementia itself was surrounded by evasion and denial. Many caregivers were cut off from their own inner source of vitality and compassion, and drawn into practices that they knew, intuitively, to be wrong. They were deprived of life-giving contact with each other, too, as they lived out the collective lie. People with dementia could not flourish under the old regimes; often they were reduced to isolation, despair and 'social death'. In contrast to this, to enter the new culture is like coming home; discovering how to draw on our feelings, intuition, spontaneity, and living more comfortably with our faults; we gain confidence in our power to know, to share, to give, to receive, to love. The fact of dementia can be openly accepted, without shame. There is an abundance of I–Thou meeting.

Sources of resistance

It is not easy to bring about a lasting change in the culture of dementia care, as experience during the last few years has already shown. A culture is all of a piece; the accepted forms of practice, the nature of common beliefs, the structure of organizations and their patterns of power all interlock together. Furthermore, if it is indeed the case that cultures are underpinned by psychological defences, these are likely to be particularly strong when the issue is as threatening as dementia. In any movement to bring about change there will be a challenge to vested interests of many kinds, and a mobilization of anxieties that had been safely hidden away.

The most obvious of all hindrances to cultural transformation is the dead weight of tradition. In Europe, at least, institutional practices to contain the misfits of society go back as long as 300 years. Only very rarely does history show examples of a serious and far-reaching attempt to take seriously the personhood of those who were old, frail or mentally disturbed. There have been many individual reformers, many radical critics; but without a culture to sustain their endeavours, their work was very easily subverted or wiped out.

One of the most damaging aspects of our inheritance is the very low status that has been given to the care of 'the elderly', and those with dementia in particular. Those working in care somehow carried, by association, the stigma attached to their clients, with the insidious consequence of low self-esteem, and a general sense of powerlessness to bring about positive change. Individuals who tried to give care beyond the norm were often subjected to pressure to reduce their efforts, even to the extent of ostracism. Some nurses, aware of the traditional prestige rankings in their profession, even went so far as to lie about their work to family and friends, lest they be tainted by the image of psychogeriatric work.

Another barrier has been the power and prestige of the medical profession. Dementia has traditionally been presented as the proper territory for psychiatry, with the implication that all other disciplines should defer to its 'higher' knowledge. Here, as we have seen, concern about personhood has not been strong, while there was a marvellous field for fundamental research. Even very recently the view has been expressed that people with dementia owe to society (read 'the biomedical research lobby') the offering of themselves for research as a form of payment for their care (Berghmans and ter Meulen 1995; see also my response, Kitwood 1995a). It is true, of course, that psychiatry and its supporting sciences have provided more accurate means of diagnosis, and a great deal of knowledge that is leading to better medical intervention. However, psychiatry has done little to help elucidate the profound personal issues surrounding dementia, and when it comes to the interpersonal process of caring, the emperor has no clothes.

There are commercial pressures, too, to keep the old culture in place. For a long time now there has been a kind of collusion between mainstream medicine and the pharmaceutical industry. Doctors in all fields are under enormous pressure to prescribe drug treatments, the more so as this has come to be what their patients expect. Medical practitioners who are in a position of having nothing curative to offer are liable to experience a sense of guilt or inadequacy, so giving a prescription is, for *them*, a kind of placebo. Geriatric medicine is a particularly susceptible field, because this typically involves chronic conditions, often several at the same time. The drug companies, for their part, know that huge profits are to be made from the medicalization of old age, and that the market is growing as the number of 'old-old' people increases.

The traditional culture of dementia care, with its tendency to use high levels of medication, especially tranquillizers of various kinds, certainly served well to increase the sales of pharmaceuticals (Thomas 1995). Now if any product can be shown by 'scientific' means to affect dementia even to a small degree, the potential for profit is staggering. The fact that many family carers are spellbound by the promises of biomedical science, and almost superstitiously hoping that miracle cures will soon be found, gives added impetus to the drug-use lobby. The new culture of dementia care, which places only a low emphasis on drug treatments and seeks to set people free from the 'chemical padded cell', comes into conflict with these commercial interests.

While strong financial pressures to preserve the old culture may be expected from the drug companies, other financial stakes are involved as well. There is the simple fact that care is relatively cheap when there is a thorough disregard for personhood. If all troublesome behaviour is sedated away, if little attention is given to maintaining continence, if nothing is done to meet psychological needs, costs can be cut to the minimum. It is possible to survive, even in specialist dementia settings, with a staffing ratio of one to 10. Person-centred care, however, requires a typical staffing ratio of one to four; and where the physical dependency level is high, a ratio of one to three or two. It is possible that some providers, especially the profit-making companies, will see person-centred care as too expensive, and maintain the old culture as far as they dare. The public sector, under extreme pressure from underresourcing, will shrug off long-term responsibility wherever it can. In Britain there is a tendency to register residential settings for dementia as nursing homes, because this category draws in more money; yet this goes against good evidence that the greater part of dementia care does not require a special input from nursing, and that registration as a residential home is sufficient (Bell and McGregor 1995).

The sources of resistance that I have mentioned thus far are accessible to ordinary methods of investigation, even if they are opaque to common sense. At many points in this book I have suggested that beyond the ordinary realities of everyday life – or perhaps beneath them – lie many forms of psychological defence: personal, interpersonal and organizational. From a psychoanalytic point of view the old culture of care, in its entirety, might be understood as having a defensive function. The medicalization of dementia, with its search for solutions exclusively within the natural sciences, served to distance those who were affected. The view that people with dementia lack insight, or even that they have ceased to be subjective beings, rationalized a lack of attention to their distress, and justified substituting to mere behaviour modification for true engagement. Stage theories implied that the pathway of global deterioration was inevitable, and so legitimated the reduction of care to the meeting of obvious physical need. Many family carers, influenced by the power of ideology, claimed that the person they once knew and loved had gone, to be replaced by another who was virtually unrecognizable. This prevented a true process of mourning, and the growth of a new kind of relationship, more empathic and intuitive than before. Even the 'alzheimerization of dementia' might be viewed as a defensive move, which has served to impede the process of cultural transformation.

The process of change

If there are such powerful forces to preserve the status quo and to sabotage the beginnings of positive change, we might well ask how a new culture of dementia care could possibly come into being. It will not happen through a paradigm shift that is merely at the level of theory. Academic arguments in themselves are powerless to bring about widespread social changes; research evidence, when it goes against deeply vested interests, is all too easily discounted or ignored. Radical improvement will not happen through the alleged freedom and flexibility that a 'market of care' is claimed to provide. As we have seen, the assumption that human services can be supplied in the same way as cars or television sets is grotesque. It will not happen through the mainstream political process, even if there were a government that put the needs of deprived minorities high on its agenda. The provision of better resources and appropriate forms of regulation constitute necessary, but not sufficient conditions for cultural change.

The experience of recent years suggests that the first stages are likely to consist of a gradual inner transformation of some of the structures that are now in place, until those structures come to function in a radically different way. The process consists of a persistent, subtle, ingenious substitution of one way of being by another. Perhaps a unit which once clearly had a type A organizational form gradually becomes one of type B (see pp. 104–6), and then generates great well-being in the clients, together with greater satisfaction and commitment in its staff. For some time the outer shell – the support group, the day centre, the residential home, etc. – might appear very much the same as before, while senior management does not realize what is occurring. Eventually, however, the truth comes out, and even former opponents are eager to identify with the evident story of success.

However tight the restrictions imposed by law, and however severe the financial constraints, there is always some freedom for movement, some possibility for doing new things. Even under totalitarianism people gradually found ways to live a more human life, subverting the system that was imposed – and we are very far from that. The remarkable fact concerning dementia is how much has been done, despite general conditions being so unpropitious. Each of the main sectors – public, private and independent – has had a creative part to play. Fortunately, there are some changes that can be brought about without huge cost implications – largely through better selection and training of staff and the drawing in of volunteers. It is also probable that there are some ways in which the new culture of care is more cost-effective than the old; because of higher levels of commitment and lower rates of absenteeism, sickness and burn-out.

In the longer term, however, a change in the culture of care can only come about where there is sufficient resourcing to enable all of those components of good practice discussed on pages 128–131 to be set in place. Any organization which claims to be providing person-centred care, but which is neglecting these, is almost certainly making fraudulent claims. The public sector is at a grave disadvantage, particularly in those capitalist economies, like that of Britain, that are undergoing steady long-term decline. Large private companies are always under pressure to cut costs so as to declare a large profit to their shareholders. At present the greatest potential lies with those smaller private settings created by deeply committed people, some of whom have put their entire assets into their venture, and with the independent but not profit-making providers. In both cases there is a clear value base, an opportunity for employees to believe in what they are doing. There can be a relative freedom from tradition and bureaucratic control, the chance for creativity and innovation.

The principal financial pressure is simply that of balancing the accounts, when all outgoings and developmental needs have been considered.

If there is to be a cultural transformation, it is essential to have a properly trained workforce at all levels. Care assistants need to be equipped not only for the essential physical aspects of their work, but also for the psychological tasks, in particular, developing those skills of interaction that we examined in Chapter 6. Senior care workers and managers, of course, need a great deal more – but here also the most important, yet highly neglected, part of their work lies at the interpersonal level. The status of the whole field must be raised, liberated from all ageist associations, and accepted as one requiring high-level expertise.

In Britain the recognition is slowly dawning that there is a vast training and educational deficit, and that none of the existing forms of professional preparation properly address the issues arising in dementia care. In recent years there have been many small and piecemeal training initiatives; at least this is a beginning. In strategic terms, my own estimate is that in the UK we urgently need around 2000 people who have the capacity to train home care assistants and staff in formal care settings, and a similar number of people who are capable of organizing and delivering a programme of carers' support (Kitwood 1997b). The scale of the problem is gigantic, and it should be tackled at the meta-level (training the trainers, etc.). This means that it is essential to have specialist courses in dementia care at both first and higher degree levels, just as we have in applied fields such as optometry and chiropody. If the first ventures that have been made in this direction are an indication, there will be no shortage of excellent applicants.

The commitment to changing the culture of care will be grounded in a range of motives very different from those which have dominated the culture of the industrial societies in recent years, as the capitalist mentality has penetrated even further into the recesses previously occupied by humanism. Among the motives for good work are the sense of strength that comes from being close to other people, the fulfilment that arises from giving freely, the pleasure of working for human betterment, the inner peace that accompanies integrity, and the satisfaction of being committed to a cause that lies beyond oneself. Also, paradoxically, ease and comfort follow from accepting that some degree of suffering is part of the human condition, rather than striving to achieve its elimination in some vain Promethean project. Many people find that there is a kind of sanity and a sense of wholeness when motives such as these are called into play. The motives that are continually evoked in present-day society – greed, self-interest, love of power and the fear of being found out – seem shoddy by comparison.

I have suggested that powerful psychological defences help to keep the old culture of dementia care in place. Drawing on a time-honoured metaphor, it might be said that vast amounts of psychic energy are involved. When, however, the defences are lowered, and people are enabled to face and work through the anxieties that are mobilized, that energy is released for constructive work. In those rare settings where this has begun to happen there is a new expansiveness and joy, and it is tremendously appealing. The new culture is an invitation to us to see those whose mental powers are failing as our fellow human beings, not as strangers or aliens. We recover the sense of community, long hidden away in the depths of our collective unconscious: a place where people can accept each other with realism, and on equal terms. With this encouragement we can more easily accept the fact of our own ageing, and even the possibility that we may be among those who have dementia before we die.

The broader implications

As the twentieth century draws towards its close, the industrialized societies of the western world find themselves in an extraordinary and paradoxical predicament. It is becoming clear that the system of liberal democracy, whose organization is allegedly rational, and whose economic life is grounded in the pursuit of profit, is fundamentally flawed. This system is deeply implicated in many kinds of global injustice, and in the ruthless spoiling of the biosphere; it is not even capable of delivering a secure and prosperous way of life to all of its own citizens. In many nation states 'welfare capitalism' has virtually come to an end, and a permanent underclass has been created, cut off from the ordinary privileges of citizenship – as in Victorian and earlier times. And yet, even while old hopes and expectations have been failing, a new and vibrant humanism has been gaining ground: more strongly committed, more psychologically aware, more culturally sensitive, more practical and pragmatic than anything that has gone before. This is the historical context in which the 'epidemic of dementia' has occurred. Among all social issues, perhaps this is the one that is the most deeply caught up in the contradictions, because the need is so intense and the size of the problem is so vast. Almost certainly the contradictions will intensify yet further, as demographic change brings even more people into the eighth and ninth decades of life.

Whatever happens to dementia can no longer remain a minor parochial matter, confined within the boundaries of geriatrics. There will, of necessity, be profound repercussions in society at large. The positive transformation of care practice – if it occurs on a widespread scale – will undermine all facile forms of determinism, and interrupt the obsessional search for technical fixes to human problems. It will challenge the stupidity and narrowness of the market mentality, and in particular the idea that human services can be effectively delivered as if they were consumer durables. It will stimulate the search for an economic process better than the one we have at present – a process which distributes the benefits of social existence far more equitably in relation to real need.

Above all else, the reconsideration of dementia invites us to a fresh understanding of what it is to be a person. The prevailing emphasis on individuality and autonomy is radically called into question, and our true interdependence comes to light. Frailty, finitude, dying and death are rendered more acceptable; grandiose hopes for technical Utopias are cut to the ground. Reason is taken off the pedestal that it has occupied so unjustifiably, and for so long; we reclaim our nature as sentient and social beings. Thus from what might have seemed the most unlikely quarter, there may yet emerge a well-spring of energy and compassion. And here, in comparison to conventional psychiatry, we may find an immeasurably richer conception of the healing of the mind.

The task of cultural transformation

Commentary by Claire Surr

In this final chapter, Kitwood focuses on the process of cultural transformation in dementia, highlighting the strides made since the 1980s but also the task still ahead in bringing about what he defined as the 'New Culture' of dementia care. In reading this chapter, I was aware that the cultural transformation has continued and that we now find ourselves in a vastly different social and political landscape to that present when Kitwood was writing. Part of Kitwood's legacy may have been in sowing the seeds of culture change towards one that focused on the centrality of persons living with dementia. However, the position of people living with dementia in society has now changed to such a degree that it is timely to go beyond Kitwood's 'new culture' to one that is truly inclusive of people living with dementia.

Kitwood defined culture as a 'settled, patterned way for providing meaning to human existence' (p. 162). He described how, once established, cultures are resistant to change and cultural norms are internalized by their members. However, other writers have presented different perspectives on how rapidly, or not, it is possible to change cultures (Varnum and Grossmann 2017). Highmore (2016) argues that culture is a lens through which individuals view the world and that shape the way life is lived. Culture is formed and maintained through the interactions between individuals within a group, via the social influences individuals or societies exert on one another. Social influence, then, is instrumental in upholding or changing a culture or its values (Nowak et al. 2012).

Over recent years there has been an array of social developments that have supported a rapid culture change relating to dementia. It is interesting to reflect on why this might be, but social media has played a role in a way that was impossible even to conceptualize in Kitwood's lifetime. People with dementia, their carers and supporters, and organizations representing their rights and perspectives, have a strong presence across a variety of social media. This has provided diverse groups of people worldwide with a vehicle through which they are able to reach an immediate global audience in order to share personal experiences, challenge the status quo and demand change. Social media has also enabled people with dementia and their carers and supporters to connect to one another in a way that had not previously been possible, supporting creation of a collective voice as well as a powerful peer support network.

In examining how societal perceptions of dementia have changed since the 1990s, I will focus in particular on three key areas operating at the macro (societal), meso (organizational) and micro (individual) levels, each of which has a complex, interconnected relationship with the others. These are:

1   Social movements and activism by people with dementia
2   Dementia as a global political and health priority, and
3   Dementia within public awareness.

Social movements and activism by people with dementia

Social movements are a series of events that are more or less connected to one another, which occur over a period of time and which serve to provide a sustained challenge to those holding power within a prevailing culture. They are not linked to one particular individual or organization, but to networks of many individuals and organizations, who interact to develop a collective action (Diani 2003). Culture change at a societal level usually occurs over a protracted period of time and is often difficult to control (Costanza et al. 2016). However, social movements are by their very nature a mechanism for supporting rapid societal culture change. Kitwood was committed to positioning the person with dementia and their experience at the centre of dementia care. It may be that his legacy has been to create the setting conditions that have made more recent social movements possible in the field. What has occurred in the field of dementia is a social movement that has, in more recent years, been led by people with dementia. Through this movement they have accomplished the changes Kitwood observed had begun by the late 1990s, when he wrote:

> Among all the changes that have occurred, one fact stands out above all others. It is that men and women who have dementia have emerged from the places where they were hidden away; they have walked onto the stage of history, and begun to be regarded as persons in the full sense.

(p. 162)

Kitwood's vision for a 'New Culture' of care was limited by his perception that understanding about dementia needs to be led by 'expert practitioners'. We have now moved far beyond this, as evidenced in the commentary on Chapter 5. It is now expected that people with dementia take on a central role in social and political activism, challenging stereotypes of people with dementia as passive recipients of care provided by expert others and emerging as the recognized experts of their own experience. The commentary on Chapter 5 outlined much of the advent of involvement and engagement groups for people living with dementia in the UK that has helped to mobilize and connect individuals living with dementia. These groups work by using the individual and collective voices of those with dementia to influence policy and societal attitudes (Bartlett 2014), as well as contributing to dementia service development and research agendas. In her Afterword that follows this commentary, Kate Swaffer who co-founded the Dementia Alliance International highlights the global growth of Dementia Advocacy.

One example of a social movement for change supported by many groups (including those led by people with dementia) has been to challenge the use of stigmatizing words when talking about dementia and those affected. This movement is underpinned by the theoretical position that the words we choose to speak about dementia, either consciously or unconsciously, are rich in meaning and describe, express and reinforce cultural perceptions (Gerritsen et al. 2016). The use of terms such as 'dementing', 'demented' and 'sufferer' can perpetuate stigmatizing and negative perceptions of people with dementia (Swaffer 2014), including fear, degeneration (Van Gorp et al. 2012) and a loss of self (Van Gorp and Vercruysse 2011), and have a negative impact on people with dementia and their family (Herrmann et al. 2018). In the words of Chris Roberts, who is living with younger-onset dementia:

> I suffer, my family does too. I am suffering daily. I do not always live well. But I am not a dementia sufferer. I'm Chris, I live with dementia.
>
> (Tweet by Chris Roberts)

Stigmatizing words and labelling phrases such as 'challenging behaviours' and 'behavioural and psychological symptoms of dementia' (to describe behaviours that are often not a symptom of the condition but the result of unmet needs) have been challenged by this movement and alternative terms promoted (Alzheimer's Australia n.d.; DEEP 2014). There undoubtedly remains a way to go in removing what is viewed as the unacceptable and stigmatizing language around dementia. However, a cultural shift around language acceptability and impact in some spheres has undoubtedly been achieved.

Within policy and national guidance development, the need to ensure that the voice of people with dementia and their carers/supporters is represented, is widely recognized. In England, for example, people with dementia and carers supported working groups that underpinned development of the country's first Dementia Strategy (Department of Health 2009) and the 'I' and 'We' statements (see Chapter 5 commentary) that underpin national policy and practice. In the academic sphere, the use of experts by experience (often referred to as patient and public involvement) has become the norm rather than the exception in dementia-related research (Boote et al. 2015; Kelly et al. 2015) and in health care workforce education (Kenny et al. 2016). Research on social activism and the application of concepts such as citizenship to those with dementia (see, for example, Baldwin 2008; Kelly and Innes 2011; Bartlett 2012, 2014) has also emerged during recent years. This has served to underpin the social movement with an evidence base, as well as permitting research to be delivered more effectively (Iliffe et al. 2013) and conducted in areas important to and driven by people with dementia and their family members.

Dementia as a global political and health priority

Over recent years there has been a rapid growth in international interest in dementia care and research, brought on by the recognition of dementia as a global health priority (WHO/Alzheimer's Disease International 2012). This has led to a number of international political summits, conferences and legacy events to support a co-ordinated global effort to increase research and improve services and support for those with dementia (RDD/10495 2013; WHO 2015), the production of many national dementia strategies, frameworks or plans globally (WHO 2017a), and a World Health Organization-led Global Action Plan on Dementia (WHO 2017b). Dementia is also a condition now covered under the United Nations convention on disability rights (UN General Assembly 2007). At the close of *Dementia Reconsidered*, Kitwood refers to the predicament in which 'industrialized societies of the western world' (p. 170) find themselves with regard to meeting the needs of those with dementia. A further cultural shift is the contemporary recognition that dementia does not affect only high-income countries. It is truly a global condition, with 68 per cent of the world's population of people with dementia set to live in low- and middle-income countries by 2050 (Alzheimer's

Disease International 2015). Dementia is on the political agenda to an extent that was unimaginable at the time Kitwood was writing *Dementia Reconsidered*. With this has come increased research investment and a range of initiatives designed to increase public awareness of dementia.

Dementia within public awareness

There can be no doubt that the general public, as well as those working within health and social care services, have never had greater awareness of dementia. The rise of dementia on the political agenda has led to awareness-raising campaigns and initiatives that have gained significant momentum, such as dementia-friendly communities (Lin and Lewis 2015). There is no single definition of what constitutes a dementia-friendly community, however the underpinning principle is that they seek to normalize dementia within society (Lin 2017), and that this can be implemented in various ways that seek to make communities accessible places for people with dementia, socially and environmentally. Within this programme of work many strands of public awareness-raising and engagement have commenced, including intergenerational and education work with young people (Galbraith et al. 2015; Parveen et al. 2015; Isaac et al. 2017) in order to create a 'dementia-friendly generation'. It is unclear if and how dementia-friendly communities will continue to develop over the coming years, but it seems likely this will be informed by a growing body of research around defining, measuring and achieving dementia friendliness. The idea that those living with dementia might be supported within society but outside of a 'caring' context, takes us beyond Kitwood's New Culture. It recognizes that what is required to meet the diverse range of people with dementia within a supportive society is not a parental caring approach but an inclusive society that supports the position of people with dementia as full and equal citizens.

Going beyond Kitwood's 'New Culture' of dementia care

Although visionary at the time in challenging a custodial, illness-based approach to dementia and promoting one that humanized those with the condition, Kitwood's New Culture, viewed through our contemporary lens, has become outdated. While there may have been a failure to consolidate much of what Kitwood aspired to, there has been a considerable shift in how dementia is conceptualized and therefore a contemporary reconceptualization of Kitwood's New Culture is now required.

I have called the post-New Culture the Inclusive Culture (Table 9.2). In the Inclusive Culture those who are living with dementia, and their family members and friends who care for them, are seen as the experts. Dementia is couched in terms beyond care provision and is seen as requiring a societal-level supportive response, which enables people with dementia to live full and active lives as equal citizens, no matter their degree of cognitive impairment. The Inclusive Culture recognizes the diversity of people who live with dementia. It does not ignore or belittle the impairments of communication, thought and reasoning that the progression of dementia brings, or the impact this has on individuals' abilities to express their needs and be included fully in society. However, it does recognize that it is only through working in full partnership with people with dementia and their family members that we will be enabled to achieve an inclusive culture. Kitwood saw culture as a relatively stable characteristic. However, in order to survive in a context of strong and rapidly changing social influence, the Inclusive Culture recognizes the need for society, communities and services to

Table 9.2 The Inclusive Culture for a Society that embraces people living with dementia as full citizens

General view of dementia

Dementia is seen as a form of disability. Those who live with dementia are full and equal citizens, and are fully included within all aspects of society. How a person experiences living with the condition is determined by the full range of biological, physical, social, psychological, spiritual and environmental factors, in conjunction with how inclusive and supportive communities and wider society are.

*We have the right to continue with day-to-day and family life, without discrimination or unfair cost, to be accepted and included in our communities and not live in isolation or loneliness.

Ultimate source of knowledge

In relation to dementia, the people who possess the most reliable and valid knowledge are those living with the condition and their family members.

*We have the right to be respected, and recognized as partners in care, provided with education, support, services, and training which enables us to plan and make decisions about the future.

Emphasis for research

There is a great deal that can be done around prevention, treatment, cure, care and support for people with dementia and their family. All of these areas require research. Research that is co-designed and delivered with people with dementia and their family members should be a priority. More funding for dementia research is urgently needed and parity between funding for prevention and cure versus care research is needed.

*We have the right to know about and decide if we want to be involved in research that looks at cause, cure and care for dementia and be supported to take part.

Supporting people with dementia and their family

People with dementia are, first and foremost, citizens. Their needs should be considered in terms broader than just provision of care. People need to be included and supported to remain active citizens with control over their own lives. When formal or informal care is required it must meet people's broad holistic needs, underpinned by the upholding of personhood.

*We have the right to an early and accurate diagnosis, and to receive evidence based, appropriate, compassionate and properly funded care and treatment, from trained people who understand us and how dementia affects us. This must meet our needs, wherever we live.

Collective understanding

It is important to recognize the broad spectrum of people who live with dementia and the variability in how it impacts on individuals' lives. Understanding is achieved through partnership and relationship between all stakeholders. We need to understand the best and most successful approaches to including and empowering all those living with dementia to express their priorities, needs and wishes.

*We have the right to be recognized as who we are, to make choices about our lives including taking risks, and to contribute to society. Our diagnosis should not define us, nor should we be ashamed of it.

(Continued)

Table 9.2 (continued)

Understanding behaviours

Words matter and so the way in which behaviour is talked or written about is important, since this can define or label how the behaviour is construed. All behaviours should be viewed, primarily, as attempts at communication, related to need. It is necessary to seek to understand the message, and so to engage with the need that is not being met. or with the experience of the individual that needs to be understood and supported.

The caring relationship

The process of support and care exists in relationship, and therefore the concerns, feelings, vulnerabilities, etc. of both the person with dementia, and their family members and formal carers must be recognized and supported. Formal and informal caregiving is recognized as emotionally and physically challenging, and those providing care need to be given the appropriate knowledge and support to care not only for the person with dementia but also for themselves.

Sustainability and context

Our societal response to dementia needs to be adaptive, and able and willing to evolve rapidly and dynamically to what people with dementia, their family, practitioners and researchers are saying is needed. Supportive communities and high-quality services for those with the condition can be achieved and sustained only through ongoing openness to improve and change. There is always going to be room for improvement. We must be willing to have an ambitious vision.

*The Dementia Statements (Dementia Action Alliance, 2017), developed by people with dementia and their carers in England.

be able and willing to constantly adapt and evolve. An Inclusive Culture is therefore not static, and recognizes that we will never be 'there' when it comes to supporting people with dementia, because through the Inclusive Culture new ways to improve and change will continually be identified and embraced. I have also included within the table (in bold) the Dementia Statements (Dementia Action Alliance 2017), developed by people with dementia and their carers in England, as an illustration of the specific expectations of people affected by the condition that should be met within an inclusive culture.

The future?

So where to in the future for the field of dementia? As the global population ages, how we will meet the needs of the growing numbers of people who will live with dementia is a question on many lips. Some of the greatest challenges are perhaps yet to come as we, as communities and nations, negotiate how to provide good-quality care and support in the context of austerity and workforce shortages. While we have yet to achieve even the basics of Kitwood's vision for a New Culture on a widespread basis, our aspirations for what could be achieved have far surpassed this. What we must ensure is that we continue to strive to achieve our ambitions and continually renew our vision of what is possible. Undoubtedly, this will be difficult at times and the way forward will not always be clear. However, as the Inclusive Culture contends, we must be willing to have an ambitious vision, just as Kitwood did.

Reflection points

- How can you support an Inclusive Culture of dementia care? What barriers do you think exist to achieving an Inclusive Culture and how can we as a society work to overcome these?

- The move towards an Inclusive Culture, where the voices of people with dementia and their family members underpin policy and practice development, has been accelerated by a social movement led by people with dementia and those who support them. While this is a positive and powerful movement, it may represent the voices and experiences of only a proportion of people living with dementia – those who are able, confident and supported to have a voice. How can we ensure the voice of people across the spectrum of those living with dementia is heard?

- An area around which there is considerable debate is the language we use to talk about dementia. Language is powerful and can perpetuate stigma, create fear and shame or empower. What terms to describe those living with dementia are supportive of an Inclusive Culture? Why do you think some groups or members of society (e.g. journalists, authors, academics, members of the public) continue to use language that many people with dementia say they find hurtful and unacceptable?

The Inclusive Culture for citizens living with dementia

Whereas the 'old culture' often forced people into isolation and estrangement, the 'new culture' is a celebration of trust, conviviality and interdependence. In the Inclusive Culture people are treated as citizens with full rights.

The 3 Nations Working Group formed in 2017 to contribute to society their lived experience as experts with personal knowledge of dementia.

Copyright: Peter Pannicia.

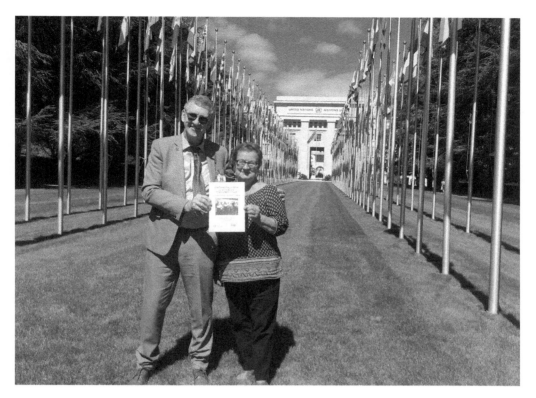

Keith Oliver and his wife Rosemary representing the case for persons living with dementia at the United Nations Committee on the Convention on the Rights of Persons with Disabilities in 2017.

Copyright: Keith Oliver.

Afterword

Kitwood's book was first published in 1997. Interestingly, dementia self-advocates were active before this time, although in very small numbers. Christine Bryden AM was diagnosed with AD in 1995 aged 46, a single mother of three small children, and the first self advocate in Australia. She encouraged patient engagement at Alzheimer's Australia (now Dementia Australia), and then worked with ADI, and was the first person with dementia to be on their board. James McKillop MBE from Scotland invented the Dementia Help Card in 2001[1], which at the time, was the first of its kind in the world. He was diagnosed with dementia aged 59, in 1999. The late Peter Ashley was diagnosed with Lewy Body Dementia in 2000, and was very active in the UK and then also globally with ADI. Following these and other pioneers, many others with dementia became active and vocal self advocates, which also led to an increasing number of Dementia Working or Advisory Groups, resulting in many more with dementia presenting at conferences and other events, or providing education about the lived experience of dementia at universities and dementia training centres or within the care service provider groups.

There has been an increasing emergence of self-advocacy and Dementia Working Groups (DWGs). In 2000, Christine Bryden and a group of international self-advocates from the USA and Canada founded the first self-advocacy group Dementia Advocacy Support Network International (DASNI), although membership was not exclusive to people with dementia. Then, in 2002, James McKillop and others founded the Scottish Dementia Working Group (SDWG). It took many years for more groups like this to emerge, and there are now a growing number of them. Peter Ashley and a strong group of British advocates were instrumental in the development and implementation of the English National Dementia Strategy and the Prime Minister's Challenge on Dementia. However, it took until 2017 for the 3 Nations Dementia Working Group covering England, Wales and Northern Ireland to be fully established.

This is a list of the known National or Regional Dementia Working or Advisory Groups:

2000: Dementia Advocacy Support Network International (DASNI)
2002: Scottish Dementia Working Group (SDWG)
2006: Alzheimer's America Early-Stage Advisory Group (EAG)
2012: Highlands Dementia Working Group (HDWG)
2012: European People with Dementia Working Group (EUPDWG)
2013: Dementia Australia Dementia Advisory Committee (DADAC)

2013: Irish Dementia Working Group (IDWG)
2014: Dementia Alliance International (DAI)
2014: Japan Dementia Working Group (JDWG)
2014: Southern (Kiama) Dementia Advisory Group (DAG's)
2015: Ontario Dementia Advisory Group (ODAG)
2016: Dementia Advocacy Awareness Team (DAAT)
2017: 3 Nations Dementia Working Group (3NDWG)
2018: NZ Dementia Advisory Committee (NZDAC)

It is also important to note countries including Taiwan and Singapore will launch their own DWG's in 2019, and there is a continuing emergence of self-advocates in countries like this primarily due to the work of DAI and also ADI members who are now determined to empower and enable the inclusion of people with dementia in their own countries.

Launched on 1 January 2014, Dementia Alliance International (DAI) is now considered the global voice of people with dementia. DAI was set up, initially to ensure we had an authentic voice and could collectively demand inclusion, as individual advocates were being ignored or silenced too often. We also mostly were receiving no services so decided to provide our own. All members are individuals diagnosed with dementia, and DAI provides grass roots support including mentoring, peer-to-peer support groups, educational webinars, cafes and other online services. As an organisation, DAI has become an activist organisation for human rights globally, at the COSP on the CRPD, the WHO, the UN and other organisations.

DAI advocated privately, then publicly for a person with dementia to be included on the World Dementia Council (WDC)[2], and there are now two people with dementia on the WDC. DAI also collaborates closely with many of the National, Regional and Local Dementia Working Groups. Through collaboration and sharing of information gleaned from all of the international meetings DAI attends, DAI aims to ensure real change. There was a lot of rhetoric about improving outcomes for people with dementia, including timely diagnosis, services and support, but little more than the production of publications prior to the World Health Organisation (WHO) First Ministerial Conference on Dementia in March 2015, where I was invited as a keynote speaker, and made three demands, including Convention on the Rights of Person's with Disabilities (CRPD) and a human rights approach to dementia. My three demands were included in Dr Margaret Chan's WHO Final Call for Action. Much has happened since then, although new DAI members still report they are only being advised to go home and prepare for end of life, rather than being supported to live positively with dementia.

One of DAI's key roles has become to empower members to live with dementia more positively and productively, and also to demand better support, rather than only to go home and die from it, as advised. Hence, this is also why I believe person centred care is in part, still a band-aid, and may be part of why this concept has never really been translated into practice. We need to change what happens to the person diagnosed, and their families, at the time of diagnosis to support disabilities, thereby promoting independence for longer, as well as significantly improving quality of life and perceived life expectancy. Whilst ever we do not change the experience of the disclosure of dementia, and the immediate post diagnostic support, and continue to receive the Prescribed Disengagement®[34], it is possible little will ever change for those of us diagnosed.

It has been due to the power of the Internet, which has allowed such global collaboration, that a global voice through DAI has really strengthened people's knowledge, and then their desire and willingness to become public self-advocates. This is partly due to being able to meet online, provide support online, collaborate and plan campaigns and presentations that have common messages, plus DAI provides those who want it a lot of advice on human rights and CRPD. Unlike ADI or other Advocacy organisations, DAI has become a member of some of the international Disability NGO's, which the national organisations are unable to become members of as their members are not persons with disabilities. Ultimately, this is giving us more knowledge and therefore more power to demand our rights. Through co-operation and collaboration, and working together, we are so much stronger.

From my experience, as a retired nurse, a past care partner for three people who have died from dementia, a person diagnosed with dementia for over ten years, and now a researcher in the field of dementia, I believe Kitwood's Person Centred Care has not generally been translated into practice, and instead has mostly been a tick-box in an organisatons' paperwork. By reviewing and providing a contemporary look at Kitwood's novel and innovative theories, this book has the potential to create real change. Self-advocates are now demanding it. My one concern, even with the review of this book, is I often feel we don't need to change the squeaky wheel; instead, we need a brand new one. People with dementia globally want real change, not rhetoric or tick boxes about perceived best practice.

Kate Swaffer
Chair, CEO & Co-founder, Dementia Alliance International
Board member, Alzheimer's Disease International
Member, World Dementia Council
PhD Candidate, University of South Australia
Global Leader, Australian 100 Women Of Influence 2018

Notes

1 https://www.ncbi.nlm.nih.gov/pmc/articles/PMC3042458/
2 https://www.dementiaallianceinternational.org/open-letters-world-dementia-council/
3 Swaffer, K. (2014). Dementia and Prescribed Disengagement™. *Dementia*, 14(1), 3–6 <http://journals.sagepub.com/doi/10.1177/1471301214548136>
4 Swaffer, K. (2014/2015), Reinvesting in a life is the best prescription, *Australian Journal of Dementia Care*, vol. 3, no 6, 31-32.

References

Absher, J.R. and Cummings, J.L. (1994) Cognitive and non-cognitive aspects of dementia syndromes: an overview. In A. Burns and R. Levy (eds) *Dementia*. London: Chapman and Hall.

Acton, G.J. and Kang, J. (2001) Interventions to reduce the burden of caregiving for an adult with dementia: a meta-analysis. *Research in Nursing and Health*, 24(5): 349–60.

Ader, R., Felten, D.L. and Cohen, N. (eds) (1991) *Psychoneuroimmunology*. San Diego, CA: Academic Press.

Albert, M.S. (1982) Geriatric neuropsychology. *Journal of Consulting and Clinical Psychology*, 49: 835–50.

Allardyce, J. (1996a) The secondary dementias: an overview. *Journal of Dementia Care*, 4(3): 28–9.

Allardyce, J. (1996b) The secondary dementias, 2: hypothyroidism. *Journal of Dementia Care*, 4(5): 28–9.

Allardyce, J. (1996c) The secondary dementias, 3: diabetes mellitus. *Journal of Dementia Care*, 4(5): 26–7.

Alston, W.P. (1976) Traits, consistency and conceptual alternatives for personality theory. In R. Harré (ed.) *Personality*. Oxford: Blackwell.

Alzheimer Scotland Action On Dementia (2017) *Scottish Dementia Working Group*. Available at: www.alzscot.org/campaigning/scottish_dementia_working_group (accessed 6 December 2017).

Alzheimer's Australia (n.d.) *Dementia Language Guidelines*, Alzheimer's Australia. Available at: www.dementia.org.au/sites/default/files/full-language-guidelines.pdf (accessed 5 April 2018).

Alzheimer's Disease International (2009) *World Alzheimer Report 2009*. London: Alzheimer's Disease International.

Alzheimer's Disease International (2017) *Dementia Friendly Communities: Global Developments*, 2nd edn. London: Alzheimer's Disease International.

Alzheimer's Disease International (2017) *Dementia Friendly Communities: Global Developments*, 2nd edn. Available at: www.alz.co.uk/adi/pdf/dfc-developments.pdf (accessed 23 March 2018).

Alzheimer's Disease Society (1996) *Opening the Mind*. London: Alzheimer's Disease Society.

Alzheimer's Society (2013) *Building Dementia Friendly Communities: A Priority for Everyone*. London: Alzheimer's Society.

Alzheimer's Society (2014) *Dementia 2014: Opportunity for Change*. London: Alzheimer's Society. Available at: www.alzheimers.org.uk/dementia2013 (accessed 15 July 2016).

Alzheimer's Society (2017) *Three Nations Dementia Working Group* . Available at: www.alzheimers.org.uk/info/20105/engagement_and_participation/1239/three_nations_dementia_working_group (accessed 6 December 2017).

Ames, D., Dolan, R. and Mann, A. (1990) The distinction between depression and dementia in the very old. *International Journal of Geriatric Psychiatry*, 5: 193–8.

Annerstedt, L. (1987) *Collective Living for the Demented in Later Life*. Lund: Gerontologiskt Centrum.

Archibald, C. (1990) *Activities*. Stirling: Dementia Services Development Centre.

Archibald, C. (1993) *Activities II*. Stirling: Dementia Services Development Centre.

Arie, T. (1983) Pseudodementia. *British Medical Journal* 286: 1301–2.

Atkinson, T., Evans., S., Darton R. et al. (2014) Creating the asset base – a review of literature and policy on housing with care. *Housing, Care and Support*, 17(1): 16–25.

Baker, C., Huxley, P., Dennis, M. et al. (2015) Alleviating staff stress in care homes for people with dementia: protocol for stepped-wedge cluster randomised trial to evaluate a web-based Mindfulness-Stress Reduction course. *BMC Psychiatry*, 15: 317.

Baldwin, C. (2008) Narrative(,) citizenship and dementia. *Journal of Aging Studies*, 22(3): 222–8.

Baldwin, C., Capstick, C., Phinney, A. et al. (2007) Personhood. In C. Baldwin and A. Capstick (eds) *Tom Kitwood on Dementia: A Reader and Critical Commentary*. Maidenhead: Open University Press.

Balfour, A. (1995) Account of a study aiming to explore the experience of dementia. *PSIGE Newsletter*, 53: 15–19.

Ballard, C., Corbett, A., Orrell, M. et al. (2018) Impact of person-centred care training and person-centred activities on quality of life, agitation, and antipsychotic use in people with dementia living in nursing homes: a cluster-randomised controlled trial. *PLoS Medicine*, 15(2): e1002500. https://doi.org/10.1371/journal.pmed.1002500.

Barham, P. and Hayward, R. (1991) *From the Mental Patient to the Person*. London: Routledge.

Barnes, B. (1980) David Malan: psychodynamic scientist. *New Forum*, August, 3–5.

Barnes, T., Sack, J. and Shore, J. (1973) Guidelines to treatment approaches. *Gerontologist*, 13: 513–27.

Barnett, E. (1995) A window of insight into quality care. *Journal of Dementia Care*, 3(4): 23–6.

Barnett, E. (1996) '"I need to be me": a thematic evaluation of a dementia care facility, based on the client perspective.' Unpublished PhD thesis, University of Bath.

Bartlett, R. (2012) The emergent models of dementia activism. *Ageing and Society*, 34(4): 623–44.

Bartlett, R. (2014) Citizenship in action: the lived experiences of citizens with dementia who campaign for social change. *Disability and Society*, 29(8): 1291–304.

Basting, A., Towey, M. and Rose, E. (2016) *The Penelope Project: An Arts-based Odyssey to Change Elder Care*. Iowa City, IA: University of Iowa Press.

Beard, R. (2011) Art therapies and dementia care: a systematic review. *Dementia*, 11(5): 633–56.

Becker, E. (1972) *The Birth and Death of Meaning*. New York: Free Press.

Bell, J. and McGregor, I. (1991) Living for the moment. *Nursing Times*, 87(18): 46–7.

Bell, J. and McGregor, I. (1995) A challenge to stage theories of dementia. In T. Kitwood and S. Benson (eds) *The New Culture of Dementia Care*. London: Hawker.

Benjamin, B. (1999) Validation: A communication alternative. In L. Volicer and L. Boom Charette (eds) *Enhancing Quality of Life in Advanced Dementia*. Philadelphia: Brunner/Mazel.

Benson, H. (1996) *Timeless Healing*. London: Simon & Schuster.

Benson, S. (1994) Sniff and doze therapy. *Journal of Dementia Care*, 2(1): 12–15.

Berghmans, R.L.P. and ter Meulen, R.H.J. (1995) Ethical issues in research with dementia patients. *International Journal of Geriatric Psychiatry*, 10: 647–51.

Berrios, G.E. and Freeman, H.L. (1991) *Alzheimer and the Dementias*. London: Royal Society of Medicine Services.

Blagg, R. and Petty, S. (2015) Sustainable staff well-being within older adult mental health. *Mental Health Review Journal*, 20(2): 92–104.

Blessed, G., Black, S.E., Butler, T. and Kay, O.W.K. (1991) The diagnosis of dementia in the elderly: a comparison of CAMCOG (the cognitive section of CAMDEX), the AGECAT program, OSM-III, the Mini Mental State Examination and some short rating scales. *British Journal of Psychiatry*, 159: 193–8.

Blessed, G., Tomlinson, B.E. and Roth, M. (1968) The association between quantitative measures of dementia and of senile change in the cerebral grey matter of elderly subjects. *British Journal of Psychiatry*, 114: 797–811.

Blum, N. (1991) The management of stigma by family carers. *Journal of Contemporary Ethnography*, 21(3): 263–84.

Blum, N. (1994) Deceptive practices in managing a family member with Alzheimer's disease. *Symbolic Interaction*, 17(1): 21–36.

Boller, E., Forette, F., Khatchaturian, Z., Pancet, N. and Christen, Y. (eds) (1992) *Heterogeneity of Alzheimer's Disease*. Berlin: Springer Verlag.

Boote, J.D., Twiddy, M., Baird, W. et al. (2015) Supporting public involvement in research design and grant development: a case study of a public involvement award scheme managed by a National Institute for Health Research (NIHR) Research Design Service (RDS). *Health Expectations*, 18(5): 1481–93.

Bowlby, J. (1979) *The Making and Breaking of Affectional Bonds*. London: Tavistock.

Bradshaw, J. (1990) *Homecoming*. London: Piatkus.

Brane, G., Karlsson, I., Kohlgren, M. and Norberg, A. (1989) Integrity-promoting care of demented nursing home patients: psychological and biochemical changes. *International Journal of Geriatric Psychiatry*, 4: 165–72.

Bredin, K., Kitwood, T. and Wattis, J. (1995) Decline in quality of life for patients with severe dementia following a ward merger. *International Journal of Geriatric Psychiatry*, 10(11): 967–73.

British Psychological Society (2014) *A Guide to Psychosocial Interventions in Early Stages of Dementia*. Faculty of Psychology and Older People. Available at: www.psige.org/public/files/A%20Guide%20 to%20Psychosocial%20Interventions%20in%20Early%20Stage%20Dementia.pdf (accessed 25 June 2016).

Brodaty, H., Green, A. and Koschera, A. (2003) Meta-analysis of psychosocial interventions for people with dementia. *Journal of the American Geriatrics Society*, 51: 657–64.

Brooker, D. (1995) Looking at them, looking at me. A review of observational studies into the quality of institutional care for elderly people with dementia. *Journal of Mental Health*, 4: 145–56.

Brooker, D. (2005) Dementia care mapping: a review of the research literature. *Gerontologist*, 45(suppl. 1): 11–18.

Brooker, D. and Latham, I. (2016) *Person Centred Dementia Care: Making Services Better with the VIPS Framework*, 2nd edn. London: Jessica Kingsley Publishers.

Brooker, D. and Surr, C. (2006) Dementia Care Mapping (DCM): initial validation of DCM 8 in UK field trials. *International Journal of Geriatric Psychiatry*, 21(11): 1018–25.

Brooker, D., Evans, S.C., Evans, S.B. et al. (2018) Evaluation of the implementation of Meeting Centres Support Programme: The impact on people living with dementia in Italy, Poland and UK; exploration of the effects on people with dementia. *International Journal of Geriatric Psychiatry*, 33: 883–892.

Brooker, D., La Fontaine, J., De Vries, K. and Latham, I. (2013) The development of PIECE-dem: focussing on the experience of care for people with living with advanced dementia. *British Psychological Society Clinical Psychology Forum*, 250: 38–46.

Brooker, D., La Fontaine, J., Evans, S. et al. (2014) Public health guidance to facilitate timely diagnosis of dementia: ALzheimer's COoperative Valuation in Europe (ALCOVE) Recommendations. *International Journal of Geriatric Psychiatry*, 29(7): 682–93.

Brooker, D., Latham, I., Evans, S.C. et al. (2016) FITS into practice: translating research into practice in reducing the use of anti-psychotic medication for people with dementia living in care homes. *Aging and Mental Health*, 20(7): 709–18.

Brooker, D., May, H., Walton, S. et al. (2007) Introducing SOFI: a new tool for inspection of care homes. *Journal of Dementia Care*, 15(4): 22–3.

Browne, C.J. and Schlosberg E. (2005) Attachment behaviours and parent fixation in people with dementia: the role of cognitive functioning and pre-morbid attachment style. *Aging and Mental Health*, 9(2): 153–61.

Bruce, E. (1995) Support through human contact for family carers. In T. Kitwood and S. Benson (eds) *The New Culture of Dementia Care*. London: Hawker.

Bruce, E. (ed.) (1996) *Focus on Dementia: A Guide to the Structured Support of Carers*. Bradford: Bradford Dementia Group.

Bryden, C. (2005) *Dancing with Dementia: My Story of Living Positively with Dementia*. London: Jessica Kingsley Publishers.

Buber, M. (1937) *I and Thou* (trans. R. Gregor Smith). Edinburgh: Clark.

Buber, M. (1970) *I and Thou* (trans. Walter Kaufmann). New York: Charles Scribner's Sons.

Buckland, S. (1995) Dementia and residential care. In T. Kitwood, S. Buckland and T. Petre, *Brighter Futures: A Report on Research into Provision for Persons with Dementia in Residential Homes, Nursing Homes and Sheltered Housing.* Oxford: Anchor Housing Association (in collaboration with Methodist Homes for the Aged).

Buetow, S. (2016) *Person-centred Health Care.* London: Routledge.

Burkitt, I. (1993) *Social Selves.* London: Sage.

Burns, A. and Forstl, H. (1994) The clinical diagnosis of Alzheimer's disease. In A. Burns and R. Levy (eds) *Dementia.* London: Chapman and Hall.

Burns, A., Jacoby, R. and Levy, R. (1990) Psychiatric phenomena in Alzheimer's disease: 1. Disorders of thought content. *British Journal of Psychiatry*, 157: 72–6.

Burns, A., Jacoby, R., Philpot, M. and Levy, R. (1991) Computerised tomography in Alzheimer's disease: methods of scan analysis, comparison with normal controls and clinical/radiological associations. *British Journal of Psychiatry*, 159: 609–14.

Butler, R.N. (1963) The life review: an interpretation of reminiscence in the aged. *Psychiatry*, 26, 65–76.

Butters, N., Heindel, W.C. and Salmon, D.P. (1990) Dissociation of implicit memory in dementia: neurological implications. *Bulletin of the Psychonomic Society*, 28(4): 359–66.

Bytheway, B. (1995) *Ageism.* Buckingham: Open University Press.

Callegaro, F. (2013) The ideal of the person: recovering the novelty of Durkheim's sociology. Part II: Modern society, the cult of the person, and the sociological project. *Journal of Classical Sociology*, 16(1): 37–52.

Camic, P.M., Tischler, V. and Pearman, C.H. (2014) Viewing and making art together: a multi-session art-gallery-based intervention for people with dementia and their carers. *Aging and Mental Health*, 18(2): 161–8.

Capstick, A. (1995) The genetics of Alzheimer's disease: rethinking the questions. In T. Kitwood and S. Benson (eds) *The New Culture of Dementia Care.* London: Hawker Publications.

Carone, L., Tischler, V. and Dening, T. (2016) Football and dementia: a qualitative investigation of a community based sports group for men with early onset dementia. *Dementia: The International Journal of Social Research and Practice*, 15(6): 1358–76.

Carpenter, B.D. and Strauss, M.E. (1995) Personal history of depression and its appearance in Alzheimer's disease. *International Journal of Geriatric Psychiatry*, 10: 669–78.

Cayton, H. (1995) Diagnostic testing, who wants to know? *Journal of Dementia Care*, 3(1): 12–13.

Chapman, A. and Marshall, M. (eds) (1996) *Dementia: New Skills for Social Workers.* London: Jessica Kingsley.

Chenoweth, L., King, M.T., Jeon, Y.H. et al. (2009) Caring for Aged Dementia Care Resident Study (CADRES) of person-centred dementia care, dementia-care mapping, and usual care in dementia: a cluster-randomised trial. *The Lancet – Neurology*, 8(4): 317–25.

Chernis, C. (1980) *Staff Burnout: Job Stress in the Human Services.* Beverly Hills: Sage.

Cheston, R. (1996) Stories and metaphors: talking about the past in a psychotherapy group for people with dementia. *Ageing and Society*, 16: 579–602.

Cheston, R. and Ivanecka, A. (2017) Individual and group psychotherapy with people diagnosed with dementia: a systematic review of the literature. *International Journal of Geriatric Psychiatry*, 32(1): 3–31.

Cheston R., Christopher, G. and Ismail, S. (2015) Dementia as an existential threat: the importance of self-esteem, social connectedness and meaning in life. *Science Progress*, 98(4): 416–19.

Clare, L. (2008) *Neuropsychological Rehabilitation and People with Dementia.* Hove: Psychology Press.

Clare, L., Kudlicka, A., Oyebode, J.R. et al. (in press) Goal-oriented cognitive rehabilitation in early-stage Alzheimer's and related dementias: a multi-centre single-blind randomised controlled trial (GREAT). *Health Technology Assessment.*

Clare, L., Nelis, S.M., Quinn, C. et al. (2014) Improving the experience of dementia and enhancing active life – living well with dementia: study protocol for the IDEAL study. *Health and Quality of Life Outcomes*, 12: 164.

Clare, L., Whitaker, R., Woods, R.T. et al. (2013) AwareCare: a pilot randomized controlled trial of an awareness-based staff training intervention to improve quality of life for residents with severe dementia in long-term care settings. *International Psychogeriatrics*, 25(1): 128–39.

Clarke, C.L., Keyes, S.E., Wilkinson, H. et al. (2013) HEALTHBRIDGE: The National Evaluation of Peer Support Networks and Dementia Advisers in Implementation of the National Dementia Strategy for England [Ref: 025/0058], Department of Health Policy Research Programme Project. Available at: https://www.gov.uk/government/uploads/system/uploads/attachment_data/file/249789/August_2013__NDS_Final_Brief_Report.pdf (accessed 15 July 2016).

Clarke, P. and Bowling, A. (1990) Quality of everyday life in long-stay institutions for the elderly. *Social Science and Medicine*, 30: 1201–10.

Coleman, P. (1986) Issues in the therapeutic use of reminiscence with elderly people. In J. Hanlay and M. Gilhooly (eds) *Psychological Therapies for the Elderly*. London: Croom Helm.

Coleman, V. (1988) *The Health Scandal*. London: Sidgewick and Jackson.

Cooper, C., Owens, C., Katona, C. and Livingston, G. (2008) Attachment style and anxiety in carers of people with Alzheimer's disease: results from the LASER-AD study. *International Psychogeriatrics*, 20(3): 494–507.

Cooper, C.L. (ed.) (1984) *Psychosocial Stress and Cancer*. Chichester: Wiley.

Costa, P.T. and McCrae, R.R. (1985) *NEOPI-R: Professional Manual*. Orlando, FL: Psychological Assessment Resources Inc.

Costanza, D.P., Blacksmith, N., Coats, M.R. et al. (2016) The effect of adaptive organizational culture on long-term survival. *Journal of Business Psychology*, 31: 361–81.

Crampton, J., Dean, J. and Eley, R. (2012) *Creating a Dementia Friendly York*. York: Joseph Rowntree Foundation. Available at: www.jrf.org.uk/report/creating-dementia-friendly-york (accessed 5 April 2018).

Crispi, E.L., Schiaffino, K. and Berman, W.H. (1997) The contribution of attachment to burden in adult children of institutionalized parents with dementia. *The Gerontologist*, 37: 52–60.

Damasio, A.R. (1995) *Descartes' Error*. London: Picador.

Danziger, K. (1978) *Socialization*. Harmondsworth: Penguin.

Davidson, D. (1970) Mental events. In L. Foster and J.W. Swanson (eds) *Experience and Theory*. Boston, MA: University of Massachusetts Press.

Davis, M. and Wallbridge, D. (1981) *Boundary and Space*. Harmondsworth: Penguin.

de Board, R. (1978) *The Psychoanalysis of Organizations*. London: Tavistock.

Dean, R., Proudfoot, R. and Lindesay, J. (1993) The Quality of Interaction Schedule (QUIS): development, reliability and use in the evaluation of two domus units. *International Journal of Geriatric Psychiatry*, 8: 819–26.

Dementia Action Alliance (2010) *National Dementia Declaration for England*. Available at: www.dementiaaction.org.uk/assets/0001/1915/National_Dementia_Declaration_for_England.pdf (accessed 5 April 2018).

Dementia Action Alliance (2011) *National Dementia Declaration for England*. London: Dementia Action Alliance. Available at: https://www.dementiaaction.org.uk/assets/0001/1915/National_Dementia_Declaration_for_England.pdf (accessed 5 March 2018).

Dementia Action Alliance (2017) *The Dementia Statements*. London: Dementia Action Alliance. Available at: www.dementiaaction.org.uk/nationaldementiadeclaration (accessed 5 March 2018).

Dementia Alliance International (2014/2015) *Dementia Alliance International*. Available at: www.dementiaallianceinternational.org/ (accessed 6 December 2017).

Dementia Australia (2018) *Dementia language guidelines*. Retrieved from https://www.dementia.org.au/sites/default/files/full-language-guidelines.pdf (accessed 28 November 2018).

Dementia Diaries (2018) *Dementia Diaries*. Available at: https://dementiadiaries.org/ (accessed 21 February 2018).

Dementia Engagement and Empowerment Project (DEEP) (n.d.) *The Dementia Empowerment and Engagement Project*. Available at: http://dementiavoices.org.uk/ (accessed 6 December 2017).

Dementia Engagement and Empowerment Project (DEEP) (2014) *Dementia Words Matter: Guidelines on Language About Dementia*. Available at: http://dementiavoices.org.uk/wp-content/uploads/2015/03/DEEP-Guide-Language.pdf. (accessed 6 December 2017).

Dementia Engagement and Empowerment Project (DEEP) (2015) *Developing a National User Movement of People With Dementia: Learning from the Dementia Engagement and Empowerment Project (DEEP)*. York: Joseph Rowntree Foundation. Available at: www.jrf.org.uk/report/developing-national-user-movement-people-dementia (accessed 5 April 2018).

Dennett, D. (1976) Conditions of personhood. In A. Rorty (ed.) *The Identities of Persons*. Berkeley, CA: University of California Press.

Dennett, D.C. (1975) *Brainstorms: Philosophical Essays on Mind and Psychology*. Brighton: Harvester.

Department for Work and Pensions and Department of Health (2017) *Thriving at Work: A Review of Mental Health and Employers*. Available at: www.gov.uk/government/ publications/thriving-at-work-a-review-of-mental-health-and-employers (accessed 5 March 2018).

Department of Health (2009) *Living Well with Dementia: A National Dementia Strategy*. London: The Stationery Office.

Department of Health (2012) *Prime Minister's Challenge on Dementia: Delivering Major Improvements in Dementia Care and Research by 2015*. London: Department of Health.

Deweer, B., Ergis, A.M., Fossati, P. et al. (1994) Explicit memory, procedural learning and lexical priming in Alzheimer's disease, *Cortex*, 30(1): 113–26.

Dewing, J. (2008) Personhood and dementia: revisiting Tom Kitwood's ideas. *Journal of Older People Nursing*, 3(1): 3–13.

Dewing, J. and McCormack, B. (2017) Tell me how do you define person-centredness? *Journal of Clinical Nursing*, 26(17–18): 2509–10.

Diani, M. (2003) Introduction: Social movements, contentious actions, and social networks: 'From metaphor to substance'? In M. Diani and D. McAdam (eds) *Social Movements and Networks: Relational Approaches to Collective Action*. Oxford: Oxford Scholarship On-line.

Dowlen, R., Keady, J., Milligan, C. et al. (2017) The personal benefits of musicking for people living with dementia: a thematic synthesis of the qualitative literature. *Arts & Health*, September, 8: 1–16.

Dröes, R.M., Meiland, F., Schmitz, M. and van Tilburg, W. (2004) Effect of combined support for people with dementia and carers versus regular day care on behaviour and mood of persons with dementia: results from a multi-centre implementation study. *International Journal of Geriatric Psychiatry*, 19(7): 673–84.

Economist (1996) A triumph of hype over experience? *Economist*, 337(7945): 111–12.

Edwards, H.B., Whiting, P., Ijaz, S. et al. (2017) Quality of family relationships and outcomes of dementia: a systematic review. *BMJ Open*, 8: e015538. doi: 10.1136/bmjopen-2016–015538.

Elvish, R., Lever, S., Johnstone, J. et al. (2012) Psychological interventions for carers of people with dementia: a systematic review of quantitative and qualitative evidence. *Counselling and Psychotherapy Research*, 13(2): 106–25.

Ely, M., Meller, D., Brayne, C. and Opit, L. (1996) *The Cognitive Disability Planning Model*. Cambridge: University of Cambridge, Department of Community Medicine.

Erol, R., Brooker, D. and Peel, E. (2016) The impact of dementia on women internationally: an integrative review. *Health Care for Women International*, 37(12): 1320–41.

Evans, N., Cheston, R. and Harris, N. (2015) Personal message cards: an evaluation of an alternative method of delivering Simulated Presence Therapy. *Dementia: The International Journal of Social Research and Practice*, 15(6): 1703–15.

Eyre, R. (2001) *Iris*. Santa Monica, CA: Miramax Films.

Eze, M.O. (2010) *Intellectual History in Contemporary South Africa*. London: Palgrave Macmillan.

Feil, N. (1982) *Validation: The Feil Method*. Cleveland, OH: Edward Feil Productions.

Feil, N. (1993) *The Validation Breakthrough*. Cleveland, OH: Health Professions Press.

Finnema, E., Van der Kooij, C., Droes, R.M. and Wolter, L. (2017) Psychosocial interventions. In S. Schüssler (ed.) *Dementia in Nursing Homes*. Switzerland: Springer International Publishing.

Fischbach, G.D. (1992) Mind and brain. *Scientific American Special Issue*, September: 24–33.

Folstein, M.F., Folstein, S.E. and McHugh, P.R. (1975) Mini-mental state: a practical method for grading the cognitive state of patients for the clinician. *Journal of Psychiatric Research*, 12: 189–98.

Fordyce, C. (2018) *Post 1 – My Symptoms from 1990 – My Diagnosis December 2015*. MyCrazy NewWorld. Available at: https://mycrazynewworld.wordpress.com/2017/01/21/first-blog-post/ (accessed 1 March 2018).

Forrester, L.T., Maayan, N., Orrell, M. et al. (2014) Aromatherapy for dementia. *Cochrane Database of Systematic Reviews 2014*, 2: CD003150.

Forstl, H., Burns, A., Luthert, P., Cairns, N., Lantos, P. and Levy, R. (1993) Clinical and neuropathological correlations of depression in Alzheimer's disease. *Psychological Medicine*, 22: 877–84.

Fossey, J., Ballard, C., Juszczak, E. et al. (2006) Effect of enhanced psychosocial care on antipsychotic use in nursing home residents with severe dementia: cluster randomised trial. *British Medical Journal*, 332: 756–61.

Foucault, M. (1967) *Madness and Civilization*. London: Tavistock.

Fox, L. and Kitwood, T. (1994) *The Quality of Care in Two Dementia Day Centres*. Bradford: Bradford Dementia Group.

Fox, P. (1989) From senility to Alzheimer's disease, the rise of the Alzheimer's disease movement. *The Milbank Quarterly*, 67: 58–102.

Frank, B. (1995) People with dementia can communicate – if they are able to hear. In T. Kitwood and S. Benson (eds) *The New Culture of Dementia Care*. London: Hawker.

Freudenberger, H.J. (1974) Staff burn-out. *Journal of Social Issues*, 30(1): 159–65.

Froggatt, A. (1988) Self-awareness in early dementia. In B. Gearing, M. Johnson and T. Heller (eds) *Mental Health Problems in Old Age*. Buckingham: Open University Press.

Funnemark, C. (1995) Changing activities to meet early to late stage Alzheimer care. *Conference Proceedings: The Changing Face of Alzheimer's Care*. Chicago, IL: Alzheimer's Association.

Gabrieli, J.D.E., Corkin, S., Mickel, S.F. and Growdon, J.H. (1993) Intact acquisition and long-term retention of mirror-tracing skill in Alzheimer's disease and in global amnesia. *Behavioral Neuroscience*, 107(6): 899–910.

Galbraith, B., Larkin, H., Moorhouse, A. and Oomen, T. (2015) Intergenerational programs for persons with dementia: a scoping review. *Journal of Gerontological Social Work*, 58(4): 357–78.

Genova, L. (2014) *Still Alice*. New York: Simon & Schuster Audio.

Gerritsen, D.L., Oyebode, J. and Gove, D. (2016) Ethical implications of the perception and portrayal of dementia. *Dementia: The International Journal of Social Research and Practice*, first published online, doi:10.1177/1471301216654036.

Gibson, F. (1994) What can reminiscence contribute to people with dementia? In J. Bornat (ed.) *Reminiscence Reviewed*. Buckingham: Open University Press.

Gibson, F. (ed.) (1991) *Working with People with Dementia: A Positive Approach*. Jordanstown: University of Ulster Publications.

Gibson, F., Marley, J. and McVicker, H. (1995) Through the past to the person. *Journal of Dementia Care*, 3(6): 18–19.

Gilhooly, M. (1984) The social dimensions of senile dementia. In I. Hanley and J. Hodge (eds) *Psychological Approaches to the Care of the Elderly*. Croom Helm: London.

Gilleard, C. (1984) *Living with Dementia*. London: Croom Helm.

Gillespie, W.H. (1963) Some regressive phenomena in old age. *British Journal of Medical Psychology*, 36: 203–9.

Goffman, E. (1963) *Stigma: Notes on the Management of Spoiled Identity*. New York: Simon & Schuster.

Goffman, E. (1974) *Stigma: Notes on the Management of Spoiled Identity*. Harmondsworth: Penguin.

Goldsmith, M. (1996) *Hearing the Voice of People with Dementia: Opportunities and Obstacles*. London: Jessica Kingsley.

Government Office for Science (2008) *Foresight Mental Capital and Wellbeing Project*. London: Government Office for Science.

Gray-Davidson, F. (1993) *The Alzheimer Sourcebook for Caregivers*. Los Angeles: Lowell House.

Gurland, B., Copeland, J., Kuriansky, J., Kellerer, M., Sharpe, I. and Dean, L.L. (1983) *The Mind and Mood of Aging: Mental Health Problems of the Community Elderly in New York and London*. London: Croom Helm.

Gwilliam, C. and Gilliard, J. (1996) Dementia and the social model of disability. *Journal of Dementia Care*, 4(1): 14–15.

Hahnemann, S. (1983) *Organon of Medicine* (trans. J. Kunzli and P. Pendleton). London: Victor Gollancz.

Handy, C. (1976) *Undertaking Organizations*. Harmondsworth: Penguin.

Handy, C. (1988) *Understanding Voluntary Organizations*. Harmondsworth: Penguin.

Harees, L. (2012) *The Mirage of Dignity on the Highways of Human 'Progress': The Bystanders' Perspective*. Bloomington, IL: AuthorHouse.

Harré, R. (1993) Rules, roles and rhetoric. *Psychologist*, 16(1): 24–8.

Harré, R. and Secord, P.F. (1972) *The Explanation of Social Behaviour*. Oxford: Blackwell.

Harrison, R., Sawa, N. and Kafetz, K. (1990) Dementia, depression and physical disability in a London borough: a survey of elderly people in and out of residential care and implications for future developments. *Age and Ageing*, 19: 97–103.

Hart, S. and Semple, J. (1990) *Neuropsychology and the Dementias*. London: Taylor & Francis.

Hawkins, P. and Shohet, R. (1989) *Supervision in the Helping Professions*. Buckingham: Open University Press.

Health Education England Skills for Health and Skills for Care (2015) *Dementia Core Skills Education and Training Framework*. London: Health Education England.

Heller, L. (1996) *The Preparation of Volunteers for Work in Dementia Care*. Bradford: Bradford Dementia Group.

Herrick, C.A. (1992) Codependency: characteristics, risks, progressions and strategies for healing. *Nursing Forum*, 27(3): 12–19.

Herrmann, L.K., Welter, E., Leverenz, J. et al. (2018) A systematic review of dementia-related stigma research: can we move the stigma dial? *American Journal of Geriatric Psychiatry*, 26(3): 316–31.

Higgs, P. and Gilleard, C. (2016) Interrogating personhood and dementia. *Ageing and Mental Health*, 20(8): 773–80.

Highmore, B. (2016) *Culture*. London: Routledge.

Hillman, A. and Latimer, J. (2017) Cultural representations of dementia. *PLoS Med*, 14(3): e1002274. doi: 10.1371/journal.pmed.1002274.

Hobson, R.E. (1985) *Forms of Feeling*. London: Tavistock.

Holden, U. (1996) Dipping into a poisonous problem. *Journal of Dementia Care*, 4(3): 10–11.

Holden, U. and Woods, R.T. (1988) *Reality Orientation: Psychological Approaches to Confused Elderly*. Edinburgh: Churchill Livingstone.

Holden, U. and Woods, R.T. (1995) *Positive Approaches to Dementia Care*. Edinburgh: Churchill Livingstone.

Homer, A.C., Honavar, M., Lantos, P.L., Hastie, I.R., Kellett, J.M. and Millard, P.H. (1988) Diagnosing dementia: do we get it right? *British Medical Journal*, 297: 894–6.

Houston, A. (2018) *Dementia Can Be More Than Memory*. Available at: https://dementiacanbemore-thanmemory.wordpress.com/ (accessed 1 March 2018).

Hughes, J.C. (2006) The heat of mild cognitive impairment. *Philosophy, Psychiatry, & Psychology*, 13(1): 1–2.

Hughes, J.C. (2011) *Thinking Through Dementia*. Oxford: Oxford University Press.

Hughes, J.C. (2014) *How We Think About Dementia*. London: Jessica Kingsley Publishers.

Hunter, S. (ed.) (1997) *Social Work with People with Dementia*. London: Jessica Kingsley Publishers.

Hydén, L-C. (2018) *Entangled Narratives: Collaborative Storytelling and the Re-Imagining of Dementia*. New York: Oxford University Press.

Ikuenobe, P. (2016) Good and beautiful: a moral-aesthetic view of personhood in African communal traditions. *Essays in Philosophy*, 17(1): 125–63.

Iliffe, S., McGrath, T. and Mitchell, D. (2013) The impact of patient and public involvement in the work of the Dementias & Neurodegenerative Diseases Research Network (DeNDRoN): case studies. *Health Expectations*, 16(4): 351–61.

Ineichen, B. (1987) Measuring the rising tide: how many dementia cases will there be by 2001? *British Journal of Psychiatry*, 150: 195–200.

Innes, A. and McCabe, L. (2007) *Evaluation in Dementia Care*. London: Jessica Kingsley Publishers.

Isaac, M.G.E.K.N., Isaac, M.M., Farina, N. and Tabet, N. (2017) Knowledge and attitudes towards dementia in adolescent students. *Journal of Mental Health*, 26(5): 419–25.

Jacoby, R.J. and Levy, R. (1980) Computed tomography in the elderly. 2. Senile dementia: diagnosis and functional impairment. *British Journal of Psychiatry*, 136: 256–69.

Jacques, A. (1988) *Understanding Dementia*. Edinburgh: Churchill Livingstone.

James, I. and Jackman, L. (2017) *Understanding Behaviour in Dementia that Challenges: A Guide to Assessment and Treatment*, 2nd edn. London: Jessica Kingsley Publishers.

James, I.A., Mackenzie, L. and Mukaetova Ladinska, E. (2006) Doll use in care homes for people with dementia. *International Journal of Geriatric Psychiatry*, 21(11): 1093–8.

Jennings, L. and the Forget Me Nots (2014) *Welcome to Our World*. Canterbury: Forget Me Nots.

Jewell, A. (2011) *Spirituality and Personhood in Dementia*. London: Jessica Kingsley Publishers.

Jitapunkel, S., Pillay, I. and Ebrahim, S. (1991) The Abbreviated Mental Test: its use and validity. *Age and Ageing*, 20: 332–6.

Jobst, K.A. (1994) Rapidly progressing atrophy of medial temporal lobe in Alzheimer's disease. *Lancet*, 343: 829–30.

Jobst, K.A. (1995) The use of scanning in diagnosis of dementia. Presentation to the conference, The Diagnosis of Dementia, Birmingham, 29 June.

Jones, G.M.M. and Miesen, B.M.L. (1992) *Caregiving in Dementia*, volume I. London: Routledge.

Jones, G.M.M. and Miesen, B.M.L. (1994) *Caregiving in Dementia*, volume II. London: Routledge.

Jorm, A.F., Scott, R., Cullen, J.S. and McKinnon, A.J. (1991) Performance of the Informant Questionnaire on Cognitive Decline in the Elderly (IQCODE) as a screening test for dementia. *Psychological Medicine*, 21: 785–90.

Jung, C.G. (1934) The stages of life. In *Modern Man in Search of a Soul*. London: Routledge and Kegan Paul.

Kaiser, P. and Eley, R. (2016) *Life Story Work with People with Dementia: Ordinary Lives, Extraordinary People*. London: Jessica Kingsley Publishers.

Kandel, E.R. and Hawkins, R.D. (1992) The biological basis of learning and individuality. *Scientific American, Special Issue*, September: 53–60.

Kant, I. (1797) The Metaphysics of Morals (1797), Part II: The metaphysical principles of virtue. In Kant, *Ethical Philosophy*, trans. James W. Ellington (Indianapolis, Indiana: Hackett, 1983), p. 127.

Karlsson, I., Brane, G., Melin, E., Nyth, A.-L. and Rybo, E. (1988) Effects of environmental stimulation on biochemical and psychological variables in dementia. *Acta Psychiatrica Scandinavica*, 77: 207–13.

Kaufman, J.C. and Beghetto, R.A. (2009) Beyond big and little: the four C model of creativity. *Review of General Psychology*, 13(1): 1–12.

Keady, J. (1996) The experience of dementia: a review of the literature and implications for nursing practice. *Journal of Clinical Nursing*, 5: 1–13.

Keady, J. and Nolan, M. (1995) IMMEL: assessing coping responses in the early stages of dementia. *British Journal of Nursing*, 4(6): 309–14.

Kelly, F. (2010) Recognising and supporting self in dementia: a new way to facilitate a person-centred approach to dementia care. *Ageing and Society*, 30(1): 103–24.

Kelly, F. and Innes, A. (2011) Human rights, citizenship and dementia care nursing. *International Journal of Older People Nursing*, 8(1): 61–70.

Kelly, S., Lafortune, L., Hart, N. et al. (on behalf of the Dementia Priority Setting Partnership) (2015) Dementia priority setting partnership with the James Lind Alliance: using patient and public involvement and the evidence base to inform the research agenda. *Age and Ageing*, 44(6): 985–93.

Kenny, J., Asquith, I., Guss, R. et al. (2016) Facilitating an evolving service user involvement group for people with dementia: what can we learn? *Journal of Mental Health Training, Education and Practice*, 11(2): 81–90.

Killett, A., Burns, D., Kelly, F. et al. (2016) Digging deep: how organisational culture affects care home residents' experiences. *Ageing and Society*, 36(1): 160–88.

Killick, J. (1994) There's so much to hear, when you listen to individual voices. *Journal of Dementia Care*, 2(5): 12–14.

Killick, J. (2016) Creativity and dementia. In C. Clarke and E. Wolverson (eds) *Positive Psychology Approaches to Dementia*. London: Jessica Kingsley Publishers.

Killick, J. (2017) *Poetry and Dementia*. London: Jessica Kingsley Publishers.

King's Fund (1986) *Living Well into Old Age: Applying Principles of Good Practice to Services for Elderly People with Severe Mental Disabilities*. London: The King's Fund.

Kinman, G. and Jones, F. (2003) Running up the down escalator: stressors and strains in UK academics. *Quality in Higher Education*, 9(1): 22–37.

Kitwood, T. (1983) Personal identity and personal integrity. In E. Weinreich-Haste and D. Locke (eds) *Morality in the Making: Thought, Action and the Social Context*. Chichester: Wiley.

Kitwood, T. (1987) Explaining senile dementia: the limits of neuropathological research. *Free Associations*, 10: 117–40.

Kitwood, T. (1988) The technical, the personal and the framing of dementia. *Social Behaviour*, 3: 161–80.

Kitwood, T. (1989) Brain, mind and dementia: with particular reference to Alzheimer's disease. *Ageing and Society*, 9: 1–15.

Kitwood, T. (1990a) The dialectics of dementia: with particular reference to Alzheimer's disease. *Ageing and Society*, 10: 177–96.

Kitwood, T. (1990b) Understanding senile dementia: a psychobiographical approach. *Free Associations*, 19: 60–75.

Kitwood, T. (1990c) Psychotherapy and dementia. *Psychotherapy Section Newsletter*, 8: 40–56.

Kitwood, T. (1990d) *Concepts in Developmental Psychology. Concern for Others: A New Psychology of Conscience and Morality*. Florence, KY: Taylor & Francis/Routledge.

Kitwood, T. (1993) Towards a theory of dementia care: the interpersonal process. *Ageing and Society*, 13: 51–67.

Kitwood, T. (1994a) Discover the person, not the disease. *Journal of Dementia Care*, 1(1): 16–17.

Kitwood, T. (1994b) Lowering our defences by playing the part. *Journal of Dementia Care*, 2(5): 12–14.

Kitwood, T. (1994c) Review of *The Validation Breakthrough* by Naomi Feil. *Journal of Dementia Care*, 2(6): 29–30.

Kitwood, T. (1995a) Exploring the ethics of dementia research: a response to Berghmans and Ter Meulen. *International Journal of Geriatric Psychiatry*, 10(8): 647–57.

Kitwood, T. (1995b) Positive long-term changes in dementia: some preliminary observations. *Journal of Mental Health*, 4: 133–44.

Kitwood, T. (1995c) Studies in person centred care: building up the mosaic of good practice. *Journal of Dementia Care*, 3(5): 12–13.

Kitwood, T. (1995d) Cultures of care: tradition and change. In T. Kitwood and S. Benson (eds) *The New Culture of Dementia Care*. London: Hawker Publications.

Kitwood, T. (1997) *Dementia Reconsidered; the person comes first*. Buckingham: Open University Press.

Kitwood, T. (1997a) The uniqueness of persons in dementia. In M. Marshall (ed.) *The State of the Art in Dementia Care*. London: Centre for Policy on Ageing Publications.

Kitwood, T. (1997b) *Strategic Training Needs Related to Dementia Care*. Bradford: University of Bradford/Bradford Dementia Group.

Kitwood, T. (ed.) (1997c) *Evaluating Dementia Care: The DCM Method*, 7th edn. Bradford: Bradford Dementia Group.

Kitwood, T. and Bredin, K. (1992a) Towards a theory of dementia care: personhood and well-being. *Ageing and Society*, 12: 269–87.

Kitwood, T. and Bredin, K. (1992b) A new approach to the evaluation of dementia care. *Journal of Advances in Health and Nursing Care*, 1(5): 41–60.

Kitwood, T. and Bredin, K. (1992c) *Person to Person: A Guide to the Care of Those with Failing Mental Powers*. Loughton: Gale Centre Publications.

Kitwood, T. and Woods, R.T. (1996) *A Training and Development Strategy for Dementia Care in Residential Settings*. Bradford: University of Bradford/Bradford Dementia Group.

Kitwood, T., Buckland, S. and Petre, T. (1995) *Brighter Futures: A Report on Research into Provision for Persons with Dementia in Residential Homes, Nursing Homes and Sheltered Housing*. Oxford: Anchor Housing Trust in collaboration with Methodist Homes for the Aged.

Knopman, D. (1991) Long-term retention of implicitly acquired learning in patients with Alzheimer's disease. *Journal of Clinical and Experimental Neuropsychology*, 13(6): 880–94.

Kokkonen, T.M., Cheston, R.I., Dallos, R. and Smart, C.A. (2014) Attachment and coping of dementia care staff: the role of staff attachment style, geriatric nursing self-efficacy, and approaches to dementia in burnout. *Dementia: The International Journal of Social Research and Practice*, 13(4): 544–68.

Kolb, D.A. (1992) *Experiential Learning: Experience as a Source of Learning and Development*. London: Prentice Hall.

Kontos, P. (2005) Embodied selfhood in Alzheimer's disease: rethinking person-centred care. *Dementia: The International Journal of Social Research and Practice*, 4(4): 553–70.

Kontos, P. and Martin, W. (2013) Embodiment and dementia: exploring critical narratives of selfhood, surveillance and dementia care. *Dementia: The International Journal of Social Research and Practice*, 12(3): 283–7.

Koo, M.Y. and Pusey, H. (2017) Photography and case study interviewing to document intergenerational family care in Singapore-Chinese families where one member is living with dementia. In J. Keady, L.C. Hydén, A. Johnson and C. Swarbrick (eds) *Social Research Methods in Dementia: Inclusion and Innovation*. London: Routledge.

Kral, V.A. (1962) Senescent forgetfulness: benign and malignant. *Canadian Medical Association Journal*, 86: 257–60.

Kramer, C.H. (1995) *Volunteer Guide for People who Care About the Aging*. Chicago, IL: Centre for Family Studies.

Kuhn, T. (1966) *The Structure of Scientific Revolutions*. Chicago, IL: University of Chicago Press.

Kurz, A. and Lautenschlager, N.T. (2017) Established treatments for Alzheimer's disease. In D. Ames, J. O'Brien and A. Burns (eds) *Dementia*, 5th edn. Boca Raton, FL: CRC Press, Taylor & Francis Group.

Laing, R.D. (1967) *The Politics of Experience*. Harmondsworth: Penguin.

Lawton, H. (1982) The myth of altruism. *Journal of Psychotherapy*, 10(3): 359–95.

LeShan, L. (1983) *How to Meditate*. London: Aquarian Press.

Levinas, E. (1985) *Ethics and Infinity: Conversations with Philippe Nemo* (trans. R.A. Cohen). Pittsburgh, PA: Duquesne University Press.

Lewis, R., Yarker, J., Donaldson-Feilder, E. et al. (2010) Using a competency-based approach to identify the management behaviours required to manage workplace stress in nursing: a critical incident study. *International Journal of Nursing Studies*, 47(3): 307–13.

Lim, J., Bogossian, F. and Ahern, K. (2010) Stress and coping in Australian nurses: a systematic review. *International Nursing Review*, 57(1): 22–31.

Lin, S.Y. (2017) Dementia friendly communities and being dementia friendly in healthcare settings. *Current Opinion in Psychiatry*, 30(2): 145–50.

Lin, S.Y. and Lewis, F.M. (2015) Dementia friendly, dementia capable, and dementia positive: concepts to prepare for the future. *The Gerontologist*, 55(2): 237–44.

Lindemann, H. (2014) Second nature and the tragedy of Alzheimer's. In L.C. Hydén, H. Lindemann and J. Brockmeier (eds) *Beyond Loss: Dementia, Identity and Personhood*. Oxford: Oxford University Press.

Lins, S., Hayder-Beichel, D., Rücker, G. et al. (2014) Efficacy and experiences of telephone counselling for informal carers of people with dementia. *Cochrane Database of Systematic Reviews*, 9: 1–113.

Lintern, T. (2001) *Quality in Dementia Care: Evaluating Staff Attitudes and Behaviour*. PhD thesis, University of Wales Bangor.

Lintern, T., Woods, B. and Phair, L. (2000a) Before and after training: a case study of intervention. *Journal of Dementia Care*, 8(1): 15–17.

Lintern, T., Woods, B. and Phair, L. (2000b) Training is not enough to change care practice. *Journal of Dementia Care*, 8(2): 15–17.

Lipinska, D. (2009) *Person-centred Counselling for People with Dementia: Making Sense of Self*. London: Jessica Kingsley Publishers.

Livingston, G. and Cooper, C. (2017) Psychological, behavioural and psychosocial interventions for neuropsychiatric symptoms in dementia: what works, what does not and what needs more evidence? In D. Ames, J. O'Brien and A. Burns (eds) *Dementia*, 5th edn. Boca Raton, FL: CRC Press, Taylor & Francis Group.

Logsdon, R.G., Pike, K.C., McCurry, S.M. et al. (2010) Early-stage memory loss support groups: outcomes from a randomized controlled clinical trial. *The Journals of Gerontology Series B: Psychological Sciences and Social Sciences*, 65(6): 691–7.

Maayan, N., Soares-Weiser, K. and Lee, H. (2014) Respite care for people with dementia and their carers. *Cochrane Database of Systematic Reviews*, 1: 1–49.

Magai, C. and Cohen, C.I. (1998) Attachment style and emotion regulation in dementia patients and their relation to caregiver burden. *The Journals of Gerontology Series B: Psychological Sciences and Social Sciences*, 53(3): 147–54.

Magai, C., Cohen, C., Gomberg, D. et al. (1996) Emotional expression during mid- to late-stage dementia. *International Psychogeriatrics*, 8(3): 383–95.

Makin, T. (1995) The social model of disability. *Counselling*, 6(4): 274.

Mangiaracina, F., Chattat, R., Farina, E. et al. (2017) Not re-inventing the wheel: the adaptive implementation of the Meeting Centres Support Programme in four European countries. *Aging and Mental Health*, 21(1): 40–8.

Margashack, D. (ed.) (1961) *Stanislavsky on the Art of the Stage*. London: Faber.

Marsh, P., Rosser, E. and Harré, R. (1978) *The Rules of Disorder*. London: Routledge.

Marshall, M. (ed.) (1988) *Guidelines for Social Workers Dealing with People with Dementia and their Carers*. Birmingham: British Association for Social Work.

Marshall, M. (ed.) (1997) *The State of Art in Dementia Care*. London: Centre for Policy on Ageing.

Marziali, E. and Donahue, P. (2006) Caring for others: Internet videoconferencing group intervention for family caregivers of older adults with neurodegenerative disease. *The Gerontologist*, 46(3): 398–403.

Maslach, C. (1978) The client role in staff burn-out. *Journal of Social Issues*, 34(4): 111–23.

Maslach, C. (1982) Understanding burn-out: definitional issues in analysing a complex phenomenon. In W.S. Paine (ed.) *Job Stress and Burnout: Research, Theory and Intervention Perspectives*. Beverly Hills, CA: Sage.

Matthews, E. (2006) Dementia and identity of the person. In J.C. Hughes, S.J. Louw and S.R. Sabat (eds) *Dementia: Mind, Meaning and the Person*. Oxford: Oxford University Press.

McCormack, B. and McCance, T. (2017) *Person-centred Practice in Nursing and Healthcare: Theory and Practice*, 2nd edn. Oxford: Wiley-Blackwell.

McDermott, O., Crellin, N., Ridder, H.M. and Orrell, M. (2013) Music therapy in dementia: a narrative synthesis systematic review. *International Journal of Geriatric Psychiatry*, 28(8): 781–94.

McGowin, D.F. (1993) *Living in the Labyrinth*. Cambridge: Mainsail Press.

McKeith, I. (1995) 'Preliminary report of the Newcastle prevalence study'. Presentation to the Conference of the Royal College of Psychiatry, York, 17–18 March.

McKeith, I.G. (2017) Dementia with Lewy bodies: a clinical overview. In D. Ames, J. O'Brien and A. Burns (eds) *Dementia*, 5th edn. Boca Raton, FL: CRC Press, Taylor & Francis Group.

McKhann, G., Drachman, D. and Folstein, M. (1984) Clinical diagnosis of Alzheimer's disease: report of the NINCDS-ADRDA work group. *Neurology*, 34: 939–44.

McMillan, F., Kampers, D., Traynor, V. and Dewing, J. (2010) An indigenous Australian experience. *Dementia: The International Journal of Social Research and Practice*, 9(2): 163–7.

Meacher, M. (1972) *Taken for a Ride*. London: Longmans.

Meiland, F., Innes, A., Mountain, G. et al. (2017) Technologies to support community-dwelling persons with dementia: a position paper on issues regarding development, usability, effectiveness and cost-effectiveness, deployment, and ethics. *JMIR Rehabilitation and Assistive Technologies*, 4(1): 31–51.

Mellody, P. (1993) *Facing Codependency*. San Francisco, CA: Harper Collins.

Memory Bridge (2007) *There is a Bridge* (documentary). Chicago, IL: Foundation for Alzheimer's and Cultural Memory. Available at: http://www.memorybridge.org/videos.php (accessed 26 February 2018).

Mental Health Foundation. (2016) *What is truth? An inquiry about truth and lying in dementia care.* Available at: www.mentalhealth.org.uk/publications/what-truth-inquiry-about-truth-and-lying-dementia-care (accessed 5 April 2018).

Menzies, I. (1972) *The Functioning of Social Systems as a Defence Against Anxiety*. London: Tavistock Institute.

Miesen, B. (1992) Attachment theory and dementia. In G.M.M. Jones and B.M. Miesen (eds) *Caregiving in Dementia*, vol. 1. London: Routledge.

Miesen, B.M.L. (1993) Alzheimer's disease, the phenomenon of parent fixation and Bowlby's attachment theory. *International Journal of Geriatric Psychiatry*, 8(2): 147–53.

Miesen, B.M.L. (1999) *Dementia in Close-up: Understanding and Caring for People with Dementia*. London & New York: Routledge.

Miesen, B.M.L. and Jones, G. (1997) Psychic pain resurfacing in dementia. From new to past trauma? In L. Hunt, M. Marshall and C. Rowlings (eds) *Past Trauma in Late Life: European Perspectives on Therapeutic Work with Older People*. London: Jessica Kingsley Publishers.

Miller, A. (1987) *The Drama of Being a Child*. London: Virago.

Miller, E. and Morris, R. (1993) *The Psychology of Dementia*. Chichester: Wiley.

Mills, M. (1995) Narrative identity and dementia. Unpublished PhD thesis, University of Southampton.

Mills, M. (1997) 'Residential care, well-being and dementia: some longitudinal evidence'. Unpublished manuscript, University of Southampton.

Mills, M. and Coleman, P. (1994) Nostalgic memories in dementia: a case study. *International Journal of Aging and Human Development*, 383: 203–19.

Mitchell, W. (2018) Which me am I today? Which me am I today? Available at: https://whichmeamitoday.wordpress.com/ (accessed 1 March 2018).

Mitchell, W. and Wharton, A. (2018) *Somebody I Used to Know*. London: Bloomsbury Publishing.

Mittelman, M. and Epstein, C. (2009) Research results. In F. Rosenberg, A. Parsa, L. Humble and C. McGee (eds) *The MoMA Alzheimer's Project: Making Art Accessible to People With Dementia*. New York: Museum of Modern Art. Available at: www.moma.org/momaorg/shared/pdfs/docs/learn/GuideforMuseums.pdf (accessed 3 April 2018).

MODEM Project (2016) *The Dementia Evidence Toolkit*. Available at: http://toolkit.modem-dementia.org.uk (accessed 15 July 2016).

Moniz Cook, E.D., Swift, K., James, I.A. et al. (2012) Functional analysis-based interventions for challenging behaviour in dementia. *Cochrane Database of Systematic Reviews*, 2: CD006929. doi: http://dx.doi.org/10.1002/14651858.CD006929.pub2.

Monti, L., Gabrieli, J.D., Wilson, R.S. and Reminger, S.L. (1994) Intact task-specific implicit memory in patients with Alzheimer's disease. *Psychology and Aging*, 9(1): 64–71.

Morgan, R.F. (1965) Note on the psychopathology of senility: senescent defence against the threat of death. *Psychological Reports*, 16: 305–6.

Morimoto, S.S., Yuen, G.S., Beres, S. and Alexopoulos, G.S. (2017) Depression with cognitive impairment. In D. Ames, J. O'Brien and A. Burns (eds) *Dementia*, 5th edn. Boca Raton, FL: CRC Press, Taylor & Francis Group.

Mork Rokstad, A.M., Røsvik, J., Kirkevold, O. et al. (2013) The effect of person-centred dementia care to prevent agitation and other neuropsychiatric symptoms and enhance quality of life in nursing home patients: a 10-month randomized controlled trial. *Dementia and Geriatric Cognitive Disorders*, 36(5–6): 340–53.

Mukulineer, M. (1995) *Human Learned Helplessness*. New York: Plenum.

Murphy, E. (1991) *After the Asylums*. London: Faber.

Murphy, E., Lindesay, J. and Dean, R. (eds) (1994) *The Domus Project: Long Term Care for Older People with Dementia*. London: Sainsbury Centre.

Murphy, J., Gray, C. and Cox, S. (2007) Talking mats: the effectiveness of a low technology communication framework to help people with dementia express their views. *Journal of Assistive Technologies*, 1(2): 30–4.

My Dementia Story (2018) Facebook.com. Available at: www.facebook.com/mydementiastory/?hc_ref=ART6Ta5Rj4wsD_gTI-x0cAk0IwMkm14yfsz7sFZCkbrhbmKcoy4PyxIU-sZMNkRTEM4&-fref=nf (accessed 1 March 2018).

Nagy, S.Z., Esiric, M.M., Jobst, K.A., Morris, J.H., King, E.M.F., McDonald, B., Litchfield, S., Smith, A., Barnetson, L. and Smith, A.D. (1995) Relative roles of plaques and tangles in the dementia of Alzheimer's disease: correlations using three sets of neuropathological criteria. *Dementia*, 6: 21–31.

Nairn, H. (1995) Discover the difference activities can make. *Journal of Dementia Care*, 3(1): 16–18.

Neary, D., Snowden, J.S. and Mann, D.M.A. (1994) Dementia of the frontal lobe type. In A. Burns and R. Levy (eds) *Dementia*. London: Chapman and Hall.

Nelis, S.M., Clare, L. and Whitaker, C.J. (2012) Attachment representations in people with dementia and their carers: implications for well-being within the dyad. *Aging and Mental Health*, 16(7): 845–54.

Netten, A. (1993) *A Positive Environment: Physical and Social Influences on People with Senile Dementia in Residential Care*. Aldershot: Ashgate Publishing Company.

New Economics Foundation (2014) *Wellbeing at Work*. Available at: http://b.3cdn.net/nefoundation/71c1bb59a2ce151df7_8am6bqr2q.pdf (accessed 5 March 2018).

NHS England (2015) *Dementia Diagnosis and Management: A Brief Pragmatic Resource for General Practitioners*. Available at: https://www.england.nhs.uk/wp-content/uploads/2015/01/dementia-diag-mng-ab-pt.pdf (accessed 19 April 2018).

NICE (National Institute for Health and Clinical Excellence) (2006) *Dementia: Supporting People with Dementia and Their Carers in Health and Social Care*. NICE Clinical Guideline 42, November. Available at: www.nice.org.uk/guidance/cg42 (accessed 5 April 2018).

NICE National Institute for Health and Clinical Excellence (2018). Dementia: assessment, management and support for people living with dementia and their carers. NICE guideline [NG97]. Available at: https://www.nice.org.uk/guidance/ng97 (accessed 28 August 2018).

Nowak, A., De Raad, W. and Borkowski, W. (2012) Culture change. The perspective of dynamic minimalism. In M.J. Gelfand, C.Y Chiu and Y.Y.Hong (eds) *Advances in Culture and Psychology*, Volume 2. Oxford: Oxford Scholarship On-line.

O'Brien, M.D. (1994) Vascular dementia: definition, epidemiology and clinical features. In A. Burns and R. Levy (eds) *Dementia*. London: Chapman and Hall.

O'Dwyer, M. and Orrell, M.W. (1994) Stress, ageing and dementia. *International Review of Psychiatry*, 6: 73–83.

Oakley, D. (1965) Senile dementia: some aetiological factors. *British Journal of Psychiatry*, 111: 414–19.

Oliver, K. (2016) *Walk the Walk, Talk the Talk*. Canterbury: Forget Me Nots.

Ollman, B. (1971) *Alienation*. Cambridge: Cambridge University Press.

Ornstein, R. and Sohel, D. (1989) *The Healing Brain*. London: Macmillan.

Orrell, M. (1995) Studies linking education and the risk of dementia. *Alzheimer's Disease Society Newsletter*, 9 December.

Orrell, M., Aguirre, E., Spector, A. et al. (2014) Maintenance cognitive stimulation therapy for dementia: single-blind, multicentre, pragmatic randomised controlled trial. *British Journal of Psychiatry*, 204(6): 454–61.

Osborne, H., Stokes, G. and Simpson, J. (2010) A psychosocial model of parent fixation in people with dementia: the role of personality and attachment. *Aging and Mental Health*, 14(8): 928–37.

Page, S., Rowett, R. and Davies-Abbott, I. (2016) Care to talk? A framework for appreciative conversations about dementia – innovative practice. *Dementia: The International Journal of Social Research and Practice*, 16(8): 1069–74.

Parveen, S., Robins, J., Griffiths, A.W. and Oyebode, J.R. (2015) Dementia detectives: busting the myths. *Journal of Dementia Care*, 23(4): 12–13.

Perren, S., Schmid, R., Herrmann, S. and Wettstein, A. (2007) The impact of attachment on dementia-related problem behavior and spousal caregivers' well-being. *Attachment and Human Development*, 9(2): 163–78.

Perrin, T. (1997) Occupational need in severe dementia: a descriptive study. *Journal of Advanced Nursing*, 25(5): 934–41.

Perry, E.K., Tomlinson, B.E., Blessed, G. et al. (1978) Correlation of cholinergic abnormalities with senile plaques and mental test scores in senile dementia. *British Medical Journal*, 2: 1457–59.

Petre, T. (1995) Dementia and sheltered housing. In T. Kitwood, S. Buckland and T. Petre, *Brighter Futures: A Report on Research with Provision for Persons with Dementia in Residential Homes. Nursing Homes and Sheltered Housing*. Oxford: Anchor Housing Association in collaboration with Methodist Homes for the Aged.

Petre, T. (1996) Back into the swing of her sociable life. *Journal of Dementia Care*, 4(1): 24–5.

Phair, L. and Good, V. (1995) How to make a change for the better. *Journal of Dementia Care*, 3(6): 15–17.

Pinquart, M. and Sörensen, S. (2006) Helping caregivers of persons with dementia: which interventions work and how large are their effects? *International Psychogeriatrics*, 18(4): 577–95.

Pool, J. (forthcoming) Facilitating occupation and enhancing well-being. *Journal of Dementia Care*.

Popper, K. (1959) *The Logic of Scientific Discovery*. London: Hutchinson.

Post, S. (1995) *The Moral Challenge of Alzheimer's Disease*. Baltimore, MD: Johns Hopkins University Press.

Post, S.G. (2000) *The Moral Challenge of Alzheimer Disease: Ethical Issues from Diagnosis to Dying*, 2nd edn. Baltimore, MD: Johns Hopkins University Press.

Post, S.G. (2006) Respectare: morale respect for the lives of the deeply forgetful. In J.C. Hughes, S.J. Louw and S.R. Sabat (eds) *Dementia: Mind, Meaning and the Person*. Oxford: Oxford University Press.

Potocny, J. (2018) *Living with Alzheimer's – My Journey to Forgetfulness!* Living-with-alzhiemers. blogspot.co.uk. Available at: http://living-with-alzhiemers.blogspot.co.uk (accessed 1 March 2018).

Prince, M., Wimo, A., Guerchet, M., Ali, G.C., Wu, Y.T. and Prina, M. (2015) *World Alzheimer Report: 2015 The Global Impact of Dementia: An Analysis of Prevalence, Incidence, Cost and Trends*. London: Alzheimer's Disease International.

Purdey, M. (1994) Anecdote and orthodoxy: degenerative nervous diseases and chemical pollution. *Ecologist*, 24(3): 100–4.

Quinton, A. (1973) *The Nature of Things*. London: Routledge.

Rabins, P.W. and Pearlson, G.D. (1994) Depression induced cognitive impairment. In A. Burns and R. Levy (eds) *Dementia*. London: Chapman and Hall.

RDD/10495 (2013) *G8 Dementia Summit Declaration*. London: G8.

Reisburg, B., Ferris, S.H., de Leon, M.J. and Crook, T. (1982) The Global Deterioration Scale (GDS) for assessment of primary degenerative dementia. *American Journal of Psychiatry*, 139: 1136, 1139.

Richards, M. and Brayne, C. (2010) What do we mean by Alzheimer's disease? *British Medical Journal*, 341: 865–7.

Richards, R. (2007) Everyday creativity: our hidden potential. In R. Richards (ed.) *Everyday Creativity and New Forms of Human Nature: Psychological, and Spiritual Perspectives*. Washington, DC: American Psychological Association.

Rinpoche, S. (1976) *Keywords: A Vocabulary of Culture and Society*. London: Fontana.

Ritchie, K., Kildea, D. and Robine, J.M. (1992) The relation between age and the prevalence of senile dementia. *International Journal of Epidemiology*, 21(4): 763–9.

Robins, J. (1995) Partnership: some effects of childhood scripts on adult relationships. *Counselling*, 6(1): 41–3.

Rogers, C.R. (1961) *On Becoming a Person*. Boston, MA: Houghton Mifflin.

Rohra, H., Stechl, E. and Förstl, H. (2016) *Dementia Activist*. London: Jessica Kingsley Publishers.

Rose, S.P.R. (1984) Disordered molecules and diseased minds. *Journal of Psychiatric Research*, 4: 357–60.

Roses, A.D. (1995) Apolipoprotein E genotyping in the differential diagnosis, not prediction of Alzheimer's disease. *Neurology*, 38(1): 6–14.

Roses, A.D., Strittmatter, W.J., Pericak-Vance, M.A., Corder, E.H., Saunders, A.M. and Schmekel, D.E. (1994) Clinical application of apolipoprotein E genotyping to Alzheimer's disease. *Lancet*, 343: 1564–5.

Roth, M., Huppert, F.A., Tym, E. and Mountjoy, C.Q. (1988) *CAMDEX 1: The Cambridge Examination for Mental Disorders of the Elderly*. Cambridge: Cambridge University Press.

Rothschild, D. (1937) Pathologic changes in senile psychoses and their psychologic significance. *American Journal of Psychiatry*, 93: 757–88.

Rothschild, D. and Sharpe, M.L. (1944) The origin of senile psychoses: neuropathological factors and factors of a more personal nature. *Diseases of the Nervous System*, 2: 49–54.

Rowe, D. (1983) *Depression: The Way Out of Your Prison*. London: Routledge.

Sabat, S.R. (1994) Language function in Alzheimer's disease: a critical review of selected literature. *Language and Communication*, 14(1): 1–22.

Sabat, S.R. (2001) *The Experience of Alzheimer's Disease: Life Through a Tangled Veil*. Oxford: Blackwell.

Sabat, S.R. (2003) Malignant positioning and the predicament of the person with Alzheimer's disease. In F.M. Moghaddam and R. Harré (eds) *The Self and Others: Positioning Individuals and Groups in Personal, Political, and Cultural Contexts*. Westport, CT: Greenwood Publishing Group, Inc.

Sabat, S.R. (2006) Implicit memory and people with Alzheimer's disease: implications for caregiving. *American Journal of Alzheimer's Disease and Other Dementias*, 21(1): 11–14.

Sabat, S.R. and Cagigas, X.E. (1997) Extralinguistic communication compensates for the loss of verbal fluency: A case study of Alzheimer's disease. *Language and Communication*, 17(4): 341–51.

Sabat, S.R. and Harré, R. (1992) The construction and deconstruction of self in Alzheimer's disease. *Ageing and Society*, 12(4): 443–61.

Sabat, S.R. and Harré, R. (1994) The Alzheimer's disease sufferer as a semiotic subject. *Philosophy, Psychiatry, & Psychology*, 1(3): 145–60.

Sabat, S.R., Napolitano, L. and Fath, H. (2004) Barriers to the construction of a valued social identity: A case study of Alzheimer's disease. *American Journal of Alzheimer's Disease and Other Dementias*, 19(3): 177–85.

Särkämö, T., Tervaniemi, M., Laitinen, S. et al. (2013) Cognitive, emotional, and social benefits of regular musical activities in early dementia: randomized controlled study. *The Gerontologist*, 54(4): 634–50.

Sauer, P.E., Fopma-Loy, J., Kinney, J.M. and Lokon, E. (2016) 'It makes me feel like myself': person-centered vs. traditional visual arts activities for people with dementia. *Dementia: The International Journal of Social Research and Practice*, 15(5): 895–912.

Sayers, J. (1994) Informal care and dementia: lessons for psychoanalysis and feminism. *Journal of Social Work Practice*, 8(2): 124–35.

Schlapobersky, J.R. (ed.) (1991) *Institutes and How to Survive Them: Selected Papers by Robin Skynner.* London: Routledge.

Schön, D. (1983) *The Reflective Practitioner.* London: Temple Smith.

Scruton, R. (2017) *On Human Nature.* Princeton, NJ: Princeton University Press.

Segal, J. (1992) *Melanie Klein.* London: Sage.

Shergill, S. and Katona, C. (1996) How common is Lewy body dementia? *Alzheimer's Disease Society Newsletter*, 6, July.

Shorthouse, T. (2018) *I'm Still Me.* Facebook.com. Available at: www.facebook.com/tracey.shorty/?hc_ref=ARRP95WpdYK3psPGNwyO9X09HjUbEsXXS5h4owpIp2HGN4zYJCwbdmpiPrbnrKj3IBk&-fref=nf (accessed 1 March 2018).

Siegel, B.S. (1991) *Peace, Love and Healing.* London: Arrow Books.

Simard, J. (2013) *The End-of-Life Namaste Program for People with Dementia*, 2nd edn. Baltimore, London, Sydney: Health Professions Press.

Sixmith, A., Stilwell, J. and Copeland, J. (1993) Dementia: challenging the limits of dementia care. *International Journal of Geriatric Psychiatry*, 8: 993–1000.

Skaog, I., Nilsson, L., Palmertz, B., Andreasson, L.A. and Svanborg, A. (1993) A population-based study of dementia in 85-year-olds. *New England Journal of Medicine*, 328: 151–8.

Smith, C. (2010) *What is a Person? Rethinking Humanity, Social Life and the Moral Good from the Person Up.* London: University of Chicago Press.

Spector, A., Orrell, M. and Woods, B. (2010) Cognitive Stimulation Therapy (CST): effects on different areas of cognitive function for people with dementia. *International Journal of Geriatric Psychiatry*, 25(12): 1253–8.

Spector, A., Thorgrimsen, L., Woods, B. et al. (2003) Efficacy of an evidence-based cognitive stimulation therapy programme for people with dementia: randomised controlled trial. *British Journal of Psychiatry*, 183: 248–54.

Stephens, A., Cheston, R. and Glesson, K. (2013) An exploration into the relationships people with dementia have with physical objects: an ethnographic study. *Dementia: The International Journal of Social Research and Practice*, 12(6): 697–712.

Stevenson, O. (1989) *Age and Vulnerability.* London: Edward Arnold.

Stevenson, O. and Parsloe, P. (1993) *Community Care and Empowerment.* York: Joseph Rowntree Foundation.

Stewart, I. and Joines, V. (1987) *TA Today.* Nottingham: Lifespan Publications.

Stokes, G. and Goudie, F. (eds) (1989) *Working with Dementia.* Bicester: Winslow Press.

Surr, C.A., Smith, S.J., Crossland, J. and Robins, J. (2016) Impact of a person-centred dementia care training programme on hospital staff attitudes, role efficacy and perceptions of caring for people with dementia: A repeated measures study. *International Journal of Nursing Studies*, 53: 144–51.

Surr, C.A., Walwyn, R.E., Lilley-Kelly, A. et al. (2016) Evaluating the effectiveness and cost-effectiveness of Dementia Care Mapping™ to enable person-centred care for people with dementia and their carers (DCM-EPIC) in care homes: study protocol for a randomised controlled trial. *Trials*, 17(1): 300.

Surr, C., Gates, C., Irving, D. et al. (2017) Effective dementia education and training for the health and social care workforce: a systematic review of the literature. *Review of Educational Research*, 87(5): 966–1002.

Surr, C., Griffiths, A.W. and Kelley, R. (2018) Implementing Dementia Care Mapping as a practice development tool in dementia care services: a systematic review. *Clinical Interventions in Aging*, 13: 165–77.

Sutton, L. (1995) Whose memory is it, anyway? Unpublished PhD thesis, University of Southampton.

Swaffer, K. (2014) Dementia: stigma, language, and dementia-friendly. *Dementia: The International Journal of Social Research and Practice*, 13(6): 709–16.

Swaffer, K. (2012) *Love, Life, Loss, A Roller Coaster of Poetry*. Kelbane, Richmond, SA: Graphic Print Group.

Swaffer, K. (2018) *Daily Blog*. Kateswaffer.com. Available at: https://kateswaffer.com/daily-blog/ (accessed 1 March 2018).

Swaffer, K., Rahman, S., Rees, G. and Taylor, R. (2016) *What the Hell Happened to My Brain? Living Beyond Dementia*. London: Jessica Kingsley Publishers.

Swanwick, G.R.J., Coen, R.F., Lawlor, D.H., Mahony, D.O., Walsh, B. and Oakley, D. (1995) Discriminating power of the Hachinski Ischaemic Score in a geriatric population with dementia. *International Journal of Geriatric Psychiatry*, 10(4): 679–85.

Symington, N. (1988) *The Analytic Experience*. London: Free Association Books.

Tatelbaum, J. (1984) *The Courage to Grieve*. New York: Harper and Row.

Taulbee, L. and Folsom, J.C. (1966) Reality orientation for geriatric patients. *Hospital and Community Psychiatry*, 17: 133–5.

Taylor, R. (2006) *Alzheimer's from the Inside Out*. Baltimore, MD: Health Professions Press.

Taylor, R. (2011) *The Voices of Dementia*. Available at: http://gpli.org/images/dementia_journal.pdf (accessed 19 April 2018).

Terry, R.D. (1992) The pathogenesis of Alzheimer's disease: what causes dementia? In Y. Chisten and P. Churchland (eds) *Neurophilosophy and Alzheimer's Disease*. Berlin: Springer Verlag.

Thomas, W. (1995) Reinventing the American nursing home. In *Conference Proceedings: The Changing Face of Alzheimer Care*. Chicago, IL: Alzheimer's Association.

Thompson, R., Heath, H. and Mills, N. (2013) *Dementia: Commitment to the Care of People with Dementia in Hospital Settings*. London: Royal College of Nursing.

Thorpe, S. (1996) Language changes in Alzheimer's disease. *Alzheimer's Disease Society Newsletter*, August: 4.

Threadgold, M. (1995) Touching the soul through the senses. *Journal of Dementia Care*, 3(4): 18–19.

Titmuss, R.M. (1969) The culture of medical behaviour and consumer care. In F.N.N. Poynter (ed.) *Medicine and Culture*. London: Wellcome Institute.

Tobin, J. (1995) Sharing the care: toward new forms of communication. In T. Kitwood and S. Benson (eds) *The New Culture of Dementia Care*. London: Hawker Publications.

Tobin, S.S. (1991) *Personhood in Advanced Old Age*. New York: Springer.

Tomlinson, B.E., Blessed, G. and Roth, M. (1970) Observations on the brains of demented old people. *Journal of Neurological Science*, 11: 205–42.

Torchia, J. (2008) *Exploring Personhood: An Introduction to the Philosophy of Human Nature*. Plymouth: Rowman & Littlefield.

Toseland, R.W., Diehl, M., Freeman, K. et al. (1997) The impact of validation group therapy on nursing home residents with dementia. *Journal of Applied Gerontology*, 16(1): 31–50.

Truthful Loving Kindness (2018) *Truthful Loving Kindness*. Available at: https://truthfulkindness.com/ (accessed 5 March 2018).

Tuchman, B.W. (1979) *A Distant Mirror: The Calamitous Fourteenth Century*. Harmondsworth: Penguin.

UN General Assembly (2007) *Convention on the Rights of Persons with Disabilities: Resolution/ Adopted by the General Assembly*. In U. Nations (ed.). A/RES/61/106.

Ussher, J. (1991) *Women's Madness*. New York: Harvester.

van den Berg, M., Wendel-Vos, W., van Poppel, M. et al. (2015) Health benefits of green spaces in the living environment: a systematic review of epidemiological studies. *Urban Forestry and Urban Greening*, 4(14): 806–16.

Van Gorp, B. and Vercruysse, T. (2011) Frames and counter-frames giving meaning to dementia: a framing analysis of media content. *Social Science and Medicine*, 74(8): 1274–81.

Van Gorp, B., Vercruysse, T. and Van Den Bulck, J. (2012) Toward a more nuanced perception of Alzheimer's disease: designing and testing a campaign advertisement. *Dementias*, 27(6): 388–96.

Varnum, M.E.W. and Grossmann, I. (2017) Cultural change: the how and the why. *Perspectives on Psychological Science*, 12(6): 956–72.

Vernooij-Dassen, M., Draskovic, I., McCleery, J. and Downs, M. (2011) Cognitive reframing for carers of people with dementia. *Cochrane Database of Systematic Reviews*, 11: 1–41.

Ward, T., Murphy, B., Procter, A. and Weinman, J. (1992) An observational study of two long-stay psychogeriatric wards. *International Journal of Geriatric Psychiatry*, 7: 211–17.

Watts, A.W. (1973) *Psychotherapy East and West*. Harmondsworth: Penguin.

Whear, R., Coon, J.T., Bethel, A. et al. (2014) What is the impact of using outdoor spaces such as gardens on the physical and mental well-being of those with dementia? A systematic review of quantitative and qualitative evidence. *Journal of the American Medical Directors Association*, 15(10): 697–705.

Whitecross, M. (2012) *Ashes*. Isle of Man, UK: CinemaNX, Fiesta Productions, Isle of Man Film.

WHO (2015) *First WHO Ministerial Conference on Global Action Against Dementia: Meeting Report*. Geneva: WHO.

WHO (2017a) *Dementia Plans*. Available at: www.alz.co.uk/dementia-plans (accessed 28 November 2017).

WHO (2017b) *Global Action Plan on the Public Health Response to Dementia 2017–2025*. Geneva: WHO.

WHO/Alzheimer's Disease International (2012) *Dementia: A Public Health Priority*. London: WHO.

Wilberforce, M., Challis, D. and Davies, L. (2016) Person-centredness in the care of older adults: a systematic review of questionnaire-based scales and their measurement properties. *BMC Geriatrics*, 16: 63.

Williams, R. (1976) *Keywords: A Vocabulary of Culture and Society*. London: Fontana.

Woods, B., Keady, J. and Seddon, D. (2007) *Involving Families in Care Homes: A Relationship-centred Approach to Dementia Care*. London: Jessica Kingsley Publishers.

Woods, R. (1995) The beginnings of a new culture in care. In T. Kitwood and S. Benson (eds) *The New Culture of Dementia Care*. London: Hawker Publications.

Woods, R.T. and Britton, P.G. (1977) Psychological approaches to the treatment of the elderly. *Age and Ageing*, 6: 104–12.

Woods, R.T., Portnoy, S., Head, D. and Jones, G. (1992) Reminiscence and life review with persons with dementia: which way forward? In G.M.M. Jones and B.M.L. Miesen (eds) *Caregiving in Dementia*. London: Routledge.

Zagzebski, L. (2001) The uniqueness of persons. *Journal of Religious Ethics*, 29(3): 401–42.

Zarit, S.J. and Femia, E.E. (2008) A future for family care and dementia intervention research? Challenges and strategies. *Aging and Mental Health*, 12(1): 5–13.

Subject Index

Name index

Commentaries Index